Nurses' Aids Series

MICROBIOLOGY FOR NURSES

Applications to Patient Care

Seventh Edition

Vivien Stucke SRN

*ENB 910 Certificate in Principles and Practice of Infection
Control Nursing;
Certificate in Cancer Nursing;
Senior Nurse, Infection Control,
West Cumbria Health Care;
Formerly Nursing Officer, Infection Control Team,
Middlesex Hospital, London*

Baillière Tindall
London   Philadelphia   Toronto   Sydney   Tokyo

Baillière Tindall 24–28 Oval Road,
W. B. Saunders London NW1 7DX

The Curtis Center,
Independence Square West,
Philadelphia, PA 19106-3399, USA

55 Horner Avenue,
Toronto, Ontario M8Z 4X6, Canada

Harcourt Brace & Company, Australia,
32–52 Smidmore Street,
Marrickville, NSW 2204, Australia

Harcourt Brace & Company, Japan,
Ichibancho Central Building,
22–1 Ichibancho,
Chiyoda-ku, Tokyo 102, Japan

First published as *Bacteriology for Nurses* 1959
Fifth edition 1978
  Reprinted 1979, 1980
Sixth edition 1982
  Reprinted 1985, 1986, 1988 and 1990
Seventh edition 1993
  Reprinted 1995, 1996, 1997

Spanish edition 1972

ELBS editions 1969, 1972, 1978, 1982

Typeset by Photo-graphics, Honiton, Devon
Printed and bound in Great Britain by
Mackays of Chatham PLC, Chatham, Kent

ISBN 0 7020 1417 6

A catalogue record for this book is available from the British
Library.

Contents

Publisher's acknowledgements		vii
Acknowledgements		ix
Foreword		x
Preface		xii
	Introduction	1
1	The history of microbiology	3
2	Structure, function and multiplication of micro-organisms	14
3	The infection process	38
4	Immunity	58
5	Chemotherapy	92
6	Cleaning, disinfection and sterilization	119
7	Diagnostic microbiology	147
8	A guide to pathogenic bacteria	186
9	A guide to viruses	239
10	A guide to fungi, protozoa, helminths and ectoparasites	282
11	Infection control—general	312
12	The patient's environment	336
13	Care of the infected/at-risk patient—aseptic techniques and basic infection control measures	366
14	Care of infected and at-risk/susceptible patients (isolation nursing)	409
Appendix:	Guide to Transmission and Management of Important Infections/Diseases	450
Glossary		476
Index		496

Publisher's acknowledgements

Figure 1.1 From original photograph in the Wellcome Institute of the History of Medicine, by courtesy of the Wellcome Trustees

Figure 1.2 Dr P N Cardew

Figure 2.6 Sleigh and Timbury, *Notes on Medical Bacteriology* (2nd Ed.) (1990), Figure 4.6, Churchill Livingstone

Figure 2.7 As 2.6, Figure 4.7

Figure 2.8 Timbury, *Notes on Medical Virology* 8th Ed.) Figure 1.3, Churchill Livingstone

Figure 2.10 Based on Gould, *Infection & Patient Care*, Figure 1.11, Heinemann Medical

Figure 2.11 As 2.10, Figure 1.10

Figure 3.2 *Infection Control*, British Medical Association (1989), Figure 46, Edward Arnold

Figure 3.3 Adapted from handout for Wallace/ICNA Teaching Pack, H G Wallace Ltd, Colchester, Essex CO2 8JH

Figure 4.8 Page 213 Pratt, R. *AIDS, Strategy for Nursing Care* (3rd Ed.) (1991), Edward Arnold

Figure 6.1 Eusol cartoon, Dr S Thomas, Surgical Materials Testing Laboratory, Bridgend General Hospital, UK

Figure 9.5 Caddow, P, *Applied Microbiology* (1989) Figure 10.5, Scutari

Figure 11.1 Meers P D et al (1981) National Survey of Infection in Hospitals. *Journal of Hospital Infection*, 2, Supplement Wallace/ICNA, H G Wallace Ltd, Colchester, Essex CO2 8JH

Figure 11.2   P D Whitehead (with minor amendments)

Figure 11.4   The role of the infection control nurse, Glenys Griffiths, Senior Nurse, Infection Control, Mayday University Hospital, Surrey, UK

Figure 11.5   Physical attributes of an infection control nurse cartoon, Mrs J E Kingston, Clinical Specialist Infection Control, James Paget Hospital, Gorleston, UK

Figure 12.1   Sources of food poisoning bacteria cartoon, published in *The Food Hygiene Handbook*, Highfield Publications, "Vue Pointe", Spinney Hill, Doncaster DN5 7LY

Figures 13.4, 13.6, 14.5, 14.6, 14.7   ICI Pharmaceuticals, UK

Figures 13.1, 13.3   Dr C A Bartzokas and P D Slade, Department of Medical Microbiology, Clatterbridge Hospital, Bebington, UK

Figure 13.2   Distribution of areas missed during hand-washing, *Nursing Times*, Vol 74, No 2 and Lynda J. Taylor, Infection Control Nurse, Public Health Laboratory Service

Figure 13.5   Factors influencing the incidence of wound infection, *Professional Nurse*, December 1988

Figure 13.7   Portals of contamination, *Nursing Standard*, Vol 5, No 28, April 3 1991

Figures 14.3 and 14.8 Mark Hayes

Particular acknowledgement to HBJ Australia for permission to use the following figures from their publication Ackerman and Dunk-Richards, *Microbiology* (1992): Figures 2.2, 5.1, 8.9, 8.10, 10.1, 10.2, 10.3, 10.4, 11.3 and 14.1 (Sister Ailsa Ritchie, Infection Control, Royal North Shore Hospital, Sydney)

Page 360   5 point plan to avoid needle stick, Bec on Dickinson UK Ltd, Oxford, UK

Acknowledgements

I would like to thank all those who have given me help during the preparation of this new edition. This includes many colleagues at West Cumberland Hospital, and the Infection Control Teams of the three Cumbrian Health Authorities. My special thanks to three people: Dr D M S Dane (now retired) and E Moya Briggs of the Department of Medical Microbiology, Middlesex and University College Hospital Medical School who gave me so much help with the chapters on diagnostic microbiology and on viruses; and Dr Geoff Scott of the Department of Microbiology at U.C.H. who has painstakingly checked almost all of the manuscript. He has made many helpful suggestions to ensure that this edition is as up-to-date as possible and has kindly consented to write the foreword. Finally my personal thanks to Martyn, Dan and Ros for many months of support while the book took shape.

Vivien Stucke
October 1992

Foreword

It gives me pleasure to introduce the 7th edition of this useful book which has now been completely updated by Vivien Stucke. When the 6th edition came out in 1982, we had just heard of AIDS, a strange susceptibility to most unusual avirulent organisms leading to death. At that time, although interesting, AIDS seemed rather distant and unimportant. Now it is a part of everyday life and nursing practice. The AIDS epidemic has, more than any other single event, influenced everyone's awareness of infection. It has had a profound effect on the provision of medical services and seems set to alter radically the population structure in the African continent and possibly in South East Asia. Yet AIDS is by no means the most important infection with which nurses will come in contact. They will see common community acquired infections and will see their patients acquiring infections while in hospital. Their practices will influence the chances of patients getting infected. Without a sound knowledge of what microorganisms are and how they can be transmitted and how infections can be prevented or treated, the advice of the Infection Control Team can only be so much mumbo-jumbo. We are now well into Project 2000 and some of you who read this book will be taking "pre-clinical" courses. I think it is difficult to remember facts about microorganisms without actually seeing them under the microscope or on plates, or seeing patients with the infections that they cause. Nevertheless, you will now be expected to learn some rather dry facts.

At least they are well-presented in this book, which should serve as a useful pocket *aide-memoire* after all the examinations are over!

Geoff Scott, M.D., M.R.C.P., M.R.C. Path, D.T.M. & H.
October 1992

Preface

As outlined by the cover and introduction, this seventh edition has been extensively revised and updated. The aim has been to produce a book which will be of use and interest to all nurses. Referencing has been included to allow the reader to pursue the subject further. More "exotic, tropical" infections have been included as there are few places to which travellers may not venture – and perhaps return with more than they bargained for! Old and new infections have tremendous implications for health care and for nursing practice. The application of scientific information to "hands-on" patient care has been stressed, and I hope the practical details included will make the subject patient-centred and relevant to the practising nurse.

Introduction

Hans Zinnsner, a microbiologist, said 'Infectious diseases are one of the few genuine adventures left in the world. The dragons are all gone and the lance lies rusty in the chimney corner' (Wenzel, 1988). This book has been written in the hope that student nurses can develop an interest in and excitement for the world of microbiology. If they can base their nursing practice, whether in a hospital or the community, on scientific principles backed with knowledge of relevant research, it can only benefit the patients in their care.

Microbiology, or the study of bacteria, viruses, fungi and protozoa, may seem to be of mainly academic interest to the student nurse, and of limited value in patient care. However, these organisms with diverse patterns of behaviour and environmental preferences vary in activity from those benefitting man, through the majority which are harmless, to those which can cause disease and death. An understanding of the way they work and the effects they can have on people will help nurses to apply the principles of safe patient care.

These involve prevention and control of infection activities designed to limit spread of infection and maintain a safe environment. The use of aseptic techniques, safe and appropriate use of disinfection and sterilisation methods, management of 'used' goods such as laundry, cutlery and crockery and clinical waste all require an understanding of the risks and transmission routes of infection.

Nurses who understand *how* infection is spread are more likely to apply correct procedures than those who are simply carrying out instructions without understanding. They can then use this knowledge when exploring the problems which infection has or might bring to the patient, and build this into the appropriate method of care. When it is realised that 20% of hospitalised patients at any one time will have an infection, and that half of these are acquired *because* of being hospitalised, the problem is obviously a major one.

The problems of infectious diseases and hospital-acquired infection are not going to vanish—indeed they are increasing. During the last 20 years we have seen (among others) the identification of Legionnaire's disease, Lyme disease and the causative agent for acquired immune deficiency syndrome (AIDS), the human immunodeficiency virus (HIV). In addition to new diseases, there has been an increase in antibiotic-resistant organisms causing hospital-acquired infection, notably in infections due to Gram-negative organisms or methicillin-resistant *Staphylococcus aureus* (MRSA). There is also the impact of new technology, and a patient population which is more 'at risk' than formerly because only the 'sicker' patients are kept in hospital for any length of time. The risks of acquiring infection in hospital are likely to continue to increase rather than diminish. In the community more patients are cared for with invasive devices *in situ*, putting them more 'at risk' than formerly. The nurse who understands how to control or prevent infection will be contributing significantly to good patient care.

REFERENCE

Wenzel RP (1988) Interaction of man and microbe: implications of the AIDS epidemic for hospital epidemiology. *Am. J. Inf. Control* **16**(5): 214–220.

1 The history of microbiology

The history of microbiology is relatively short, since it is the study of organisms not directly visible to the naked eye and needed the invention of the microscope in order to develop. However, measures to protect people from communicable diseases, even though the causes were not understood, have been taken for over 2000 years. In the Babylonian era, dead bodies were removed from the living area, and many other public-health regulations existed which would protect people from infection (Coleman, 1985), because illnesses were then thought to be caused by demons. The Egyptians thought illnesses were the wrath of the gods, and this view continued to Biblical times, where sin was the presumed cause (this is still heard in some circles in the twentieth century, e.g. concerning the AIDS epidemic). The approach to leprosy included separation of the sufferer, with weekly examinations by the priest and, if the signs were confirmed after 2 weeks, the individual was declared to be a leper (*Leviticus*: 13, 14). Unfortunately most lepers did not have leprosy as we now recognise the disease, but were deformed due to many different illnesses.

The philosophers and physicians of ancient Greece and Rome made great advances in suggesting that natural laws govern the world and that diseases had natural causes such as earthquakes or, more importantly, changes in atmosphere. From this came the miasmal theory, where disease was thought to be due to vapours fouling the air, a theory which continued until Pasteur. The historian Thucydides noted that in an outbreak of plague in 430 B.C., the physicians caring for the victims themselves fell prey to the disease, and Virgil describes anthrax among animals and how the tanners avoided the hides of the animals because they might themselves be affected and die (*The Cell—A Small Wonder*, 1985).

The Middle Ages saw three main causes of illness and death, which were leprosy, plague and syphilis. Leprosy was responsible for the development of the first isolation hospitals; plague devastated vast areas and some estimates of European deaths suggest that a quarter of the population of Europe may have succumbed at its height. The Venetians introduced the concept of quarantine for plague, in an attempt to prevent visitors from the East bringing the disease into Venice. Would-be visitors spent 40 days and 40 nights on an island before gaining access to the city (Glasschieb, 1963). Syphilis spread across Europe in a vast pandemic in the late fifteenth century and served to strengthen the retributional approach to infectious disease.

'Modern' ideas can be said to originate with Fracostoro, a poet and scholar from Verona, who produced a paper 'De Contagione' in 1546 in which he suggested that infection is composed of minute, insensible particles and is spread by means of them. He noted that the infection was the same for 'he who received as for he who had given' the infection. This was a great advance as it recognised the transmission of disease, which he attributed to actual contact between people, or their clothing and other objects, and also through air. However, it was not until the discovery of the microscope that others could be persuaded to take up this dramatic view.

For centuries all races used the products of bacterial growth and fermentation without realising the implications of the changes or the processes involved. In fact, the relationship between fermentation and infectious disease was not suspected until two centuries after bacteria were first seen by Antonius van Leeuwenhoek in 1676, using primitive microscopes of his own design and making.

In 1776, Spallanzani first cultivated bacteria in sterilised media, with and without air. He failed, however, to realise the importance of this and either was unaware of Fracastoro's work or failed to relate it to his own.

While this work was being carried on by the scientists, the causation of infectious disease was being investigated empirically by the clinicians of the day. In 1767 John Hunter, investigating the cause of syphilis, experimentally infected himself. Unfortunately, he induced a mixed infection of gonorrhoea and syphilis and his results were rather confused. In 1796, Jenner, a pupil of Hunter, introduced vaccination, making use of the practical observation that those who had had cowpox were immune or partially immune to smallpox. Jenner was unaware of the activities of both Indian and Chinese physicians some 2000 years earlier, who apparently used the first known inoculation of smallpox vesicle fluid for protection against the disease (so-called variolation) (McGrew, 1985).

In 1843, Oliver Wendell Holmes reviewed work on puerperal fever and concluded that this was a contagious disease spread by medical staff and midwives to their patients, and suggested hygienic measures to avoid spread (Holmes, 1843). This paper went largely unheeded for many years, in the same way that Semmelweiss' observations did in 1847. Semmelweiss, a Viennese obstetrician, also realised that puerperal fever was transmitted from one patient to another on the hands of the attendants. He showed conclusively that infection could be greatly reduced by hand-washing and the use of a mild antiseptic (chlorinated lime) on the skin. He used the chlorine initially to get rid of the offensive smell on his hands, and only subsequently discovered that rates of puerperal sepsis were reduced. This discovery is the foundation stone of all modern aseptic techniques in use in hospitals. Unfortunately, his aggressive and disordered approach to communication lost him his job, and his findings were largely ignored by his colleagues.

A few years later in 1854 Dr John Snow demonstrated that cholera was transmitted through drinking water by showing the geographical relationship of the cases to the Broad Street pump in London and then stopping the outbreak by removing the pump handle.

Improvements in the microscope led to special diseases being associated with certain organisms of characteristic morphology. Davaine in 1850 saw what he called minute 'infusoria' in the blood of sheep dead from anthrax and he was able to transmit the disease by inoculation of greatly diluted blood.

Figure 1.1 Louis Pasteur (1822–1895).

The techniques of modern microbiology were largely initiated and enormously developed by Pasteur, Lister and Koch. Pasteur, a pure chemist, became interested through investigation of industrial fermentation problems. He demonstrated that alcoholic fermentation was brought about by specific bacterial enzymes, and gave a logical explanation for a process which had been carried on for hundreds of years.

Lister followed up Pasteur's work on fermentation and carried out experiments to test the deduction that if fermentation of sugar and starch was due to micobial action, sepsis and putrefaction of proteins were due to a similar cause. He therefore attempted to prevent bacterial invasion of operation wounds and injuries and the many forms of sepsis which resulted in suppuration, hospital gangrene and septicaemia. He used phenol to destroy germs and prevent them gaining a foothold in wounds. He published the successful results of his work in 1867, though it was many years before his sceptical colleagues accepted his teaching. By applying carbolic putty to cases of compound fracture, he was able to save limbs which would previously have been amputated because of gangrene or septicaemia. In the course of his experiments he devised a technique for obtaining pure cultures originating from a single organism, the first man to do so.

While Pasteur was working in France and Lister in England, Koch in Germany was developing the bacteriological techniques which form the basis of modern diagnostic bacteriology. Today it is relatively simple to identify an unknown organism. The necessary tests have been laid down and are simply a matter of applying routine knowledge, but in 1870 Koch had no such rules to help him and new disciplines had to be worked out. Koch first isolated the anthrax bacillus in pure culture.

He then devised liquid and solid culture media which included both serum and blood agar and noted that the organisms grew in clusters called 'colonies' which eventually became visible to the naked eye. He saw that these colonies were characteristic and had defined conditions of growth. After this start, the causative organisms of numerous other infectious diseases were identified and their conditions of growth noted in the same way.

In 1881, Klebs and Loeffler isolated the diphtheria bacillus. The discovery of this organism necessitated a reassessment of the preformed theories of bacterial infection. It was discovered that filtrates of growing cultures of this organism, that is to say material in which the organism had been growing but from which it had been removed by means of filtration, were still able to cause death in animals. This led to the discovery of exotoxins, powerful tissue poisons, often enzymes or ferments, which are produced by some organisms during growth and which diffuse into the surrounding tissues to be carried through the body in the bloodstream to produce injurious effects remote from the site of bacterial growth.

In 1890, von Behring showed that diphtheria could be prevented and cured by the administration of serum from a horse convalescent from diphtheria. This was the discovery of antitoxins. In 1891, Ehrlich standardised diphtheria toxin so that its potency could be assessed and the antitoxin measured against it.

At the beginning of this century, Ehrlich was investigating the possibility of finding a 'magic bullet', a chemical sufficiently non-toxic to give to a patient, but capable of destroying all bacteria in his body. In 1910 he discovered an effective chemotherapeutic agent, the arsenical drug salvarsan 606, able to destroy *Treponema pallidum*, and this was used for many years in the treatment of syphilis.

Following Ehrlich's lead the hunt for chemotherapeutic agents was intensified. In 1935 Domagk found the dye prontosil to be effective against streptococci and this drug and many other members of the same chemical family,

Figure 1.2 Sir Alexander Fleming (1881–1955).

the sulphonamides, are still widely used to treat suitable infections. In 1929 Fleming discovered penicillin, which after it had been developed in 1940 by Florey and Chain, proved to be a 'magic bullet' that revolutionised the treatment of infections. The outstanding success of penicillin stimulated research that has resulted in the discovery of many chemicals and antibiotics effective against bacteria. At the present time there are a great many antibiotics covering virtually all types of known bacteria.

Virology has developed along broadly similar lines to bacteriology, but necessarily more slowly because of the extremely small size of the infective particles and because they can only multiply within living cells. Pasteur, in 1884, did pioneer work on protection against rabies. Loeffler and Trosch showed filterability of foot-and-mouth disease virus through bacteria-retaining filters in 1898. Culture difficulties have been overcome to a considerable extent by the development of tissue culture techniques only since the 1950s, and classification of viruses greatly advanced with the development of the electron microscope.

Some outstanding successes in protection have taken place against virus diseases. Notable amongst these are Jenner's vaccination against smallpox. Theiler's yellow fever vaccine, and the Salk (1953) and Sabin (1955) vaccines for poliomyelitis. More recently vaccines have been used to protect against measles, mumps, rubella and hepatitis B virus.

There are sporadic records throughout history of the observation that infection with a particular disease can lead to resistance to reinfection with the same disease. This concept was advanced in the eighteenth century following the discovery by Jenner of vaccination against smallpox as mentioned above, and was further developed by Pasteur and many others in the nineteenth century. In the last decade of the nineteenth century it was observed that the serum of immune animals contained factors which neutralised the toxins of the infecting organism. This led rapidly to the development of vaccines against toxin-producing organisms (e.g. diphtheria and tetanus) and to the discovery of the serum components (antibodies) responsible for the neutralisation. Meanwhile it became apparent that specific immunity to some diseases such as tuberculosis is mediated not by serum factors, such as antibody, but rather by certain types of cell. We now know that specific antibody-mediated and cell-mediated immunity result from the activity of the lymphoid system, particularly specialised lymph tissue in the respiratory tract and gut and the lymph nodes, spleen and thymus. Modern immunology has revealed that these organs contain numerous distinct subclasses of lymphocyte, some of which are purely regulatory in function, while others are dedicated to the production of antibody, or to one of the ever increasing number of cell-mediated mechanisms. Within the next few years immunologists hope to discover precisely which antibody-mediated or cell-mediated mechanisms are needed to protect against each of the major infectious diseases so that vaccines can be designed to evoke the right kind of response. The development of such 'tailor-made' vaccines will require detailed understanding of how the different mechanisms are regulated. Such knowledge will also facilitate control of rejection of transplanted organs, and of auto-immune disease.

Perhaps one of the greatest challenges of all to the science of microbiology lies in the present search for both a vaccine to protect against infection with the human immunodeficiency virus, and an effective agent to treat those already infected.

REFERENCES

Coleman V (1985) *The Story of Medicine*. London: Robert Hale.

Glasschieb HS (1963) *The March of Medicine*. London: Macdonald.

Holmes OW (1843) The contagiousness of puerperal fever. *N. Engl. Q. J. Med. Surg.* **1**: 503–530.

McGrew R (1985) *Encyclopaedia of Medical History*. London: Macmillan.

The Cell—A Small Wonder (in the series on *The Human Body*) (1985). New York: Torstar Books.

FURTHER READING

Ashhurst AP (1927) The centenary of Lister (1827–1927). A tale of sepsis and antisepsis. *Ann. Med. Hist.* **9**: 205–221.

Baldry P (1976) *The Battle Against Bacteria: A Fresh Look*. Cambridge: Cambridge University Press.

Bristowe JS (1864) Mortality in hospitals: *Lancet* i: 451–452.

Bristowe JS and Holmes T (1864) Hospital hygiene no. I and II. *Lancet* ii: 498–500, 532–533, 700–702.

Buer MC (1968) *Health, Wealth and Population in the Early Days of the Industrial Revolution*. London: Routledge and Kegan Paul.

Burnet M and White D (1972) *Natural History of Infectious Disease*. Cambridge: Cambridge University Press.

Devenish EA and Miles AA (1939) Control of *Staphylococcus aureus* in an operating theatre. *Lancet* i: 1088–1094.

Farr W (1864) Hospital mortality. *Med. Times Gaz.* **1**: 242–244.

Fleming A (1919) The action of chemical and physiological antiseptics in a septic wound. *Br. J. Surg.* **7**: 99–129.

Gordon R (1983) *Great Medical Disasters*. London: Hutchinson.

Guthrie D (1949) *Lord Lister. His Life and Doctrine*. Edinburgh: Churchill Livingstone.

Hastings RP (1974) *Medicine and International History*. London: Ernest Benn.

Maurois A (1963) *The Life of Alexander Fleming*. Harmondsworth: Penguin.

McNeil W (1979) *Plagues and Peoples*. London: Penguin.

Meleney FL (1935) Infection in clean operative wounds. *Surg. Gynaecol. Obst.* **60**: 264–276.

Murchison C (1864) On the isolation of infectious diseases. *Med. Times Gaz.* **1**: 210–211.

Parish HJ (1968) *Victory with Vaccine*. Edinburgh: Churchill Livingstone.

Semmelweiss IF (1861) *The Aetiology, the Concept and the Prophylaxis of Childbed Fever* (trans. FP Murphy). Republished in *Classics of Medicine Library* (1981) Birmingham.

Williams G (1981) *The Age of Miracles: Medicine and Surgery in the 19th Century*. London: Constable.

Wilson JR (1963) *Margin of Safety. The Story of Poliomyelitis Vaccine*.
    London: Collins.
Zeigler P (1969) *The Black Death*. London: Collins.

2 Structure, function and multiplication of microorganisms

Human infections can be caused by the following groups of microorganisms: bacteria (including mycoplasmas, rickettsiae and chlamydiae), viruses (and small pieces of viral DNA called 'prions'), fungi and protozoa. In poorer countries, large parasites such as worms (helminths) are also a major cause of morbidity.

PROKARYOTES AND EUKARYOTES

Living creatures are composed of one of two cell types: *prokaryotic* or *eukaryotic* cells. Prokaryotic cells have a simpler structure and, in particular, the nuclear material is free within the cytoplasm (see Figure 2.1); they include bacteria. Eukaryotic cells have their DNA enclosed within a nuclear membrane, and a clear nucleus can be seen under the microscope (see Figure 2.2). The simplest single-cell eukaryocytes are protozoa, fungi and some algae. These represent a basic structure seen in higher animals, helminths and plants. Viruses are organisms which require other living cells in order to reproduce.

Prokaryotic cells

Figure 2.1 shows diagrammatically the structures that may be demonstrated in bacteria with the help of an

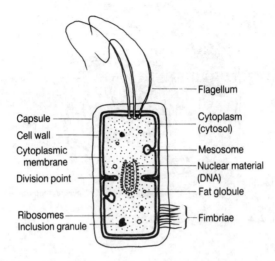

Figure 2.1   The anatomy of a bacterium (prokaryotic cell).

electron microscope. A rigid cell wall which preserves the shape of the organism encloses a thin flexible cytoplasmic membrane. Mycoplasmas, rickettsiae and chlamydiae do not have the rigid outer cell wall. The membrane allows diffusion to take place between the cell cytoplasm and the environment. The cell contents inside the membrane are liquid, and include the following.

1. The *cytoplasm* which contains the mechanisms necessary for maintaining the cell and allowing reproduction.
2. Nuclear material, or *deoxyribonucleic acid* (DNA), circular and double stranded. It is not bounded by a nuclear membrane as occurs with animal and plant cells, but it is too large a molecule to fit within a bacterium without coiling and supercoiling.

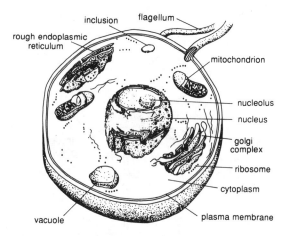

Figure 2.2 A eukaryotic cell.

3. *Ribosomes*—numerous granules of *ribonucleic acid* (RNA) which manufacture protein.
4. *Mesosomes*—granules which sometimes may be formed by invagination of the cytoplasmic membrane, and act as respiration centres.
5. Other inclusion granules and fat globules.
6. Division points, partial septa consisting of cell wall and cell membrane which grow completely across the cell at the time of cell division (see below).

One or more of the following may be seen outside the bacterial cell wall in some species.

1. *Flagella*, filaments which propel species by a rotating movement. Common to most Gram-negative (and a few Gram-positive) bacilli (see p. 23). This movement, or *motility*, is used in laboratory identification of organisms.

2. *Capsule*, a protective carbohydrate layer which helps the bacterium to reist phagocytosis (see Chapter 4).
3. *Fimbriae (pili)*, short, stout hair-like processes, not concerned with motility, but with adhesion to host cells and the transfer of genetic material.

Cell division in prokaryotes

Most bacteria multiply by dividing in two in a simple process known as *binary fission*. The DNA, contained in the *one* double-stranded chromosome of a bacterial cell simply *replicates* and the cell divides in two (see Figure 2.3). Each daughter cell contains only one strand of the chromosome and they are, therefore, identical. The daughter cells, in turn, will replicate again.

Eukaryotic cells

The cell membrane or cell wall forms the outer boundary of the eukaryotic cell (Figure 2.2). There is rarely any extra coating equivalent to the capsule of prokaryotes. Filamentous fungi, however, do have a rigid cell wall composed of chitin and other carbohydrates. The cytoplasm is more complex than in prokaryotic cells and eukaryotes have distinct structures in the cytoplasm called *organelles*. These have specific functions, e.g.

1. *Nucleus*—bounded by a double membrane and containing DNA and the *nucleoli* which are involved with ribonucleic acid (RNA) production within the nucleus.
2. *Endoplasmic reticulum*—the framework for transport of proteins, lipids and other materials.
3. *Ribosomes*—produce protein, as in prokaryotes.
4. *Mitochondria*—for respiration/energy production.

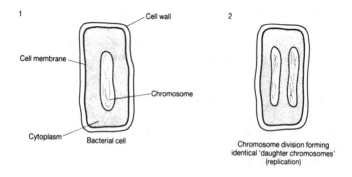

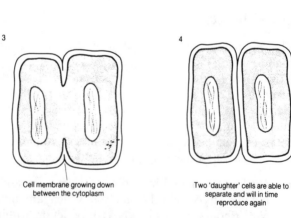

Figure 2.3   Binary fission.

5. *Golgi complex*—concerned with secretion of substances from the cell.
6. *Lysosomes*—enzymes made in the Golgi complex often contained in small vesicles which can break down foreign substances such as bacteria.

Cell division in eukaryotes

As eukaryotic cells have many chromosomes, cell division is more complex than for prokaryotes. The number of chromosomes present is characteristic of a particular species, e.g. man has 46. The chromosomes consist of two strands of DNA but they are *paired*, usually (but not always) being duplicates of each other. These cells, containing two of each chromosome, are known as *diploid* cells. Most reproduce by simple, asexual division known as *mitosis*, but occasionally reproduction is sexual and is then known as *meiosis*.

1. Mitosis—when the chromosomes replicate, they condense into *chromatids* which are joined at a *centromere*. They are drawn apart by the *mitotic spindle* and finally a nuclear membrane forms around each set of chromatids and two identical cells are produced (see Figure 2.4). Each daughter cell will have a complete set of chromosomes.
2. Meiosis—a sexual reduction division involving pairs of chromosomes separating into haploid cells (gametes), resulting in mixing of genes and thus giving scope for much variation in and alteration of the organism.

BACTERIA

Bacteria are minute organisms ranging in size from 0.3 to 14 μm in length (1 μm = 0.001 mm)—300 of the

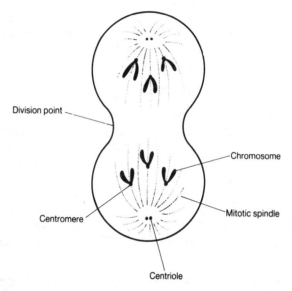

Figure 2.4 The final stage of mitosis, where identical sets of chromosomes are at opposite poles.

smaller organisms could be placed end to end on the diameter of a pin's head. They cannot be seen with the naked eye and a microscope is necessary to see the shape of individual organisms.

Bacteria vary enormously in the substances which they can utilise as food and there are some bacteria in all environments where active steps have not been taken to remove them—in the soil, in hot springs, in the sea, in the atmosphere, in vegetable matter, on animals and in dust—their type depending on the available foodstuff and the prevailing physical conditions. Some organisms are particular and require exacting conditions in order to flourish, such as the presence of animals or insects upon which they live; when the existence of the organisms is wholly dependent on the presence of these animals or insects, the latter are said to act as vectors or carriers.

Most bacteria are not harmful; indeed many are essential and a great many are useful. A large group of soil bacteria have the power of using atmospheric nitrogen for their growth; as they grow, reproduce and die, organic nitrogenous material is liberated into the soil enriching it and making it available to plants which do not have this power of 'fixing nitrogen'. Bacteria in the soil elaborate vitamins necessary for animal life, and bacteria in the healthy bowel synthesise vitamins essential to human well-being. Bacteria are used to turn curd or cream into cheese, and the products of fungi turn grape juice into wine and wine into vinegar. These reactions are carried out commercially and their products are of benefit to mankind.

The term 'bacteriology', therefore, covers the study of a vast number of organisms, most of which are not met with in medical work and do not cause disease. Those which are encountered in medical bacteriology have become accustomed to living on organic material or animal tissues, and many have lost the power of using simple inorganic substances as a source of food; they have become, to a lesser or greater degree, parasitic.

Classification

Bacteria can be classified according to a variety of characteristics, but 'the most important are *morphology* or shape, *nutritional requirements*, the reaction to *staining* and *structural differences*.

Shape or morphology (see Figure 2.5)

1. *Cocci* are round bacteria and may appear in *chains* (streptococci), *clumps* (staphylococci) or *pairs* (diplococci).
2. *Bacilli* are rod-shaped bacteria and these vary from chains to threads or club-shaped organisms. Some may be curved, e.g. *Vibrio* spp. Some form very short rods and look like cocci, these are called 'coccobacilli'.
3. *Spiral* forms include:
   (a) *spirilla*—longer, rigid, curved organisms with several spirals, e.g. *Spirillum minus* which is one cause of rat-bite fever in the tropics; and
   (b) *spirochaetes*—even longer, but flexible spiral organisms, e.g. *Borrelia, Treponema* and *Leptospira*.

Nutritional requirements

Like other living things, bacteria need food and water. Different bacteria have different requirements for certain substances such as vitamins and amino acids, but all bacteria require *carbon dioxide*; most grow better in neutral or slightly alkaline solutions; all need phosphates.

Bacteria require *water*; drying will cause their death, but some bacteria can survive for long periods effectively in suspended animation (see below) as *spores*.

Bacteria can be divided into three groups with regard to their need for *oxygen*.

1. *Strict or obligate aerobes*, which must have oxygen to grow. They will be found on the surface of wounds, on skin and mucous membranes, e.g. *Pseudomonas aeruginosa*.

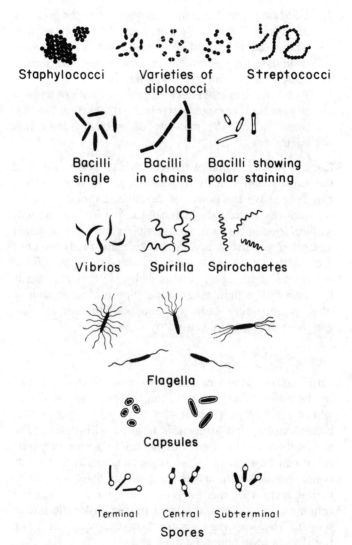

Figure 2.5 Some common bacterial shapes and arrangements.

2. *Obligate anaerobes*, which cannot grow in the presence of oxygen. These will particularly affect deep wounds where tissue is dead (e.g. stab, gunshot and crush wounds); they include the *Clostridium* spp. which cause tetanus and gas gangrene.

3. *Facultative anaerobes*, which can grow with or without oxygen, and perhaps better in 5–10% carbon dioxide; these include the majority of medically important bacteria.

Certain species, notably those which cause anthrax and the *Clostridium* species responsible for tetanus and gas gangrene, have the power of developing *spores*, a highly resistant resting phase which can survive for long periods without food or water and resist wide temperature changes and other adverse conditions. Like plant seeds they can grow and mature again when suitable conditions (food, water and temperature) are available. Spores may easily be seen with a light microscope. Sporulating organisms often manufacture exotoxins and both tetanus and gas gangrene are actually caused by these toxins.

Staining

The bacterial kingdom can be roughly divided into two by the action of a staining technique developed by *Gram*, which consists of staining the cells with a basic dye, methyl violet, and afterwards treating with iodine. The film is then decolourised with alcohol or acetone until no more can be removed. The organisms are subsequently counterstained with a red contrasting dye, e.g. dilute carbol fuchsin or neutral red. *Gram-positive* organisms retain methyl violet and appear purple under the microscope; *Gram-negative* ones are those which do not retain the dye and are counterstained red.

The tubercle bacillus (*Mycobacterium tuberculosis*) and

some related organisms are stained only with difficulty by Gram stain. They can be reliably stained by using hot, strong carbol fuchsin which is impossible to remove with acid and alcohol. This is the basis of the *Ziehl–Neelsen* stain and the organisms so stained are said to be 'acid/alcohol fast' bacilli (AAFB).

The flagella which enable some bacteria to move can only be stained by using special techniques. Some organisms such as the pneumococcus are surrounded by a thick carbohydrate capsule which can be demonstrated by special stains.

Structural differences between Gram-positive and Gram-negative bacteria

The cell walls of Gram-negative and Gram-positive organisms differ. Gram-positive organisms have cell walls made up of chains of carbohydrate which are cross-linked by amino acids so that they are enclosed in one huge molecule. This framework is several layers thick and is called *peptidoglycan* or *mucopeptide*. It occurs also in Gram-negative organisms but is far less thick. Gram-negative organisms have an outer membrane that is not present in Gram-positive organisms. This consists of a complex *lipopolysaccharide* (LPS) composed of sugars, phosphate and fatty acids, and *lipoprotein* bilayer membrane. LPS or *endotoxin* may be responsible for a shock reaction in patients with Gram-negative organisms in the blood (for further information on endotoxins see p. 40). Some Gram-positive organisms have an additional layer of *teichoic acid* which is a sugar and phosphate complex. Both Gram-positive and Gram-negative organisms may be surrounded by a *capsule*, as already described. The cell wall acts as a defence mechanism as well as being responsible for the shape of the organism (but see Chapter 5 for effects of antibiotics).

Multiplication of bacteria

As stated earlier, bacteria reproduce by *binary fission* (see p. 17 and Figure 2.3). Most bacteria under optimal conditions will divide every 20–30 min, although some organisms, such as *Mycobacterium tuberculosis*, divide much more slowly (even under optimal conditions). For a more detailed description of bacterial reproduction see Sleigh and Timbury (1986) and Thomas (1988).

Bacterial genetics

Plasmids

Most bacterial DNA is contained as a single chromosome, but a small amount (approximately 1–2%) is extrachromosomal in small circles in the cytoplasm called *plasmids*. Plasmids are important in that they can multiply both independently of the host cell, and also during normal binary fission, carrying important genetic information with them. This may include resistance to certain antibiotics.

Organisms can evolve by acquiring new genes from others. This is known as *genetic recombination*. In bacteria it can occur in one of three ways: transformation, transduction or conjugation.

Transformation

Fragments of free or 'naked' DNA may be taken up by cells and incorporated into the recipient cell's chromosome. This only occurs naturally in a few genera, but can be performed artificially in the laboratory when it is known as *recombinant technology*. *Escherichia coli* can be easily manipulated in this way.

Transduction by bacteriophages

Transfer of genetic material known as *transduction* occurs when plasmid DNA is carried from one bacteria to another by a *bacteriophage*, a virus which parasitises bacteria. Phages are highly specific to strains of bacteria. The bacterial DNA is contained in the head of the phage (see Figure 2.6) and effectively injected into the body of the bacterium. *Virulent* phages will destroy the bacteria they enter, but *temperate* phages allow their hosts to survive although may destroy them later after reproducing themselves by *lysis* or breaking down the bacterial cell walls. Phages are used within the laboratory, for example to separate strains of *Staphylococcus aureus* (see Chapter 5).

Conjugation

As described above, many bacteria carry independent plasmids. Plasmids may be transferred between similar strains by conjugation, in which a *pilus* or tube forms between two cells allowing the plasmid to be propelled from one cell to the other when they are in direct contact (see Figure 2.7). The donor cell also must have a fertility factor (F factor). This is a form of primitive sexual reproduction. It happens more easily and frequently in Gram-negative than in Gram-positive organisms although, from a clinical point of view, it is probably equally important in both.

VIRUSES

There are three important ways in which viruses differ from other microorganisms.

1.   They are so small that most are not visible with a

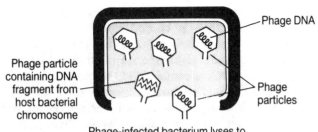

Phage DNA

Phage particle containing DNA fragment from host bacterial chromosome

Phage particles

Phage-infected bacterium lyses to release new phage particles

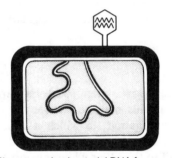

Phage carrying bacterial DNA fragment enters recipient bacterium

Bacterial DNA from phage recombines into chromosome of recipient bacterium

Figure 2.6 Transduction.

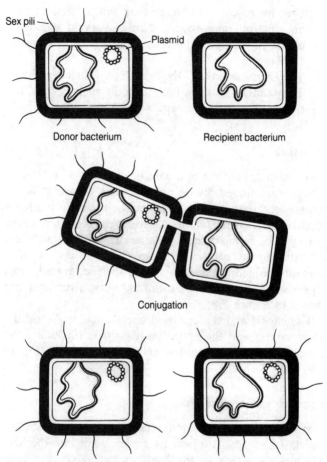

Figure 2.7   Conjugation, showing gene transfer by plasmids.

light microscope, although they can be studied with
an electron microscope. Viruses vary in size from
about 20 to 300 nm, whereas staphylococci measure
1000 nm.
2. They possess either DNA or RNA, but never both.
3. They cannot grow on lifeless media such as agar, but
only within living susceptible cells.

Structure

Virus particles consist of a core of nucleic acid (DNA *or*
RNA) surrounded by a protein coat (*capsid*). Some
viruses, e.g. herpesviruses, are enclosed by a further layer
or *envelope*. Viruses without envelopes are called *naked*
viruses. The capsid protects the nucleic acid and facilitates
the attachment of the virus to the host cell; it also
contains antigenic material which is specific for each virus
type. Some examples of different virus structures are
shown in Figure 2.8.

The capsid and the enclosed nucleic acid make up the
nucleocapsid and the entire virus particle (including the
envelope if there is one) is called a *virion* (see Figure
2.9).

Function and replication

The virus recognises protein receptors on the host cell to
which it attaches. It injects its nucleic acids into the host
where they attach to the host nuclear DNA and take
over host cell protein and DNA synthesis so that new
virus particles can be made. They can then be released
to continue the cycle. The protein of the outer coat is
responsible for much of the immunological response to
the virus as it is antigenic. Enveloped viruses are released
from the cell by budding. The envelope is part of the

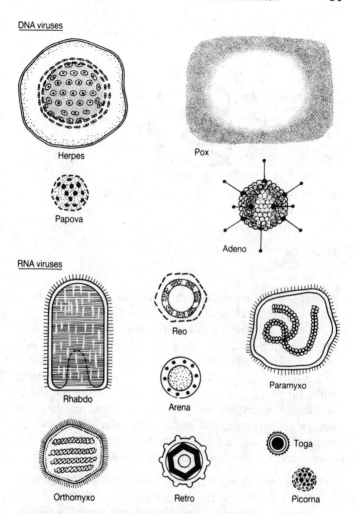

Figure 2.8 Some different virus structures.

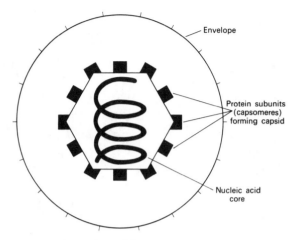

Figure 2.9 A complete virion.

parent cell membrane and these viruses are not infectious
without the envelope.

Viruses are true parasites, i.e. they cannot reproduce
outside living cells and many viruses do not survive long
outside living cells. Viruses are everywhere: many cause
us no harm but, like bacteria, they are responsible for a
wide range of diseases. These include influenza, many
childhood infections such as measles and chickenpox,
several types of hepatitis and the more recently discovered
acquired immune deficiency syndrome (AIDS). They may
take effect on the host cell in three ways:

1. *cytopathic effect* (CPE)—the infection kills the cell,
   e.g. adenovirus, respiratory syncytial virus.
2. *latency*—has no obvious effect but remains potentially
   infectious, e.g. Varicella–Zoster virus.
3. *transformation*—transformation of the host cell to a
   malignant form, e.g. Hepatitis B associated with liver

carcinoma, and Epstein Barr virus with Burkitt lymphoma.

RICKETTSIAE AND CHLAMYDIAE

These organisms, like viruses, multiply only within living cells but, like bacteria, they contain both DNA and RNA. Unlike viruses, both rickettsiae and chlamydiae can be killed by antibiotics and they are larger than most viruses. They are, therefore, classed with bacteria.

Rickettsiae are usually transmitted by fleas or ticks and are found world-wide, although rarely in temperate climates. Chlamydiae are also found world-wide; they cause pneumonia (psittacosis), trachoma (a form of chronic conjunctivitis) and some sexually transmitted diseases (see Chapter 8).

MYCOPLASMAS

Mycoplasmas are tiny bacteria (smaller than large viruses) which lack cell walls, but can live independently and will grow on artificial media. They may be found everywhere— in all animals, and in sewage and compost. In humans, some species may cause atypical pneumonia, pelvic inflammatory disease (PID) or puerperal fever.

PROTOZOA

These are *eukaryotic* cells. They are the smallest single-cell animals, and can range in size from 5 to 50 μm, much larger than most bacteria. They possess a nucleus surrounded by a limiting membrane lying within the cytoplasm, which in turn is divided into endoplasm (concerned with nutrition) and ectoplasm (which obtains

the food). The ectoplasm may actively flow into pseudo-
podia to allow movement or the cell may have flagella
or cilia (see Figure 2.10). Species causing human disease
include *Plasmodium* (causing malaria), *Entamoeba*
(amoebic dysentery), *Giardia* and *Cryptosporidia*
(diarrhoeal diseases).

FUNGI

These are *eukaryotic* cells. Fungi are more complex than
bacteria, consisting of a nucleus containing chromosomes
inside a membrane. The surrounding cytoplasm contains
mitochondria and ribosomes. Fungi may reproduce sexually or by spore formation and are divided into four
groups.

1. *Yeasts*—round/oval cells which reproduce by budding
    e.g. *Cryptococcus neoformans*.
2. *Yeast-like fungi*—like yeasts, most will reproduce by
    budding, but some form filaments, e.g. *Candida
    albicans*.
3. *Filamentous fungi*—these grow as filaments (hyphae)
    which interweave into a mesh (the *mycelium*); they
    reproduce by asexual spores, e.g. *Aspergillus*, and
    ringworm fungi.
4. *Dimorphic fungi*—these grow in two forms, according
    to their situation: as yeasts in the body, but form
    mycelia in the environment or in culture e.g. *Blasto-
    myces* and *Histoplasma*.

Fungal disease (*mycoses*) can be divided into those
affecting the skin only, e.g. ringworm (superficial), and
those affecting the whole system, e.g. histoplasmosis
(deep). The latter are usually only pathogenic as 'opportunists', taking advantage of lowered host resistance. (See
Chapter 10.) Some pathogenic fungi are shown in Figure
2.11.

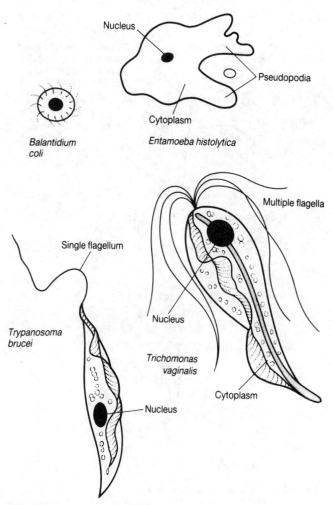

Figure 2.10 Some pathogenic protozoa.

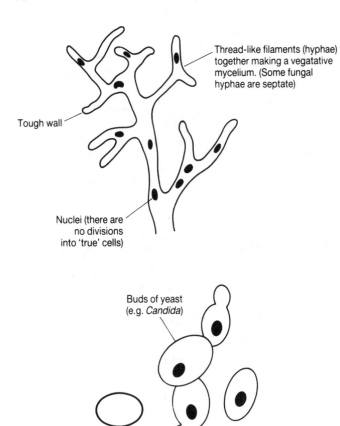

Thread-like filaments (hyphae) together making a vegatative mycelium. (Some fungal hyphae are septate)

Tough wall

Nuclei (there are no divisions into 'true' cells)

Buds of yeast (e.g. *Candida*)

Thick-walled spore

Figure 2.11   Some pathogenic fungi.

REFERENCES

Sleigh JD and Timbury MC (1986) *Notes on Medical Bacteriology*, 2nd edn. London: Churchill Livingstone.

Thomas CGA (1988) *Medical Microbiology*, 6th edn. London: Baillière Tindall.

3 The infection process

INTRODUCTION

This chapter is intended to provide information on the procss of infection—how and why it occurs. The terms used are all explained in the glossary, but concepts such as *pathogenicity* are described in more detail. *Sources* of infection (human, environmental and other animals) are explored. In order to understand the scope for potential infection, *normal flora* and *carrier* states are described in some detail. Susceptibility of people to infection is discussed briefly, but is described further in Chapters 4 and 11. The chapter concludes with a discussion of the routes by which infecting organisms can enter and leave the body.

The factors essential to the process of infection are:

1. a pathogenic organism,
2. a susceptible host (allowing the pathogen to enter and multiply), and
3. a means of transmission (exit and transference).

These three factors will be discussed in depth in Chapters 4 and 5. An understanding of how an infection can be transmitted and, therefore, how transmission risks can be reduced, will help the nurse take appropriate action when caring for infected and 'at risk' patients. A knowledge of the sources of potential infection, and the body mechanisms for fighting infection, will enable nurses to maintain a positive approach to health and to avoid infection in themselves, their patients and their fellow workers.

The principles of infection control is to prevent infection being transmitted by *breaking the chain* of infection (see Figure 3.1).

PATHOGENIC ORGANISMS

Before discussing the *sources* of pathogenic organisms, *pathogenicity* itself needs explanation. Most organisms do not automatically cause disease, rather their ability to do so depends upon their virulence, which in turn depends on their structure, invasiveness and ability to manufacture toxins. The susceptibility of the host is discussed later.

Only a low *number* of a highly virulent organism are required to cause disease, whereas a less virulent one may need to be present in vast numbers to do so.

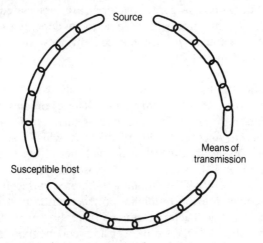

Figure 3.1 The chain of infection.

Virulence is a measure of how effective the organism is at causing disease. 'High virulence' infers that relatively low numbers are needed to produce disease in healthy subjects.

Invasiveness means the ability to enter and multiply in the host. Virulence and invasiveness often go together. Colonisation and invasion depend on the structure of the organism and on the susceptibility of the host.

Colonisation is a critical step in the process of infection. When an organism enters the body it must gain a foothold at the entry site. Mostly this involves binding of the microorganism to a susceptible cell. *Invasion* may then follow. This may be made possible by the following:

1. Some bacteria possess a capsule (see Chapter 2) which can resist the killing activity of white blood cells which fight infection (*polymorphonuclear phagocytes*). *Streptococcus pneumoniae*, *Haemophilus influenzae* and *Salmonella typhi* all possess capsules.
2. Adhesiveness—some bacteria are associated with extra virulence which appears to depend on their possession of *pili* on the cell surfaces (or *plasmids* (see Chapter 2)).

Some organisms produce chemicals which damage tissues, i.e. they are *toxigenic*. These organisms are divided into exotoxins and endotoxins. *Exotoxins* are potent enzymes excreted by bacteria which can cause serious disease and death (e.g. diphtheria, botulism and tetanus) and a range of food poisoning illnesses (e.g. cholera, *E. coli*). These toxins are secreted extracellularly. *Endotoxins* are the outer lipopolysaccharide part of the Gram-negative bacterial cell and are liberated on cell death. Effects range from fever and leucopenia to shock, disseminated intravascular coagulation (DIC) and death.

SOURCES

There are three sources of infection, the first of which is the most important:

1. humans,
2. environment (inanimate, including food and water), and
3. other animals and birds.

Examples of sources of infection are given in Figure 3.2.

Humans

People are not sterile. They are *colonised* by about 1 kg of a wide variety of microorganisms, most of which can become pathogenic given the right conditions. Table 3.1 gives some examples of 'normal flora' by body site. At their natural site these flora actually help to prevent colonisation by other virulent organisms. Before discussing pathogens further, it is important to understand the role of *normal flora* in human beings and their ability to cause infection under certain conditions.

Normal flora

Normal body flora of the healthy individual vary from one person to another, depending on age, general health, temperature and specific local conditions such as acidity in the stomach. If normal conditions are altered, then the normal flora may be destroyed and replaced by harmful organisms. For example, there are normally few bacteria in bronchi and alveoli, but in patients with chronic bronchitis whose respiratory tract mucosa is damaged, normal upper respiratory tract organisms such as *H. influenzae* are able to colonise the lower respiratory tract and will proliferate during acute viral infection.

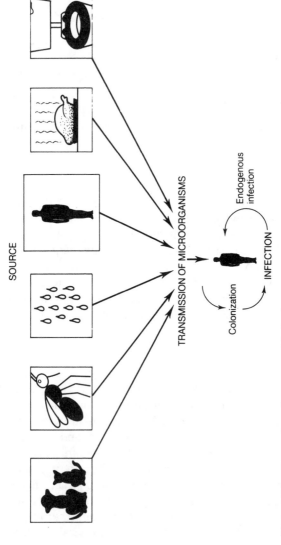

Figure 3.2 Examples of sources of infection

Table 3.1 Examples of normal body flora.

Site	Organism
Upper respiratory tract and nasopharynx	Viridans-type or β-haemolytic streptococci *Moraxella (Branhamella) catarrhalis* *Haemophilus influenzae* *Streptococcus pneumoniae* Coryneforms *Staphyloccus aureus* (mainly anterior nares)
Skin	*S. epidermidis* *Acinetobacter* spp. Transient organisms from nearby sites, e.g. bowel, mouth, nose
Eye	Coryneforms *S. epidermidis* *Neisseria* spp. α-Haemolytic or non-haemolytic streptococci
Mouth	Mixed anaerobes, predominantly Spirochaetes α-Haemolytic streptococci
Stomach	Usually sterile
Upper gut	Predominantly aerobic, e.g. *E. coli*, *Proteus* spp., etc. *Enterococcus faecalis* *Proteus* spp.
Lower gut	Mixed anaerobes predominate, e.g. *Clostridium* spp. Lactobacilli. *Bifidobacterium* spp. etc. Yeasts
Urethra (only anterior third; same organisms as on skin)	*S. epidermidis* Lactobacilli Coryneforms α-Haemolytic streptococci
Female genital tract	Lactobacilli *S. epidermidis* *Mycoplasma hominis* *Staphylococcus aureus* (5%)

N.B. Almost any organism may be transiently carried on the hands, but may not form part of the normal flora of that individual.

Escherichia coli is a normal inhabitant of the gut where it causes no harm; if it is transferred to the bladder it will cause a urinary infection. Only *E. coli* with pili are able to stick to and colonise the bladder mucosa. The normal process of micturition is powerful protection against bladder colonisation. Thus an organism from a healthy carriage site (gut), imbued with particular virulence may invade and produce disease (cystitis), particularly if there is any damage to the urinary tract or a problem with micturition.

It is important that hospital staff are aware that both they and their patients can carry a variety of organisms which may be transferred from transient or permanent carrier sites to a site where they may cause infection.

The normal flora is exceedingly complex. There is, for example, a quite different flora in different parts of the mouth. The vaginal secretions have been found to contain over 50 different species of bacteria. Considering how many bacteria individuals carry, it is remarkable that there is not more invasive disease. However, although one individual may carry microorganisms harmlessly to which he or she is adapted, they may be relatively virulent to other quite healthy subjects. Furthermore, in hospitals, patients are more susceptible to infection by less virulent organisms.

Any individual can thus be a source of infection. Although it is traditional to call exogenous infection 'cross-infection', both endogenous and exogenous infection can be caused by cross-infection. For example, a nurse may catheterise a patient but fail to maintain the sterility of the catheter by (a) contaminating it from her own hand skin flora (exogenous), (b) by contaminating it with the patient's own bowel flora (endogenous), or (c) by contaminating the system by leaving the bag on the floor (exogenous). All these can be a source of urinary tract infection. In each case this is cross-infection.

Figure 3.3 shows examples of exogenous infection.

'Carriers' and infected individuals

In addition to their normal flora, a person may be incubating an infection, acutely ill, recovering from an infection but still a potential source of the organism, or be a chronic carrier of an organism without having any symptoms. All are potential sources of infection for others.

1. *Incubating infection*—many infections have a short *prodromal* phase, consisting of non-specific symptoms such as those of a cold, when the organisms are capable of transmission to others but have not yet produced a diagnostic rash or other definite sign. For mumps this prodromal period may be 6 days and for infections with β-haemolytic streptococci may be 1–2 days. In others such as hepatitis B, the organism is circulating for a long period before jaundice develops. By the time the patient is admitted to hospital because of jaundice, the virus has been present (and the patient *'infectious'*) for about 2 weeks, yet may be no longer infectious.

2. *Acute or chronic infection*—the infecting organisms are often present (and transmissible) in large numbers from one or more of the following: urine, faeces, respiratory tract secretions, discharges from other body systems, or blood, depending on the responsible organism. *Influenza* and *measles*, for example, can spread rapidly by aerosol droplet among susceptible people exposed to the agent. *Tuberculosis*, although less easily transmitted, if not effectively treated can

(a) Environmental cross-infection

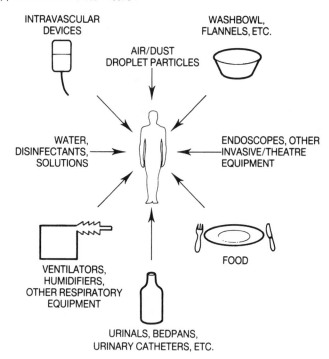

(b) Person-to-person cross-infection

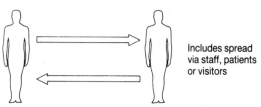

Figure 3.3 Exogenous cross-infection: (a) environmental; (b) person to person.

continue as a chronic active infection for months or years. Transmission to others may be found to have occurred during the period before tuberculosis was diagnosed.

3. *Convalescent carriage*—the organism which caused the infection may still be present after the patient's symptoms have resolved. Usually numbers decrease as time passes, but *typhoid* organisms may continue to be excreted in faeces for years. A food handler, 'recovered' from his infection, may unwittingly be the source of further cases by contaminating food during preparation.

4. *Asymptomatic carriage*—people who have come into contact with someone suffering from infection may unwittingly acquire this organism and then be able to transmit it again. Within the community, streptococci and meningococci are spread in this way, causing no illness in the majority of carriers, but being a source of infection for occasional susceptible hosts. In hospitals, the transfer by staff of methicillin-resistant *S. aureus* (see Chapter 8) between patients may cause infections in susceptible patients, and is the reason for extensive *screening* for colonisation under certain conditions.

The inanimate environment

Although almost any item, from walls and floors to the utensils with which we eat, harbours organisms, the majority of such contamination does not lead to overt infection (see Maki et al, 1982). It is mainly the break down of basic hygiene or of disinfection and sterilisation techniques in hospitals which leads to infection from the inanimate environment. Invasive equipment such as a tracheal, intravenous or urinary catheter causes a break in the skin or interferes with normal clearance mechanisms. They are a portal of entry for environmental organisms.

However, soil, food and water can harbour organisms which act as a source of infection under the right conditions. Soil can contain *Clostridium* spp. and, if a traumatic penetrating injury carries these organisms deep into tissue, anaerobic conditions may permit the organism to multiply. Cooling towers for air-conditioning systems may provide suitable conditions for multiplication and airborne spread of *Legionella* spp., as in the outbreak of legionellosis at Stafford in 1985 (Department of Health and Social Security, 1986). On a smaller scale, a bottle of 'sterile' saline which becomes inadvertently contaminated with Gram-negative organisms because of a failure of aseptic practice and is then used to clean a succession of wounds, is an equally relevant example.

Other animals and birds

A variety of diseases can be spread from animal to man and these are called *zoonoses*. Table 3.2 gives examples of these diseases, their causative organisms, which routes of transmission are involved, and the chief animal or bird hosts. Asterisked diseases are those most likely to be seen in the UK.

In general, it is the agricultural worker, veterinary surgeon or abattoir worker who is most at risk of infection from animals (for more detail see Chapters 8 to 10), and also travellers to other countries. However, many animal products can transmit infection *in food*, such as *salmonellosis* from infected poultry, their eggs, meat and dairy products.

SUSCEPTIBLE HOST

This subject is discussed in more detail in Chapter 4, but some discussion and a description of means of entry to the host is given here. It is important for the nurse to realise how circumstances affect susceptibility to infection. Nursing care for patients may have to be adjusted according to either patient or staff susceptibility, or both.

Example

> Nurses on a paediatric ward may or may not have had chickenpox. Those who have, can safely take care of a child with the disease, being concerned only to avoid bringing contaminated material into contact with susceptible people. Those who are not immune should not nurse the child because they may catch the disease. If a nurse does acquire chickenpox, there is a possibility of transferring the virus to others during the prodromal period of mild upper respiratory symptoms. Because the incubation period is 2–3 weeks, the susceptible nurse may well have forgotten the exposure to chickenpox and may not realise the implication of the 'cold' symptoms. The immunocompromised child with leukaemia is likely to develop severe, sometimes fatal, chickenpox if exposed, particularly while in hospital on chemotherapy.

The *design* and *function* of any hospital brings sick people together, and exposes them to further risk of infection from surgery or invasive techniques which bypass natural defences. Particular factors affecting susceptibility include:

1. extremes of age (neonates and the elderly);
2. drug treatments and radiotherapy, which artificially suppress immunity; and
3. underlying diseases such as diabetes or neoplasia.

Table 3.2 Examples of zoonoses.

Disease	Causative organism	Mode of transmission	Chief host
Anthrax	*Bacillus anthracis*	Contact with infected tissue/hides (cutaneous). Inhalation of spores (pulmonary)	Cattle
Brucellosis	(*) *Brucella abortus*	Contact with infected tissues. Ingestion of infected milk or dairy products	Cattle
	Brucella melitensis	Ingestion of infected milk or dairy products	Sheep or goats
	Brucella suis	Ingestion of infected meat or meat products	Pigs
Tuberculosis	*Mycobacterium bovis*	Ingestion of contaminated meat or dairy products	Cattle
Q fever	(*) *Coxiella burnetii*	Airborne or direct contact with infected tissues, e.g. placentae	Cattle, sheep
Food poisoning	*Salmonella* spp.	Ingestion of contaminated food	Cattle, poultry, eggs
	Campylobacter spp.	Ingestion of contaminated food	Cattle, poultry, other animals

Disease	Organism	Mode of infection	Animal source
Listeriosis	*Listeria monocytogenes	Ingestion of contaminated food. *Trans-placental* route important	Cattle, hens, other animals
Contagious pustular dermatitis	*Orf	Direct contact with infected animals (skin trauma)	Sheep
Chlamydiosis	*Chlamydia psittaci	Direct contact with infected animals, e.g. placentae and inhalation. *Trans-placental* infection or abortion may occur	Sheep
Psittacosis	(*) Chlamydia psittaci	Direct contact with infected birds; inhalation	Parrots
Ornithosis	(*) Chlamydia psittaci	As above	Other birds
Leptospirosis (canicola fever)	*Leptospira canicola	Direct contact with infected animals or with water contaminated with infected urine involving inoculation of mucous membranes, or inhalation	Dogs (puppies)
	*Leptospira hardjo	Inoculation of mucous membranes, or inhalation	Cattle
(Weil's disease)	*Leptospira icterohaemorragiae	Direct contact with infected animal or urine, or inhalation	Rats
Plague	Yersinia pestis	Flea-bite inoculation, or inhalation, or direct contact with infected animal tissues	Wild rodents, chiefly rats

---

Table 3.2 Continued.

Disease	Causative organism	Mode of transmission	Chief host
Tularaemia	*Francisella tularensis*	Inoculation from arthropod bite or of mucous membranes from infected animals; also inhalation or ingestion	Rodents and rabbits
Lassa fever		Inoculation with infected rodent urine	Rats (West Africa)
Toxoplasmosis	*Toxoplasma gondii	Ingestion of faecally contaminated soil or undercooked meat. *Transplacental* infection occurs	Cats
Rabies		Inoculation from bite of infected animal	Dogs, foxes, bats
Lyme disease	*Borrelia burgdorferi	Inoculation from tick bite from infected animal host	Deer

* Likely to be seen in the UK.
(*) Possibility of being seen in the UK.

N.B. Secondary person-to-person transmission can occur in plague, tuberculosis, brucella, Lassa fever and food poisoning.

This is discussed in more detail in Chapter 11.

Hospital-acquired (nosocomial) infection is infection acquired in hospital, whether originating from a patient, a member of staff or the environment or equipment. Two large studies of hospital-acquired infection show the extent of the problem for susceptible hosts **in** hospital. They reveal that a considerable proportion of infections in hospitalised patients are acquired in hospital. The report on the national prevalence survey of infection in hospitals in England and Wales (Meers et al, 1981) showed that 19% of patients were infected, half of these with nosocomial infections. The report of the US study on the efficacy of nosocomial infection control (Haley et al, 1985) found that the overall incidence of nosocomial infections was 5.7 per 100 admissions. These surveys are discussed in more detail in Chapter 11. The fact that so many hospitalised people do acquire infection, at least some of which is preventable, should cause concern for all health-care workers. As nurses give so much 'hands-on' care to patients, they must be particularly aware of the dangers to patients, and of the safe procedures which are designed to prevent spread of infection. Chapters 12 to 14 discuss this in detail.

With regard to *community infection*, Meers et al (1981) found that half of those admitted to hospital already had infections. The majority of these were respiratory tract infections, both bacterial (especially *Haemophilus influenzae* in chronic bronchitis) and viral (influenza and other 'flu-like' illnesses). Elderly people with chronic 'wounds' such as leg ulcers colonised with bacteria often require hospital admission, as may some with gastroenteritis. Children are not usually admitted with mild childhood infectious diseases such as mumps, varicella or whooping cough, but it is still occasionally necessary.

Within the community itself, bacterial infections are less likely to cause 'outbreaks' of infection, disease being a product of an individuals' underlying disease or misfortune. However, viral infections of the respiratory tract easily spread within households and workplaces. It is usually only the most vulnerable, such as infants with respiratory syncytial virus bronchiolitis, who require hospitalisation. Nevertheless, the already infected individuals may be susceptible to further infection, or be the cause of cross-infection on a small scale.

So, in both hospital and community, there is a large population of people who are more than usually susceptible to infection. If health-care workers understand the process of infection and the susceptibility of their patients, they can attempt to minimise the risk by interrupting the chain of infection.

Routes of entry

1. **Respiratory tract**, by *inhalation* of organisms such as common cold viruses, tuberculosis, diphtheria, influenza, mumps.
2. **Alimentary tract**, by *ingestion* of organisms such as dysentery bacilli or amoebae, hepatitis A virus, poliovirus, *Salmonella* spp.
3. **Skin and mucous membranes**, by *inoculation* to deeper tissues by surgery (*Staphylococcus aureus*), insect bites, injection with contaminated products, trauma (*Clostridium* spp.), or sexual contact (HIV). Intact skin is a natural barrier to infection. Mucous membranes, although more permeable than skin, are a good defence mechanism against many organisms, the mucous acting as a barrier and hindering the adherence of organisms to the surface.
4. **Trans-placentally**, a few organisms (such as cytomega-

lovirus, rubella virus and *Listeria monocytogenes*) can be transmitted from mother to fetus *in utero*.

ROUTES/MEANS OF TRANSMISSION

The main routes of transmission fall into five categories.

1. **Contact transfer**—the most important in nosocomial infection:
    (a) *direct contact*, e.g. transfer of organisms from one patient to another via staff hands; endogenous infection where commensal organisms are carried from a patient's skin to a susceptible site during surgery; and sexually transmitted diseases; or
    (b) *indirect contact*, via 'fomites' (inanimate objects) such as bedding or communal equipment.
2. **Airborne transfer**—involving inhalation of organisms:
    (a) in *droplets* from one individual to another during kissing, coughing or sneezing, e.g. streptococcal infection;
    (b) in *droplet nuclei*, i.e. bacteria or viruses in protective droplets of fluid which remain suspended in the air indefinitely to be inhaled by another individual, e.g. tuberculosis and measles.
3. **Common vehicle**—by contaminated food (salmonellosis), water (cholera), solutions (*Pseudomonas* spp.), drugs or blood products (hepatitis B and others).
4. **Vector-borne**—via arthropods, e.g. ticks. Mosquitoes, which commonly transmit infection in many countries (e.g. malaria), are rare in Britain. See Chapter 10.
5. **Blood-borne**—via inoculation injury or sexual transmission. HBV and HIV infection are the main organisms of concern and inoculation injury is the

main route for health-care settings. Other viruses and syphilis may also be involved. (Sometimes included as part of *direct contact* transfer.)

Note that more than one route of transmission may be involved with some organisms.

The practising nurse needs to understand the relevance of these routes of transmission in order to care safely for his/her patients. For example, there is no point in isolating the patient with malaria because he/she cannot transmit the disease directly to others. However, blood for transfusion is not taken from individuals who have been to the tropics because of the risk of transfusion-associated malaria in the recipient.

Conversely, it would be a foolish nurse who allowed a child with chickenpox to be nursed in a communal ward where immunosuppressed children would be put at grave risk.

Chickenpox illustrates the point that many organisms can be spread by more than one route. Chickenpox can be spread to susceptible people by the *airborne* route, by *direct contact* with the lesions, and by *indirect contact* via recently contaminated articles such as linen or tissues. In this instance, the patient will need to be nursed by immune staff in a single room, with the door closed, and care taken to safely contain contaminated articles. (See also Chapters 9, 12 and 14.)

REFERENCES

Haley RW, Culver DH, White JW, et al (1985) The efficacy of infection surveillance and control programs in preventing nosocomial infections in the US hospitals. *Am. J. Epidemiol.* **121**(2): 182–205.
Department of Health and Social Security (1986) *The Report of the Committee of Inquiry into an Outbreak of Food Poisoning at Stanley Royal Hospital.* London: HMSO.

Maki DG, Alvarado CJ, Hassemer CA and Zilz MA (1982) Relation of the inanimate environment to endemic nosocomial infection. *New Engl. J. Med.* **307**: 1562–1566.

Meers PD, Ayliffe GAJ, Emmerson AM, Leigh DA, Mayon-White RT, McKintosh CA and Stronge JL (1981) Report of the National Survey on Infection in Hospitals. *J. Hosp. Inf.* **2** (Suppl. 2).

4 Immunity

INTRODUCTION

This chapter is concerned with the mechanisms which make up the immune responses protecting the individual against infection. *Non-specific defence mechanisms*, the natural barriers to infection such as skin, mucous surfaces, secretions and mechanical structures, are discussed first. The *inflammatory process* and *phagocytosis* or the engulfing of organisms are explained, and the *complement system* is discussed in some detail. *Specific immune responses* (which come into force if non-specific mechanisms fail) are then described. An initial meeting of an individual with a particular organism will lead to the formation of *antibodies* (*humoral immunity*); these directly neutralise viral infectivity and combine with complement to aid killing of bacteria. *Cell-mediated immunity* concerns the actions of T-lymphocytes, which are sensitised to react to 'foreign' antigens, and are also involved in delayed hypersensitivity and transplant rejection. A brief summary of the immune response explains how all these mechanisms are linked; and the chapter concludes with a description of vaccination and immunisation.

The term 'immunity' in relation to infectious disease derives from the original meaning of the term 'exemption from military service or paying taxes'. It had been recognised from early times that those who had suffered and recovered from infectious disease, e.g. smallpox, measles or diphtheria, were exempt from further attacks of that disease. Such people have developed a *specific immune response* to the infecting organism. The mechanism of this immune response which involves lymphocytes in the lymph nodes and spleen is discussed in detail later (p. 69). Briefly, in the immune individual, re-exposure to the infection results in rapid recognition and destruction of the organisms before they can cause disease. But this is only true for organisms to which the patient has developed an immune response, as a result of either vaccination or previous infection. There is no such thing as generalised immunity to all infectious diseases. Immunity is specific, that is it indicates the ability of the host to resist one particular invader.

The specific immune response is not the only defence against pathogenic organisms. There are a number of *non-specific mechanisms*, not dependent on previous exposure to the organism, which attempt, not always successfully, to prevent the establishment of infection even in non-immune people. It is when these mechanisms fail that the specific immune response becomes of vital importance. These mechanisms will be discussed in the order corresponding roughly to that in which they would act in an individual exposed to infection for the first time.

Non-specific defence mechanisms

1. Prevention of invasion:
   (a) skin,
   (b) mucous surfaces,
   (c) secretions, and
   (d) mechanical arrangement of structures.
2. General influences.
3. Non-specific mechanisms following invasion: inflammation and phagocytosis; interferon production in virus infections.
4. The complement system.

Specific immune responses

1. Induction of the immune response.
2. Mechanisms of action of the specific immune response:
   (a) B-lymphocytes and antibody production (*humoral immunity*); and
   (b) T-lymphocytes and *cell-mediated immunity*.

NON-SPECIFIC DEFENCE MECHANISMS

Prevention of invasion

The body is surrounded by organisms, both pathogenic and non-pathogenic, since they are present on everything we touch and eat and the air we breathe; therefore the skin and mucous surfaces must form the first line of defence. (See Figure 4.1.)

The skin

The skin has often been said to be impermeable to invasion by pathogenic organisms, but this is only a half-truth. The skin is a complex structure, constantly renewing itself and containing hair follicles, sweat and sebaceous glands. The hair follicles and sweat glands harbour many organisms which it is impossible to remove in spite of the most meticulous treatment, and pathogenic organisms frequently invade from these sites. Axillary abscesses and beard infections are common results of such infection and are difficult to treat. Intact skin does, however, form a barrier against many pathogenic bacteria, and its secretions have antibacterial properties.

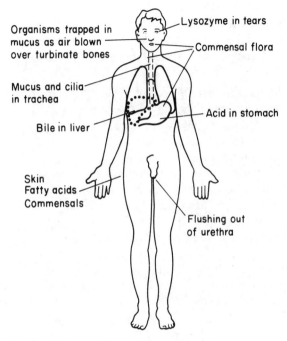

Lysozyme in tears

Organisms trapped in mucus as air blown over turbinate bones

Commensal flora

Mucus and cilia in trachea

Bile in liver

Acid in stomach

Skin
Fatty acids
Commensals

Flushing out of urethra

Figure 4.1 Non-specific barriers to infection.

Mucous surfaces

In certain situations where the number of bacteria is high the surfaces are moistened with a mucous secretion to entrap the organisms until they can be removed; the nose, mouth and vagina are good examples of this.

Secretions

All organs in the body which are in contact with the external environment produce secretions. These are most appreciable in places where there is potentially the greatest danger of bacterial invasion. These secretions act in two ways.

1. *Mechanical action*—secretions of the bronchi entrap organisms and the flow of secretion is moved away from the alveoli by the action of the cilia on the bronchial walls. Tears also wash organisms away from the conjunctivae.

2. *Chemical action of their constituents*—these secretions may be acid, like sweat, adult vaginal secretion and gastric juice, or contain fatty acids, like sweat, or be strongly alkaline, like bile. Abrupt changes from an acid to an alkaline environment are known, for example, to keep the bacterial flora of the alimentary canal in check. Tears and certain other mucosal secretions, for example nasal mucus and saliva, contain an active antibacterial substance, lysozyme.

The mechanical arrangement of structures

As air is inspired, it is taken in at high velocity as if by a vacuum cleaner, and this air may contain many pathogenic organisms. The arrangement of the mucus-covered turbinate bones in the nose is such that the air impinges upon them and bacteria stick to the mucous surfaces. The speed of flow of air is considerably reduced, due to the increasing area of the bronchial passages, with the result that by the time the air reaches the alveoli it is travelling very slowly and contains very few organisms. The mucus, swept by the cilia up the air passages into the pharynx, is subsequently swallowed and many of the organisms are killed by the acid in the gastric juice.

The direction of the bronchi may have something to do with the localisation of lung infections and the short straight auditory tubes in infants may play a part in the greater frequency of middle-ear infections in comparison with infections in adults. The shortness of the urethra in the female compared with that of the male accounts for the ease with which organisms can ascend to the bladder and cause cystitis.

General influences

These include a wide range of factors which will vary from one individual to another and will affect that person's response to any invading organism. General health, any underlying disease, state of nutrition, metabolic activity, hormonal influences and genetic factors all play a part.

Non-specific defence mechanisms following invasion

If an organism succeeds in getting through the non-specific barriers above, and so enters the tissues, further non-specific defence mechanisms are activated. These are still not dependent on the specific immune response but, as will be seen later, their efficiency is greatly enhanced by it.

Non-specific inflammation and phagocytosis

Most organisms, once they have entered the tissues, will cause inflammation. The signs of inflammation are heat, redness, swelling and tenderness or pain. These signs are similar whether the tissue irritant is a *Staphylococcus*, a sterile splinter or a chemical irritant.

Capillary dilatation results in an outpouring of fluid, white cells and some red cells from the blood vessels into

the tissues. This outpouring of cells and serum is
important, since it brings them into contact with the
organisms. Serum contains substances which attach non-
specifically to the surfaces of many organisms. This can
lead, after further interactions with yet another series of
serum factors called the *complement system*, to engulfment
of the organisms by phagocytic cells.

Interferon

When cells are infected by viruses they may release
interferon, which increases the resistance of neighbouring
cells to the infection. Interferon is mentioned on pp. 113
and 239 as a substance released by infected cells. It is
now clear that there are many related types of interferon
which play a complex regulatory role in cellular processes,
which need not involve viruses. They appear to be the
first line of defence against viral infection, appearing
within 48 h of infection, several days before antibody
production. They do not act as antiviral agents themselves,
but stimulate proteins to be synthesised in cells which
inhibit replication of the virus. There are three main
types of human interferon:

1. *alpha*, from leucocytes (IFNα);
2. *beta*, from fibroblasts (IFNβ); and
3. *gamma*, from antigenically stimulated lymphocytes
   (IFNγ).

There has been some excitement about possible anti-
tumour effects, and genetically engineered interferon is
now available in sufficient quantity to permit extensive
use in clinical trials. Treatment with interferon has had
some useful effect against herpes eye infections and also
in chronic hepatitis B and varicella zoster virus infections
in immunocompromised patients (see Thomas, 1988;
Jawetz et al, 1989; Zuckerman et al, 1990).

In the process of *phagocytosis* (see Figure 4.2), phagocytic cells ingest invading organisms and destroy them with enzymes. Two types of white cell are involved, both arising in stem cells of the bone marrow.

1. *Polymorphonuclear leucocytes (neutrophils)*—these circulate in the blood for only a few hours and are attracted to the scene of infection by chemotactic substances (chemicals released in the inflammatory process).
2. *Mononuclear phagocytes*—these pass into the blood as *monocytes* and are then integrated into tissue as *fixed macrophages* or wander as *free macrophages*. They can maintain their activity for a considerable period of time. They also process antigens (see p. 69) and secrete interleukin-2 (see p. 83) which is responsible for activating T- and B-lymphocytes.

The complement system

The complement system (abbreviated as C′) consists of numerous enzymes and co-factors which interact with each other in an orderly sequence, often called an 'enzyme cascade'. When the complement system is activated, there are several important consequences which help in the destruction of infecting organisms.

Activation of the complement system

The complement system can be activated by contact with the surfaces of some organisms (see Figure 4.3). This type of complement activation is called the 'alternative pathway'. The other type of complement activation, called the 'classical pathway' because it was the first to be described, involves antibody and will be considered later with the 'specific' immune response. The two

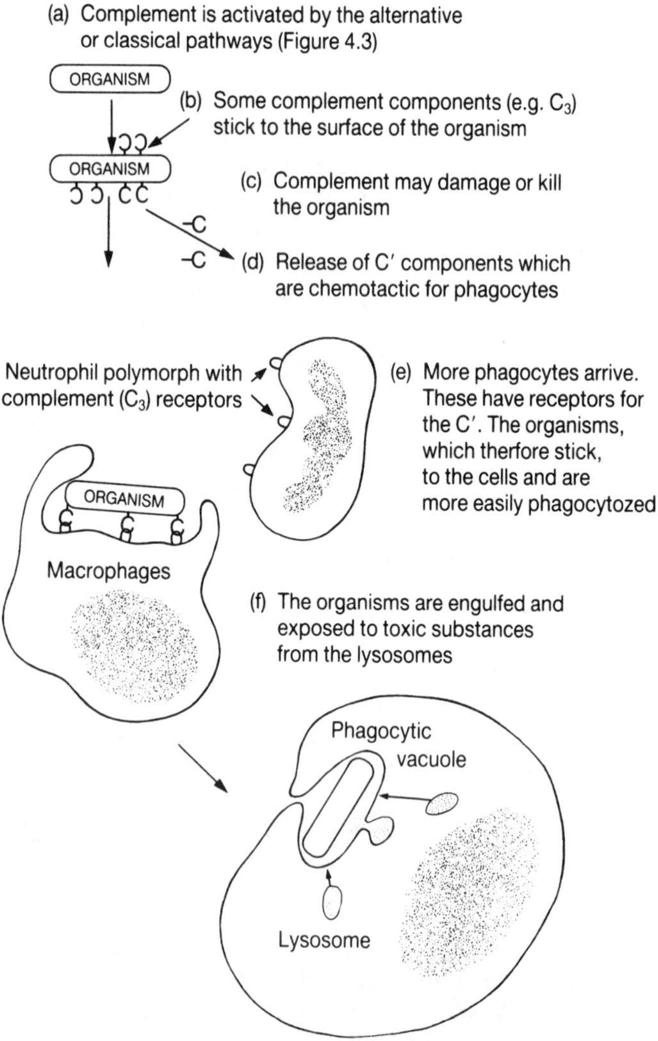
(a) Complement is activated by the alternative or classical pathways (Figure 4.3)
ORGANISM
(b) Some complement components (e.g. C3) stick to the surface of the organism
ORGANISM
(c) Complement may damage or kill the organism
(d) Release of C′ components which are chemotactic for phagocytes
Neutrophil polymorph with complement (C3) receptors
(e) More phagocytes arrive. These have receptors for the C′. The organisms, which therfore stick, to the cells and are more easily phagocytozed
ORGANISM
Macrophages
(f) The organisms are engulfed and exposed to toxic substances from the lysosomes
Phagocytic vacuole
Lysosome

Figure 4.2 Phagocytosis.

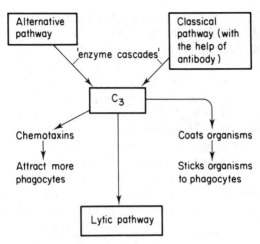

Figure 4.3 Activation of the complement system.

pathways lead, via 'enzyme cascades', to the activation of the most important complement component, known as C_3.

Antimicrobial effects of the complement system

Complement components from the blood will leak out into a site of inflammation and infection (see Figures 4.2 and 4.3). Once activated at such a site the following things may happen:

1. The organisms may become coated with derivatives of one of the complement components known as C_3. This causes the organisms to adhere strongly to the membranes of phagocytic cells which have a binding site or 'receptor' for C_3. This attachment of the organisms to phagocytes greatly increases the efficiency with which they are engulfed. Indeed C_3 is so important that congenital absence of it leads rapidly to death from infection.

2. Other components are then modified enzymically and become active as chemotaxins. That is to say that they attract more phagocytic cells to the site of infection.

3. Another group of complement components can lyse cell membranes (*the lytic pathway*). These are the factors which lyse red blood cells when an unmatched blood transfusion has been given. A few species of bacteria and viruses can be killed by this lytic pathway, but this function of complement, although the most well known, is not as important as the binding to membranes via C_3 and congenital absence of one of the factors involved can be symptomless.

Destruction of engulfed organisms

Once engulfed by phagocytes (polymorphs or macrophages) with the help of the alternative complement pathway and C_3, the organisms are contained within membrane-bound vacuoles called 'phagosomes', where they are exposed to a variety of microbicidal mechanisms. Then the contents of the lysosomes are emptied into the phagosomes. Lysosomes contain a number of digestive enzymes which help to eliminate the organisms. Occasionally the situation is reversed and the organisms kill the phagocytes. Pus is an accumulation of living and dead phagocytes, other blood and tissue cells, cell debris and bacteria.

THE SPECIFIC IMMUNE RESPONSE

While the struggle outlined above is going on, the lymphocytes in the lymphoid system are beginning to mount the specific immune response, which then comes to the aid of the non-specific mechanisms.

The induction of the immune response (See Figure 4.4)

Stage 1

Every organism is made up of a unique mixture of cell wall components, cytoplasm, enzymes and perhaps toxins. Most of these molecules are unlike anything present in the patient's own tissues and so are recognised as 'foreign'. These are known as *antigens*. Antigens from the infecting organism pass along the lymphatics, free or in macrophages, to the draining lymph nodes.

Stage 2

In the draining lymph node, the antigens come into contact with the surfaces of lymphocytes. Each lymphocyte carries on its surface *receptors* which enable it to recognise one particular type of antigen. When antigen attaches to lymphocytes with receptors of the right specificity the cells begin to proliferate. This proliferation leads to a great increase in the number of lymphocytes able to recognise the antigen in question.

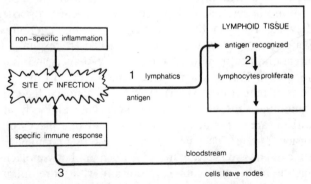

Figure 4.4 Induction of the immune response.

Stage 3

The lymphocytes leave the lymph node via the efferent lymphatics and travel to the site of the infection via the blood stream. Here they assist in the struggle against the infection in a number of ways.

Humoral immunity

Mechanisms of action of the specific immune response B-lymphocytes and antibody production

The lymphocytes discussed above are of two kinds: B-lymphocytes (B-cells) derived from bone marrow and T-lymphocytes (T-cells), also derived from bone marrow but become thymus dependent, requiring the thymus gland for development (see p. 75).

The *B-lymphocytes* are the basis of *humoral immunity* and they are the precursors of *antibody-producing cells* (plasma cells). Plasma cells release molecules similar to the antigen-recognising receptors already described and these molecules, which are referred to as *antibody*, accumulate in the serum and may be present in astonishingly large quantities. Antibodies are subdivided into several classes, each of which has different properties; they are referred to collectively as 'immunoglobulins'. They are proteins which are produced in response to infection. The immunoglobulins are Y-shaped and made up of two Fab fragments (the arms of the Y) and one Fc fragment (the Y stem). The Fab fragments have the combining sites for specific antigens, and antibody and antigen are constructed so that they fit like pieces of a jigsaw puzzle. The Fc fragment has the complement attachment site (see Figure 4.5). Each antibody molecule has the ability to combine specifically with more antigen of the kind which induced the proliferative lymphocyte

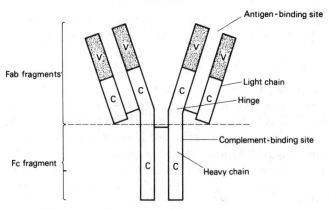

Figure 4.5 Antibody structure and function.

response in the draining lymph node. In fact since each antibody molecule may have several antigen-specific combining sites, it may be able to attach to several antigen molecules. Other B cells develop into *memory cells* the function of which is to respond quickly to any further invasion by the same antigen. They spread through the lymphatic system to be 'on guard'. The development of these cells to form an immunological memory takes several weeks, but that memory then lasts for life. Second exposure to antigen will lead to a much more rapid and powerful production of antibody. This is seen clearly when giving a booster immunisation many years after the initial course.

The major types (classes) of antibody

IgG

The most abundant class of antibody in the serum is immunoglobulin G (IgG). Each molecule of IgG has two antigen-binding sites. IgG crosses the placenta and so is present in babies at birth. It appears in an individual 1–2 weeks after infection and lasts for a considerable time.

IgM

The other major class of antibody in serum is IgM. It is larger than IgG and each molecule has 10 antigen-binding sites. It is the first to appear, about 1 week after the onset of an acute infection, and lasts for 4–6 weeks. Small amounts of IgM may be produced in chronic infections. How recent an infection is can be guessed by measuring IgM and IgG antibodies to an organism, but this is not infallible.

Other antibodies

Other classes of antibody are usually present only in small quantities in serum and have rather special properties.

IgA is actively secreted into the gut, bronchi, tears and saliva. It helps to block adherence of bacteria and viruses to mucous surfaces.

IgE is the immunoglobulin class responsible for hay fever because, rather than circulating in the blood, it attaches itself to mast cells and basophils. These are triggered to release compounds such as histamine in the presence of the antigen to which the IgE binds. IgE is also found in high serum levels in worm infections.

IgD remains an uncertain quantity, but appears to have no antibody function.

Figure 4.6 illustrates the ways in which antibody (mainly IgM and IgG) protect the host.

1. By combining with the active parts of toxins, such as those released in diphtheria or tetanus, antibody can neutralise their effects.

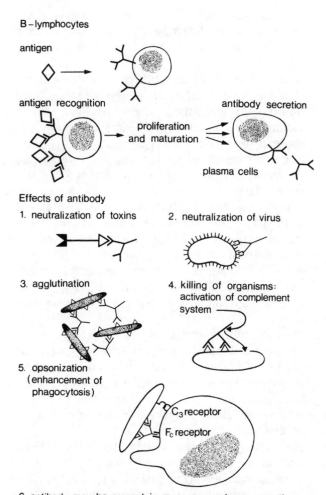

Figure 4.6 B-lymphocyte mechanisms in the specific immune response.

2. Viruses must attach to cells before they can enter them and cause infection. Antibody can cover the virus and block its ability to do this, e.g. influenza virus.

3. Since each antibody molecule can combine with more than one antigen molecule, antibody can agglutinate antigens or antigen-carrying organisms. Such big clumps of, for instance, small viruses are more easily engulfed by phagocytic cells.

4. Some organisms become coated with complement (p. 65) by means of a direct interaction with various serum factors. Other organisms do not activate complement until antibody molecules have attached to their surfaces. After this has occurred, the antigen-bound antibody itself can activate the complement system (classical pathway, see Figure 4.3), which leads to attachment of complement to the surface of the organism. Some organisms are lysed by these complement components (lytic pathway, see Figure 4.3).

5. Receptors for complement (C_3 receptors) are found on the membranes of phagocytic cells (p. 65). There are also receptors for the free end of antibody molecules (F_c receptors) and the 'opsonised' organism thus sticks firmly to macrophages and polymorphs which can then phagocytose the organism very efficiently.

6. Antibody (IgA) is secreted into the bronchi, the gut and tears and so can reinforce the non-specific barriers such as mucus and cilia (p. 59). Antibody is also secreted in the maternal milk and some subclasses (IgG) can cross the placenta so that babies are protected for the first few months of life by the mother's antibody. Meanwhile they begin to develop their own immune responses.

Cell-mediated immunity

T-lymphocytes and cell-mediated immunity

T-lymphocytes are the cells responsible for cell-mediated immunity, which protects an individual from intracellular bacterial infections, viral and some fungal infections. It is also the major element of defence against parasites and tumours and is involved in transplant rejection.

Several types of cell are involved in this system but the primary effector cells are the *T-lymphocytes* which are so called because they are dependent, particularly in early life, on the *thymus* gland where these cells mature. These lymphocytes are absent in the rare children with congenital absence of the thymus and such children have very low resistance to infection, due primarily to loss of cell-mediated immunity. As the name implies, this involves the direct interaction of T-lymphocytes with antigen.

Two important ways in which T-cell mediated immunity protects the host are illustrated in Figure 4.7.

1. When a T-cell encounters the antigen which its receptors recognise, it may release mediators known collectively as 'lymphokines'. IFNγ is an example of a lymphokine. The lymphokines make macrophages in the vicinity become activated. This involves a number of complex metabolic changes, the most important of which is an increased ability to destroy microorganisms. For example, tubercle bacilli, even when coated with antibody and complement, appear not be killed by normal macrophages but activated macrophages can destroy them. This is also the mechanism of defence against leprosy.

2. T-cells and their 'assistants', the activated macrophages, are also able to recognize and damage cells

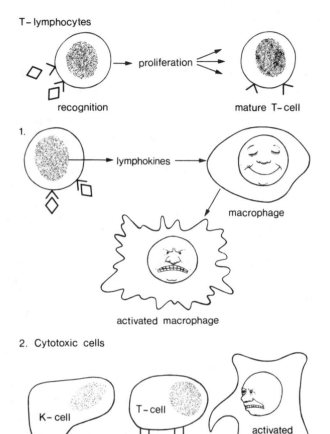

Figure 4.7 T-lymphocyte mechanisms in the specific immune response.

which have become foreign to the host. For instance, virus-infected cells may express viral antigens on to their surface. The cell-mediated response can recognise these antigens and help to localise the infection by attacking such cells and interrupting the virus replication cycle (the attacking cells are known as 'cytotoxic cells'). This mechanism is of particular importance for defence against viruses such as varicella–zoster which can pass directly from cell to cell without being released into the body fluids where they would be exposed to antibody. This is why it is common to see an exacerbation of varicella–zoster when T-cell function is compromised, e.g. in patients undergoing cytotoxic therapy.

When T-cells proliferate they differentiate into two main types of cell.

1. *Helper* T-cells which activate or encourage B-cell proliferation and so encourage antibody production (humoral immunity) by the new plasma cells. These react to antibodies to the CD4 cell surface antigen, and they comprise about 65% of the total.
2. *Suppressor* T-cells which counteract the helper cells, preventing excessive reaction and damage to tissues. They make up approximately 35% of the total, and react to antibodies to CD8 antigens.

Within this population there are further subgroups including *cytotoxic* T-cells which destroy foreign cells, tumour cells, infected cells; and lymphokine-producing cells which stimulate phagocytosis.

The interaction between the main population and the subpopulations is extremely complex but, in summary, the balance between the two is crucial: if the helpers are in excess this will lead to autoimmune disease, whilst if the helpers are decreased this will result in immune deficiency disease.

Memory T-cells are also formed with each new meeting with an invader cell and the immunological memory will last for many years. They can then produce a rapid response to any future contact with a particular antigen in the same way as memory B-cells.

Imbalance in the immune system

In some genetic diseases, either or both B- and T-cells can be absent. T-cells are necessary for stimulation of B-cells, leading to antibody production. Lack of B-cells and antibodies leads to agammaglobulinaemia (relative or total lack of one class of antibody) which can leave the child susceptible to overwhelming infection.

Autoimmune diseases such as rheumatoid arthritis and systemic lupus erythematosus (SLE) are thought to be connected with some failure of balance in the immune system, possible failure of suppressor T-cells leading to the body's defences attacking itself.

The action of T-cells and macrophages in controlling cancers has already been mentioned. The increased incidence of malignancies in old age may be connected with the decreasing influence of the thymus gland itself. T-cell numbers in the blood progressively fall with age.

In treatment of infection with HIV measurement of the ratio of CD4 to CD8 cells is used to define the progression of the disease and the need for therapy.

SKIN TESTS

If a quantity of antigen too small to cause non-specific inflammation is introduced into the skin of a non-immune individual, nothing can be seen at the site of injection.

If the individual has developed a cell-mediated immune response to the antigen in question, T-lymphocytes and macrophages accumulate at the site of injection and cause inflammation, swelling and induration, reaching a peak at 48 or 72 h. This phenomenon, referred to as delayed hypersensitivity is the basis of the tuberculin test. It can be used to test for cell-mediated responsiveness to many other antigens apart from tuberculin (see below).

However, at least two other phenomena can occur at such a skin-test site, and these must be distinguished from delayed hypersensitivity.

Thus if the individual has IgE antibody to the test antigen (see p. 72) there may be an immediate reaction within minutes due to mediator release from mast cells. Similarly, if there is much IgG or IgM, antigen/antibody complexes may form in the blood vessel walls at the test site. This causes inflammation within 8 h which then declines. Thus tuberculin tests should always be read at 72 h.

Hypersensitivity tests suggesting a previous dose of a pathogenic organism

Hypersensitivity reactions may be:

1. *immediate*, when they are an allergic response of the body to foreign proteins, e.g. hay fever; or
2. *delayed*, when the response is dependent on immunologically activated lymphocytes reaching the entry site of the antigen. The delay is due to the fact that the lymphocytes have to migrate to this site.

This reaction of delayed hypersensitivity is the basis of the tuberculin test (e.g. Mantoux or Heaf test). A positive reaction does not necessarily mean that the patient has active tuberculosis at the time of the test, but that at some previous date he/she has been exposed to the relevant antigens. The diagnostic value of a positive tuberculin test is, therefore, limited. Many people have a mild primary infection with tuberculosis in childhood or adolescence, which resolves spontaneously and with minimal symptoms. Others have BCG (a live mycobacterial organism) immunisation in adolescence, so the majority of adults in the UK are tuberculin test positive.

Another well-known skin test is the Schick test, now regarded as insensitive and non-specific. *Corynebacterium diphtheriae* toxin is injected into the skin. If local redness and swelling develops, the patient has no antibodies and should be immunised. A lack of reaction indicates that antigen was neutralised by the patient's antibodies.

SUMMARY OF THE IMMUNE RESPONSE
(See Figure 4.8)

In the last few pages the most important mechanisms which contribute to the immune response have been described. It is essential to realise that during an actual infection all of these mechanisms will play some part, so that an analysis of what is happening at any one time becomes very complicated. This is partly because they are all interrelated. For instance macrophages are important for both antibody responses and cell-mediated responses, and the presence of some antibody and complement is probably essential for the optimal functioning of cell-mediated responses.

If the various mechanisms are understood it is possible to predict the sequence of events in a particular disease. For example, a virus enters by the mouth or respiratory tract and initially infects the mucosa in one of these sites. Physical barriers oppose this, and secreted antibody may prevent it in the immune individual. If the virus succeeds

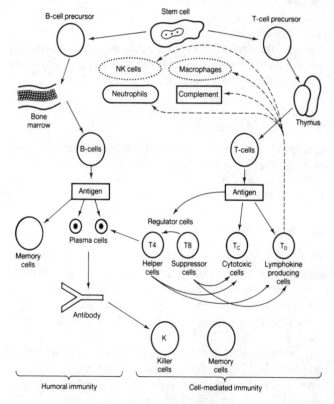

Figure 4.8 Mechanisms of acquired immunity.

in establishing itself in the cells of the mucosa, it replicates and is released into the blood stream. This is a critical stage. If antibody is present the virus is neutralised, agglutinated and coated with antibody and complement so that it adheres to phagocytes in the blood, liver and spleen via the complement and antibody receptors. It is then rapidly removed and destroyed. In the absence of antibody, the tiny virus particles are not efficiently removed and survive to reach their target organ (the nervous system in poliomyelitis etc.). They then enter cells again, so that antibody is of little help except to mop up any further released virus; the cell-mediated response must take over by recognising infected cells and limiting local spread. Thus all the mechanisms discussed have occurred in one disease.

NEW DEVELOPMENTS

Immunology is a very rapidly developing field and there are a number of advances of which the reader should be aware, in addition to the very simplified scheme described earlier in this chapter.

Immunogenetics

When studying the antigens against which the immune response is directed during graft rejection, it was noticed that most of these were coded for only one chromosome, in a closely linked group of loci now known as the major histocompatibility complex (MHC). This stretch of DNA codes for several immunologically relevant molecules and, in particular, for two major classes of cell surface glycopeptide. Apart from their role in graft rejection these glycopeptides are involved in 'communication' between lymphoid cells, and between macrophages and lymphocytes. Moreover, antigens are recognised in association with these glycopeptides on the surfaces of antigen-presenting or infected cells. Thus they may have fundamental regulatory roles in deciding *which antigens* should evoke responses and which *type of response* should be activated.

There are many different alleles which can occur at each locus within the major histocompatibility complex. These code for subtly different variants of these important glycopeptides. Thus in some ways it resembles the blood group system, although far more complex. Possession of some of these variants is associated with an increased incidence of certain diseases. Since the human major histocompatibility complex has been named the 'human leucocyte antigen' (HLA) system, such diseases are described as HLA-linked. Ankylosing spondylitis is the most clear-cut example.

Interleukins

These are substances which affect functioning of lymphocytes and some other cells. More than 10 interleukins have now been described, three important examples of which are given below.

1. Interleukin-1—derived from macrophages, and leads to a temporary increase in T-cells. Causes fever.
2. Interleukin-2—derived from T-lymphocytes; used to increase T-cell lines in tissue culture.
3. Interleukin-3—produced by T-cells to help increase differentiation in some other white blood cell types.

Monoclonal antibodies

It is now possible to fuse antibody-producing cells with tumour cells, to make an 'immortal' clone of dividing antibody secreting cells, known as a hybridoma (see Figure 4.9). A hybridoma can go on making antibody of one specificity forever, providing unlimited quantities of a perfectly standardised reagent. Such monoclonal reagents are more specific than immune serum which contains mixtures of antibodies derived from large numbers of B-cells of slightly different specificity.

These monoclonal antibodies are revolutionising biology because they provide astonishingly precise probes for analysing the structure of complex organic molecules. Moreover their clinical importance is becoming apparent, because selected monoclonal antibodies can be used to identify viral and bacterial antigens, and for blood and tissue typing. Human hybridomas have now been used in treatment, e.g. a monoclonal antibody has been used to treat Gram-negative bacteraemia (Thomas, 1988). Work is still being done on use of monoclonal antibodies against tumour cells.

VACCINATION AND IMMUNISATION

Immunisation to prevent infectious diseases is an example of a highly effective medical development. Even 'straightforward' childhood diseases such as measles and chickenpox have some degree of associated mortality (annual average of 13 deaths from measles in the UK in 1970–1988 (Department of Health, 1990)) and the congential abnormalities associated with rubella during early pregnancy are well known. Smallpox is an example of a disease with a high mortality rate which has been totally eradicated by a campaign to immunise all contacts of cases in the endemic areas.

Immunisation, which is *artificially acquired immunity*, may be short-term passive immunity or active immunity when the production of specific antibody is stimulated in

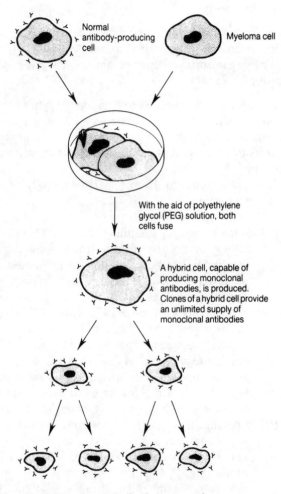

Figure 4.9 Monoclonal antibody preparation.

response to administration of specific antigen, but without causing a clinical attack of the disease.

Passive immunity

Serum from an individual or animal convalescing from a particular infection contains specific antibody to the infecting organism. This specific antibody is given in the following three situations.

1. It is given *therapeutically* to a patient who has already succumbed to the same disease and is not producing sufficient antibody to combat the causative organism or its toxins, e.g. diphtheria antitoxin and antitetanus serum.
2. It is given *protectively* to a person already at high risk from infection:

    (a) human normal immunoglobulin (HNIG) consisting of pooled plasma from many donors, containing antibody to prevalent viruses, can be given to protect susceptible children with conditions such as leukaemia or congenital heart abnormalities if exposed to a child with measles, for example. HNIG has also been used prophylactically against hepatitis A for travellers to and those working in countries where there is a high prevalence or where sanitation is poor. It is also used repeatedly as protection against infection for patients with agammaglobulinaemia.

    (b) Specific immunoglobulin from pooled convalescent sera can be given for hepatitis B, varicella–zoster virus, tetanus or rabies as appropriate, e.g. if a member of staff is accidentally inoculated with blood from a patient with hepatitis B.

3. It is given *transplacentally* in that a fetus will receive antibodies from the mother. Such immunity is relatively short lived, usually lasting for a few months but sometimes as long as a year. Immunisation against measles, for example, is usually given to children at 12–18 months of age as transplacentally acquired immunity protects for about 6 months and cases do not usually occur until children start to mix. In tropical Africa, however, where mortality due to complications following measles infection is high, the peak incidence of the disease occurs earlier than in developed countries, so vaccination is recommended at 9 months of age.

Active immunity

Active immunity is induced by:

1. suffering from the disease; or
2. inoculation of the organism, or the product of the organism (toxin), responsible for the disease. The organism has to be treated so that it induces the immune response but does not produce the disease.

Vaccines and antitoxins are produced in the following ways:

1. Killing the organism, e.g. typhoid.
2. Attenuation of the organism, e.g. BCG, poliomyelitis. Attenuated strains have lost the power to produce invasive infection but induce the same antibody response as fully virulent strains.
3. Modification of exotoxins, e.g. diphtheria and tetanus. In diseases purely due to toxaemia the only antigen capable of inducing the immune response is the exotoxin so that in these diseases it is not necessary to inoculate the complete organism. The

exotoxin causes the disease and therefore has to be modified before administration. This is usually done by treatment with formaldehyde and the modified toxin is called *toxoid*. Toxoid induces the same immune response as toxin but does not result in symptoms of the disease.

Length of protection

An attack of a disease or immunisation against it does not necessarily confer life-long immunity. The length of protection time varies, but antibody level and therefore resistance to attack is always greatest immediately after recovery from the acute phase of the disease. In streptococcal infections the antibody level falls relatively quickly and further attacks are not uncommon. In other diseases such as measles the antibody level declines equally rapidly but the immune response remains and it is unusual to have more than one attack of the disease. Some infections such as the common cold appear to recur but this is due to the multiplicity of strains of the virus, each antigenically different but each producing comparable symptoms. That is, a series of different colds is due to different antigenic strains not to repeated attacks by exactly the same virus.

Immunisation schedules

The diseases against which routine immunisation is advised by the Department of Health are diphtheria, pertussis, tetanus, *Haemophilus influenzae* b (Hib), polio-myelitis, measles, mumps, rubella (MMR) and tuberculosis. Rubella (German measles) immunisation with single antigen rubella vaccine will still be given to girls aged 10–14 years who have not had the disease or immunisation, and to non-immune women before pregnancy and after delivery (Department of Health, 1990). Hepatitis A vaccine is now available for adults (see Chapter 10).

In the past it was considered unwise to immunise babies under 6 months of age, for a number of reasons. Recent

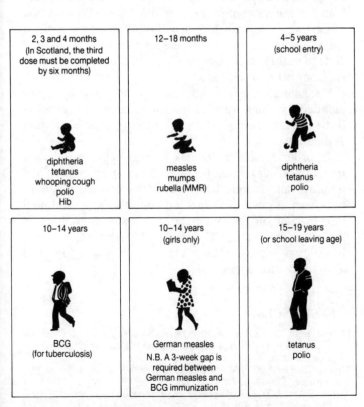

2, 3 and 4 months (In Scotland, the third dose must be completed by six months)	12–18 months	4–5 years (school entry)
diphtheria tetanus whooping cough polio Hib	measles mumps rubella (MMR)	diphtheria tetanus polio
10–14 years	10–14 years (girls only)	15–19 years (or school leaving age)
BCG (for tuberculosis)	German measles N.B. A 3-week gap is required between German measles and BCG immunization	tetanus polio

Figure 4.10 The immunisation schedule recommended in Great Britain.

studies, however, suggest that antibody levels against diphtheria, pertussis (whooping cough), tetanus and poliomyelitis were comparable under the extended original schedule and the recent accelerated schedule of immunisation (Department of Health, 1990). This amended schedule (see Figure 4.10) has been altered in order to allow the primary course of three injections to be completed by 6 months of age so that those very young children who are most at risk have full protection against whooping cough. A schedule allowing a combined vaccine also helps to reduce the number of visits needed and, therefore, increases the likelihood of completion of the course of vaccination.

Vaccination against smallpox is no longer recommended. Rabies vaccination may be given prophylactically for people visiting or working in areas of high endemicity.

In order to avoid the risk of travellers introducing infectious diseases, many countries insist upon travellers holding valid immunisation certificates on entry. Countries vary a good deal in their requirements. Detailed information on recommendations for immunisation is available from the UK Health Departments. Advice includes a rapid schedule for those needing to travel abroad at short notice.

REFERENCES

Department of Health, Welsh Office, Scottish Home and Health Department (1990) *Immunisation against Infectious Disease*. London: HMSO.

Jawetz E, Brooks GF, Melnick JL et al (1989) *Medical Microbiology*, 18th edn. London: Prentice-Hall.

Mims CA (1987) *The Pathogenesis of Infectious Disease* 3rd edn. Academic Press, London.

Thomas CGA (1988) *Medical Microbiology*, 6th edn. London: Baillière Tindall.

Zuckerman AJ, Banatvala JE and Pattison JR (1990) *Principles and
Practice of Clinical Virology*, 2nd edn. Chichester: Wiley.

FURTHER READING

Campbell AGM (1988) Immunisation for the immunosuppressed
child. *Arch. Dis. Childhood* **63**(2): 113–114.

Dawson M (1988) Series of articles on the immune system. *Nursing
Times* **84**(17); **84**(18): 73–76; and **84**(19): 69–72.

Dept. of Health, Welsh Office, Scottish Office Home and Health
Dept., DHSS (N.I.) 1992 edn. *Immunisation against Infectious
Disease*. London: HMSO.

Jones AE, Johns A, Magrath DI, Melville-Smith M and Sheffield
F (1989) Durability of immunity to diphtheria, tetanus and
poliomyelitis after a three dose immunisation schedule completed
in the first eight months of life. *Vaccine* **7**: 300–302.

Roitt IMR (1984) *Essential Immunology*, 5th edn. Oxford: Blackwell.

World Health Organisation. *Vaccination Requirements for International Travel*. Geneva: WHO.

5 Chemotherapy

HISTORY

Although the concept of infectious or transmissible diseases has been accepted for at least 2000 years, their treatment by destroying invading microorganisms within the body was virtually unknown before the pioneering work of Ehrlich in the early twentieth century. In 1904, Ehrlich succeeded in curing experimental trypanosomiasis (sleeping sickness) by using a dye (trypan red), and in 1910 showed that the organic arsenical compound salvarsan 606 could cure certain protozoal and spirochaetal infections in man. This was used in syphilis treatment for many years. This remained virtually the extent of specific drug therapy against infection for the next 25 years.

The modern era may be said to have begun in 1935, when Domagk reported some successes against bacterial diseases caused by the β-haemolytic *Streptococcus* with prontosil, a drug of the sulphonamide group. Since 1935, other drugs belonging to this family have been synthesised to give a wider range of activity against more bacteria, with greater potency, less toxicity, and different physico-chemical properties. The action of these drugs is *bacteriostatic* rather than *bactericidal*, i.e. the organisms are prevented from growing and multiplying and the normal defence mechanisms of the body are needed to deal with the infection. (See Glossary for further explanation of terms).

In 1940, Woods and Fildes formulated the hypothesis that bacteriostasis occurs by blocking metabolic pathways of the organism. This was based on Woods' observation on the mode of action of sulphonamide. All bacteria which are sensitive to the sulphonamides require as an essential *metabolite* p-aminobenzoic acid which is a precursor of folic acid. This substance reacts with an enzyme specific to the bacterium which uses p-aminobenzoic acid. Once the enzyme has reacted with the drug, the natural chain of reactions become blocked and folic acid cannot be synthesised. Folic acid is necessary for the formation of nucleotides and DNA, so this is a critical pathway in the growth of the bacterial cell (see p. 96).

A later drug, *trimethoprim*, was shown to potentiate the action of sulphonamides by blocking the next sequential step to that blocked by sulphonamide. Combinations of these drugs (e.g. cotrimoxazole) are *synergistic*, i.e. they have a greater effect in combination than would be expected individually. Trimethoprim is usually prescribed in combination, but may be used alone in some urinary (and respiratory) tract infections due to sensitive bacteria, as it produces less side-effects than cotrimoxazole, particularly in older patients.

Antibacterial substances which are produced naturally by living cells are known as 'antibiotics', although the term is now used also for synthetically produced agents. It has been known for many years that substances produced by various bacteria or moulds will inhibit the growth of other organisms. Many of these are also toxic to animal tissues, but a few are sufficiently selective in their action to be used therapeutically. It was not until 1929 that the full importance of these substances began to be recognised.

In 1928, Alexander Fleming had noticed that colonies of staphylococci were 'dissolved' around a mould of *Penicillin notatum* which was growing by accident on a culture plate. He published his findings in 1929, showing that substances produced by the mould destroyed several kinds of bacteria without being toxic to the animal involved. However, the extract was difficult to produce in quantity and it was not until 1940 that Florey and Chain managed to produce purified penicillin in Oxford. By the end of World War II, penicillin was in widespread use.

Resistance to penicillin was soon being noted and this in turn stimulated the search for more antibiotic substances. Many were produced from soil bacteria, notably the *Streptomyces* group, of which streptomycin was one of the first. Chloramphenicol followed, first derived from *Streptomyces venezuelae* found in mulch in a Venezuelan stubble field (British Medical Association, 1989). Later, in 1948, the tetracycline group were discovered and these were considered the first broad-spectrum antibiotics, which act against many bacteria.

Further developments are erythromycin, gentamicin and other aminoglycosides (see below), the cephalosporins and, much more recently, the quinolones and teicoplanin. The search for an ideal antibiotic continues, as all have some problems. These include toxicity to the host, acquisition of resistance, problems in administration, and expense. In order to enhance the care of patients receiving treatment, a brief description follows of how these drugs work, the different groups of agents currently available, and some of the associated problems. Nurses need this understanding to enable them to explain treatment to the patients in their care, and also to be aware of possible side-effects for prompt recognition and treatment.

MECHANISMS OF ACTION

There are four main mechanisms involved in the action of antimicrobial drugs (see Figure 5.1):

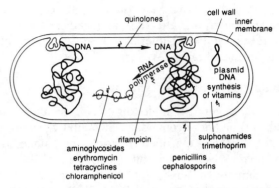

Figure 5.1 Sites of action of antibiotics on the bacterial cell.

1. inhibition of cell-wall synthesis,
2. alteration of the cell membrane,
3. inhibition of nucleic acid synthesis, and
4. inhibition of protein synthesis.

Inhibition of cell-wall synthesis

Bacterial cells differ from mammalian cells in that most have a cell wall (the exceptions are mainly tiny bacteria like chlamydiae, mycoplasma and rickettsiae). Certain antibiotics act by inhibiting the synthesis of the cell wall as the cell divides, leading to death of the cell without harm to the host cells, e.g. penicillins and cephalosporins.

Some agents (e.g. vancomycin and teicoplanin) interfere with the passage of the mucopeptide units (which make up the cell wall) through the cell membrane.

Alteration of cell membrane

The cell membrane of both fungi and bacteria have a different structure to mammalian cells and can be disrupted, allowing the cytoplasm contents to escape. For example, polymyxins affect Gram-negative bacterial cell membranes, and amphotericin B and nystatin affect fungal cell membranes (Walters, 1989).

Inhibition of nucleic acid synthesis

This may occur by inhibiting RNA synthesis (e.g. rifampicin) or, more commonly, by inhibiting some stage of DNA synthesis e.g. metronidazole, quinolones (such as nalidixic acid or ciprofloxacin) (see Table 5.1), sulphonamides (mistaken by bacterial enzymes for an essential metabolite in some DNA or RNA synthesis); also antifungal agents including 5-flucytosine, griseofulvin; and antiviral agents such as acyclovir and zidovudine.

Inhibition of protein synthesis

The ribosomes of bacterial cells appear to have sufficient differences in structure and function from mammalian cells to allow antimicrobial drugs to inhibit bacterial protein synthesis while leaving the host cells relatively undamaged. Examples of drugs that work in this way are aminoglycosides (gentamicin, neomycin, etc.), tetracyclines, macrolides (erythromycin), chloramphenicol, lincomycin and fusidic acid.

MAIN GROUPS OF ANTIMICROBIAL AGENTS

The uses and side-effects of these are summarised in Table 5.1. A brief description of the development of and some problems with the major groups is given below.

Penicillins

In general, it may be said that the Gram-positive cocci and bacilli, some pathogenic Gram-negative cocci and the spirochaetes are sensitive to penicillin, while most Gram-negative rods and bacteria without a cell wall are penicillin resistant. Gram-negative organisms have an extra membrane through which the antibiotic must traverse.

Organisms which are resistant to penicillin are resistant for one of three reasons:

1. production of enzymes which inactivate penicillin (e.g. β-lactamase);
2. the alteration of the binding substrates 'penicillin binding proteins'; or
3. impermeability of the outer membrane of Gram-negative organisms.

In all antibiotic-sensitive cultures there are a few organisms which are relatively more resistant than the rest; these arise by natural mutation. In the presence of concentrations of penicillin sufficient to kill the majority, this minority are not killed and, unless inactivated by normal host defences, they may multiply. Thus a resistant strain is established. The regular use of penicillin rapidly resulted in an increase in the number of resistant strains of several bacteria.

From modifications to the basic nucleus of penicillin have come other compounds, including the following.

1. Acid-stable compounds which can be taken orally (flucloxacillin, ampicillin and amoxycillin).
2. Penicillinase-resistant compounds which will be active in penicillinase-producing staphylococcal infection (flucloxacillin) (but see later).
3. Compounds with broad-spectrum activity, including against Gram-negative rods (ampicillin and amoxycillin). Also, augmentin (amoxycillin with clavulanic acid which inactivates the β-lactamase produced by

Table 5.1 Summary of antimicrobial agents

Agent	Route of administration*	Indications for use†	Disadvantages/side-effects
Penicillins			
Benzylpenicillin (Penicillin G)	P	Streptococcal infection (e.g. tonsillitis, erysipelas, endocarditis), pneumococcal and meningococcal meningitis; sensitive staphylococcal infections, clostridial infection, diphtheria; tetanus; gonorrhoea; syphilis; actinomycosis; anthrax. Prophylactically in orthopaedic surgery	Inactivated by bacterial penicillinases and gastric acid. Hypersensitivity may occur, and can (rarely) cause anaphylactic shock. Occasional cause of convulsions
Phenoxymethylpen. (Penicillin V)	O	For mild infections, e.g. tonsillitis, otitis media	Inactivated as above. Absorption variable
Methicillin	P	Staphylococcal infections due to penicillinase producers	Rarely used now in UK
Flucloxacillin, cloxacillin	O or P	Staphylococcal infections due to penicillinase producers	Flucloxacillin preferred to cloxacillin as better absorbed in gut. Resistance problems in hospitals
Broad-spectrum penicillins			
Ampicillin and amoxycillin	P or O (before food)	Chronic bronchitis, middle ear infections, UTI, and gonorrhoea. Also *Listeria*	Resistance increasing both by β-lactamases and some GNB

Drug	Route	Uses	Notes/Side effects
Augmentin (amoxycillin + clavulanic acid)	O or P	Infections due to penicillinase producers; clavulanic acid inactivates them, allowing amoxycillin to act	Diarrhoea and skin rashes
Antipseudomonal penicillins			
Ticarcillin	P	*Pseudomonas* and *Proteus* infections (serious)	Some resistance seen. Inactivated orally. Occasional hypersensitivity. Renal function may be affected
Piperacillin	P	Serious Gram-negative infections, especially in immunocompromised patients. Usually combined with an aminoglycoside	
Mezlocillin	P	As above	Less prone to resistance
Azlocillin	P	Particularly effective against *Pseudomonas* infection, but less resistant to β-lactamases than piperacillin	
Timentin (ticarcillin + clavulanic acid)	P	Respiratory and abdominal infections, and UTI	
Cephalosporins *First generation*			
Cephradine	O or P	Severe infections while awaiting bacteriology results, sometimes in combination with other antibiotics. Gram-negative infections resistant to other antibiotics. May be used in pregnancy	Hypersensitivity as with penicillin. Also allergic skin rashes, diarrhoea, occasional interference with clotting factor
Cephazolin	P		
Cefaclor	O		
Cephalexin	O		
Cefadroxil	O		

Table 5.1 Continued.

Agent	Route of administration*	Indications for use†	Disadvantages/side-effects
Second generation			
Cefuroxime	O or P	Less susceptible to inactivation by penicillinase producers, e.g. resistant strains of gonorrhoea and *Haemophilus influenzae*. Surgical prophylaxis in *major* surgery	As for other cephalosporins
Cefamandole	P		
Third generation			
Cefotaxime	P	Better than second generation against Gram-negative infections but not so effective against Gram-positive organisms.	May encourage superinfection with resistant bacteria and fungi
Ceftazidime	P		
Ceftizoxime	P	Ceftazidime active against *Pseudomonas*. Some major surgical prophylaxis	
Monobactams			
Aztreonam	P	Gram-negative infections only. May be tolerated by penicillin-sensitive patients	
Other β-lactams			
Imipenem	P	Broad-spectrum including anaerobes, especially for bacteria resistant to other β-lactams. Affinity for brain tissue	Too early in experience to assess possible side-effects fully

	Route	Notes	Side effects / Precautions
Tetracyclines			
Tetracycline	O (usually)	Broad-spectrum, but increased resistance has led to reduced use. Chronic bronchitis, chlamydia, rickettsial infection, Lyme disease, brucella and mycoplasma infections	Poor CSF penetration. Nausea and diarrhoea. Stains teeth, avoid in children and pregnant women. Altered gut and vaginal flora can lead to superinfection with *Candida*, or enterocolitis
Oxytetracycline	O		
Doxycycline	O	May be used in renal impairment. Penetrates CSF so may be used for meningococcal prophylaxis	Dizziness and vertigo
Minocycline	O		
Macrolides			
Erythromycin	O or P	Gram-positive infections, and can be used for penicillin-allergic patients. Some anaerobic, chlamydial, mycoplasma, legionella and campylobacter infections	Myalgia. Gastrointestinal upset
Aminoglycosides			
Gentamicin	P	Serious Gram-negative infections. In conjunction with penicillins or penicillin + metronidazole for serious infections as 'blind' therapy	Oto- and nephro-toxic. Inactive against anaerobes. Renal function and antibiotic assays essential
Netilmicin	P	Similar spectrum to gentamicin	Less effective against *Pseudomonas*, but slightly less toxic than gentamicin
Amikacin	P	Useful for gentamicin-resistant organisms	
Tobramycin	P	Better than gentamicin against *Pseudomonas*	

Table 5.1 Continued.

Agent	Route of administration*	Indications for use†	Disadvantages/side-effects
Neomycin	O and T	Topically and for gut 'sterilisation' before surgery	Severe oto- and nephrotoxicity Not given parenterally
Streptomycin	P	First aminoglycoside, now used mainly for tuberculosis, and then only rarely, in combination therapy	Poorly absorbed from gut. Resistant strains emerge rapidly if used alone
Spectinomycin	P	Related to aminoglycosides. Used in resistant strains of gonorrhoea or penicillin hypersensitivity	Pain at injection site Nausea and fever
Sulphonamides and trimethoprim			
Sulphadiazine	O or P	Meningococcal meningitis	Bacterial resistance has developed. Rashes, blood disorders and renal failure. May crystallise in kidneys if fluid intake low
Sulphadimidine	O or P	Meningococcal meningitis, and susceptible UTIs. Almost never used now	
Trimethoprim	O or P	Acute and long-term use for UTIs, also acute and chronic bronchitis	Not used in pregnancy. Nausea, gastro-intestinal (G-I) disturbances
Cotrimoxazole	O or P	UTIs, chronic bronchitis, severe salmonella, brucella and *Pneumocystis carinii* infections	Not used in pregnancy. Nausea, vomiting, rashes, blood disorders

	Route	Clinical use	Adverse effects
Others			
Chloramphenicol	O, P or T	Life-threatening infections only, e.g. typhoid fever or *Haemophilus influenzae* meningitis. Topical use in eye drops for conjunctivitis	G-I disturbances, neuritis, haematological disturbances—even aplastic anaemia, hence restricted use
Lincomycin Clindamycin	P O or P	Lincomycin less well absorbed orally, used for difficult staphylococcal infections. Clindamycin used for bone and joint infection and abdominal sepsis *Bacteroides* infections usually susceptible but superceded by metronidazole	Mild diarrhoea Pseudomembranous colitis (rare)
Fusidic acid (sodium fusidate)	O	Osteomyelitis, in conjunction with another agent for penicillin-resistant staphylococci	Nausea (give after food). I/V use avoided as jaundice more common
Vancomycin	O or P	Multiple-resistant (especially MRSA and MRSE) staphylococcal infections, e.g. septicaemias and other Gram-positive infections. Penicillin-allergic *S. viridans* endocarditis. Orally for pseudomembranous colitis. Most useful for *S. epidermidis* infections	Rashes and fever. Oto- and nephro-toxic. Serum assays essential
Teicoplanin	P	Many streptococcal and staphylococcal infections, including MRSA Similar spectrum to vancomycin	Appears less toxic than vancomycin. Blood dyscrasias, tinnitus and headache

Table 5.1 Continued.

Agent	Route of administration*	Indications for use†	Disadvantages/side-effects
Metronidazole	O, P and R	Anaerobic bacterial infections, especially *Bacteroides*, in surgical infections and surgical prophylaxis. Protozoal infection including amoebiasis and giardiasis	Nausea and mild gastrointestinal upset. Peripheral neuropathy if treatment prolonged. Avoid alcohol
Nitrofurantoin	O	Usually for 'coliform' or *S. saphrophyticus* UTI	Gastrointestinal disturbance. Concentrates in the urine, not blood, hence used for UTI only
Quinolones Nalidixic acid	O	Gram-negative UTIs only	Resistance develops rapidly. Mild gastrointestinal upset, possible allergy and neurological effects. Concentrates in urine
Ciprofloxacin	O or P	Broad-spectrum, especially good for Gram-negative infections including salmonella and shigella. Has been used for MRSA	Gastrointestinal or neurological effects

Antitubercular drugs

First-line drugs

Isoniazid	O or P	(Only for tuberculosis)

Peripheral neuritis. Some organisms always resistant, hence combination therapy

Rifampicin	O or P	(Broadspectrum agent particularly active against staphylococci but resistance selected rapidly so used in combination)

Gastrointestinal disturbance and altered liver function. Colours urine, sweat and contact lenses orange. Rarely, rashes and thrombocytopaenia. Leads to failure of low dose oestrogen oral contraceptive

Ethambutol	O

Visual disturbances. Avoid if renal function impaired

Pyrazinamide	O

Good meningeal penetration, used in tubercular meningitis

Nausea, vomiting, arthralgia. Liver damage

Second-line drugs (if sensitivities show alternative therapy required)

Capreomycin	P

Not to be given with ototoxic drugs, not in pregnancy. Renal and hepatic damage possible, and hypersensitivity

Cycloserine	O

Neurotoxicity, and skin allergy. Severe psychiatric disturbance

Table 5.1 Continued.

Agent	Route of administration*	Indications for use†	Disadvantages/side-effects
Antifungal agents			
Amphotericin B	O, P or T	Systemic infection with *Candida*, *Cryptococcus*, or *Aspergillus*. Topically to *Candida albicans* e.g. orally or vaginally	Nephrotoxic, also fever, nausea and vomiting. Localised phlebitis at injection site. Dose needs to be built up gradually.
Flucytosine	O or I/V	Effective against systemic infections with yeasts including *Candida* and *Cryptococcus*	Less toxic than above. Prolonged treatment can lead to bone marrow depression and liver failure. May be used synergistically with amphotericin B. Penetrates CSF well
Griseofulvin	O	Effective against dermatophytes so used for fungal skin infections, e.g. ringworm. Prolonged treatment necessary	May give rise to headaches, photosensitivity, rashes and gastrointestinal upsets
Nystatin	O or T	Mainly for *Candida* infections of mouth, gut and vagina	Not absorbed from the gut

Imidazoles (act on cell membrane function)			
Clotrimazole and econazole	T	Topical use for vaginal *Candida* infection and dermatophyte skin infections	Not prone to develop resistance
Miconazole	T or I/V	Topical use as above. Systemically for *Cryptococcal* and *Candida* infections	Toxic at injection site. Rashes, nausea and vomiting
Ketoconazole	O	Persistent mucocutaneous and vaginal candidiasis, also used for histoplasmosis	Nausea and rashes occasionally. *Rarely*, fatal liver damage
Fluconazole	O	Similar to ketoconazole	Less hepatic damage
Antiviral agents			
Idoxuridine (IDU)	T	Herpes simplex conjunctival or corneal infection. First antiviral agent; no longer used systemically. Used topically in shingles infection if given early	Too toxic when used systemically and replaced by acyclovir
Acyclovir	O or I/V	Herpes simplex including genital infection, and varicella–zoster virus. Requires prompt administration to be effective	Usually non-toxic but may cause rashes, gastrointestinal and neurological upset, renal and liver abnormalities
Ganciclovir	I/V	Similar to acyclovir, but more effective against cytomegalovirus, especially in immunosuppressed cases	
Vidarabine	I/V	Herpes simplex, e.g. corneal lesions. Systemic use now replaced by acyclovir	Low toxicity but may cause nausea and phlebitis

Table 5.1 Continued.

Agent	Route of administration*	Indications for use†	Disadvantages/side-effects
Inosine pranobex	O	Herpes simplex, mucocutaneous. Genital warts	Contraindicated in renal impairment. Doubtful efficacy
Zidovudine (AZT)	O	Infection in HIV-positive patients, now also being used prophylactically on diagnosis of HIV-positive	Bone marrow depression and anaemia. Expensive. Headaches, nausea and vomiting, rashes, anorexia and insomnia. Long-term effects unresolved
Amantadine	O	Active against influenza A virus if given early enough	Rashes, insomnia
Ribavirin	I/V and aerosol	Aerosolised to treat severe RSV bronchiolitis. I/V for patients with Lassa fever	

Interferons (see Chapter 4)

* O, oral; P, parenteral; T, topical; I/V, intravenous.
† UTI, urinary tract infections; CSF, cerebrospinal fluid; MRSA, Methicillin-resistant *Staphylococcus aureus*; MRSE, Methicillin-resistant *Staphylococcus epidermidis*; RSV, Respiratory syncytial virus.

some bacteria, enabling the amoxycillin to take effect).

4. Compounds active against *Pseudomonas aeruginosa* (azlocillin, mezlocillin, ticarcillin and piperacillin).

Carbenicillin was the first penicillin compound to become available in the late 1950s with activity against *Pseudomonas aeruginosa*. However, its activity was low and large daily doses of 20–30 g, which had to be given by intravenous injection, were necessary. Newer drugs with the same general antibacterial sprectrum but a greater weight-for-weight activity include azlocillin and piperacillin.

The cephalosporins

These are a family of antibiotics broadly similar chemically and in their spectrum of activity to penicillin. Like penicillin, a part of the molecule can be substituted in various ways to produce compounds with differing antibacterial action. The first cephalosporin (cephalothin) became available in the mid-1960s. 'Second generation' cephalosporins (see Table 5.1) followed the early (first) cephalosporins and have certain uses, e.g. against penicillinase-producing gonococci and resistant strains of *Haemophilus influenzae*, and also in major surgical prophylaxis.

The 'third generation' cephalosporins are a continually expanding range. They are less active against Gram-positive bacilli, but have uses in Gram-negative infection, e.g. meningitis in neonates caused by Gram-negative bacteria, and in some surgical prophylaxis. They have many advantages, but have also been subject to wide-spread and sometimes inappropriate use, leading to possible problems with *superinfection*. This implies the acquisition of a more resistant strain of the organism already causing infection, or the replacement of normal

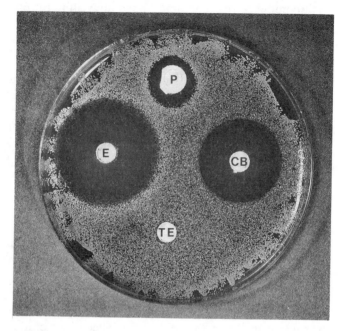

Figure 5.2 Estimation of antibiotic sensitivity. In the culture of *Staphylococcus aureus*, sensitivity is indicated by the inhibition of growth around discs. P, penicillin; CB, methicillin; TE, tetracycline; E, erythromycin.

flora by antibiotic-resistant organisms because of antibiotic use. A recent survey in the UK showed that, despite a 15-fold rise in use of ceftazidime (third generation) over 4 years, no accompanying resistance had occurred (Brown et al, 1990). However, in a leukaemia unit which uses ceftazidime frequently in almost every patient, the proportion of ceftazidime-resistant blood-culture isolates is gradually increasing year by year (G. Scott, personal communication). Resistance to second and third generation cephalosporins by many Gram-negative bacteria (*Drugs and Therapeutics Bulletin*, 1986) and the risk of colonisation by resistant bacteria in hospital patients demand constant attention.

There are newer related drugs such as *carbapenems* (e.g. imipenem which has a very broad spectrum of activity), and *monobactams* (e.g. aztreonam which is only active against Gram-negative organisms) (see Table 5.1).

Aminoglycosides

Streptomycin is a member of the family of aminoglyco-sides, which includes neomycin, gentamicin, netilmicin, amikacin and tobramycin. Broadly speaking, the amino-glycosides have the same range of activity as streptomycin but are more reliably active against Gram-negative bacilli. All are associated with oto- and nephro-toxicity, and renal function and antibiotic levels must be monitored with each drug. Aminoglycosides cannot be mixed with other drugs in solution.

Chloramphenicol

Derived originally from strains of *Streptomyces*, this is now produced synthetically. Although toxicity is rare, about 1 in 40 000 patients develop fatal aplastic anaemia, and the drug is reserved for use in life-threatening situations. It is one of the cheapest and most popular antibiotics used in the Third World. Resistance in coliforms and typhoid is now commonplace.

Quinolones

This group of drugs is derived synthetically from *nalidixic acid* and includes ciprofloxacin, ofloxacin and norfloxacin. Nalidixic acid and norfloxacin concentrate in the urine and are used only for treatment of urinary tract infections. Ciprofloxacin is active against both Gram-negative and Gram-positive bacteria, but is mainly used for the former (see Table 5.1). It is the only effective agent against *Pseudomonas* which can be taken orally.

Broad-spectrum antimicrobials

Drugs such as chloramphenicol, the tetracyclines and ampicillin have a wide range of antibacterial action, so their administration also inhibits the growth of non-pathogenic organisms which are normally present on the healthy mucous membranes (the 'normal flora'). These organisms play an important role (see Chapter 3) and help in protection against virulent organisms. The bacterial flora of the gut and respiratory tract are profoundly altered after giving ampicillin or chloramphenicol, and this change produces deleterious effects. The normal flora is rapidly replaced by antibiotic-resistant strains of species, not usually found in these sites or only present in small numbers. For example, the gut flora may be overwhelmed by tetracycline-resistant staphylococci and the patient will suffer from the acute diarrhoeal disease of staphylococcal enteritis. There may also be vitamin B deficiency associated with the destruction of intestinal flora. Overgrowth of *Candida* produces symptoms of oral, vulval and anal irritation.

Metronidazole

This was once regarded solely as an antiparasitic agent, widely used in the treatment of *Trichomonas* and certain gut infestations. It is now used effectively in the treatment of anaerobic infections including those due to *Bacteroides* spp. Its use prophylactically for bowel and vaginal surgery has considerably reduced the incidence of infection.

Metronidazole reacts with alcohol to cause vomiting (see Table 5.1).

ANTI-FUNGAL AGENTS

Most important antibiotics are produced by fungi, and it is not surprising that fungi should be resistant to their effects. There are, however, a few substances that are effective in the treatment of certain human fungal infections and they specifically interfere with the cell wall lipid structure based on cholesterol peculiar to fungi. For the most important of these see Table 5.1.

ANTIVIRAL AGENTS

The main reason for the slow and limited development of antiviral agents is the nature of virus replication. Viruses are obligate intracellular parasites and require cell metabolic processes to replicate. Any agent must be able to target viral replication without damaging the host cell.

The first agent found to affect viruses was *interferon*. Interferons are a family of natural proteins, produced by cells in response to viral infection, and discovered in 1956 by the British virologist Alick Isaacs. Interferon appears to prompt the synthesis of other proteins which then inhibit viral replication (see Chapter 4). Interferon is produced naturally in virus infections even before the first symptoms appear. These often appear only when viral multiplication may be almost over, so the substance is not of much use in the treatment of acute infections.

Idoxuridine was the first specific antiviral drug used against herpesviruses since the 1960s. Next came amantadine, effective against influenza A (although not widely used). More recently, acyclovir, gancyclovir, ribavirin, vidarabine and inosine pranobex have been used.

Stimulated by the advent of HIV infection and treatment, there is tremendous research into antiviral agents. As retroviruses actually become integrated into the host-cell DNA, once so integrated it is not possible to target them without damaging other cells. Drugs are, therefore, required which act during virus replication, but there would still be a problem of interfering with normal cell growth. Also, many antiviral drugs cannot cross the blood–brain barrier in sufficient concentration to act effectively in virus-infected brain cells (Roth, 1989). Zidovudine (AZT) is the first antiviral agent to be developed for use against HIV and further drugs, including dideoxyinosine (DDi), are currently on trial; others will surely follow.

RESISTANCE TO ANTIBIOTICS

There are a variety of mechanisms by which bacteria may become resistant to antibiotic agents. Detailed descriptions can be found elsewhere (e.g. Thomas, 1988; Jawetz et al, 1989; Shanson, 1989), but a brief outline is given below. Antibiotic resistance may be coded for on chromosomes or on plasmids. Resistance may be divided into *natural* and *acquired* resistance.

1. *Natural resistance* occurs irrespective of antibiotic usage. This may be due to:
   (a) the production of drug-destroying enzymes,
   (b) the resistance of cell membranes (e.g. of Gram-negative bacteria) which prevent the access of antibiotics to the organism, or
   (c) bacteria may lack a target site for the drug to act on.

2. *Acquired resistance* is often associated with inappropriate or excessive use of antibiotics.

   (a) *Chromosomal resistance* occurs when mutant strains of a bacterium survive in the presence of an antibiotic and eventually multiply and predominate if exposure to the antibiotic persists.

   (b) *Plasmid-mediated resistance* occurs when plasmid transference takes place between strains involving genes coding for antibiotic resistance (*R-factors*), even crossing species in some Gram-negative organisms.

Examples of resistance are the following:

1. Enzymes such as penicillinases which destroy penicillin; there are other drug-destroying enzymes which affect Gram-positive and Gram-negative bacilli and lead to major antibiotic resistance in these oganisms. These are known as 'β-lactamases' and can hydrolyse almost all the β-lactams described.

2. Gradual adaptation, e.g. gonococci, initially fully susceptible to penicillin, but later requiring larger and larger doses for effect.

3. Some bacteria develop new metabolic processes which bypass the target site of the antibiotic.

Moss et al (1981) found that one-half of antibiotics were being used with no bacteriological evidence of infection and a US study (Kunin 1981) also found that one-half of hospital patients received unnecessary antibiotics.

Although it is not the nurse who prescribes an antimicrobial, it is frequently he/she who administers it and, under the UKCC Code of Professional Conduct (1984; Suppl. 1986) the nurse thereby accepts responsibility for it. He/she needs to understand and be aware of the uses and abuses of these agents and to be in a position to help avoid misuse, just as knowledge of how the drugs work will enable him/her to give safer nursing care. The nurse can alert the doctor if antibiotics are being given for too long, or if the patient does not seem to require them.

Significance of current antibiotic resistance

Methicillin-resistant *Staphylococcus aureus* (MRSA) will be dealt with again in a later chapter, but the organism *Staphylococcus aureus* is a prime example of acquired resistance. Initially always sensitive to penicillin, less than 10% of hospital strains can now be found which are sensitive to penicillin following widespread use of the antibiotic in the 1950s. The ability to produce β-lactamase was primarily responsible for resistance of the organism but methicillin was designed as a β-lactamase resistant penicillin. Resistance to methicillin has subsequently developed and some strains of the organism are now so resistant to antibiotics that they can only be treated with glycopeptides such as vancomycin or teicoplanin. (Methicillin is not used therapeutically in this country because it can only be given intravenously and is toxic. Flucloxacillin can be taken parenterally or orally as its equivalent.)

Gram-negative bacilli have been affected by plasmid-mediated resistance; the bacillus for dysentery (*Shigella dysenteriae*) was found in 1959 in Japan to be resistant to all suitable antibiotics. Other Gram-negative organisms in the stools of hospital patients infected with *Shigella* at that time were found to have the same antibiotic resistance; plasmids were being transferred between species.

This appears to occur more rapidly and frequently where antibiotics are used indiscriminately. The potential for disastrous epidemics is obvious, where treatment with antibiotics has been made difficult or impossible.

Hospital strains of various bacteria show a greater tendency to develop resistance because of the extent of antibiotic use. Bacteria which are resistant to all useful antibiotics are now found in intensive care units where antibiotics are used extensively. The community is also being affected. Nurses can play a part here too, because patients need reassurance that the answer to every infection is not necessarily an antibiotic. It is far better to reserve them for serious infections. To date, man's ingenuity in designing new antibiotics has stayed one step ahead of the bacteria, but we cannot continue to rely on coming up with another alternative when resistance develops to the current treatment.

The problems of superinfection and drug resistance resulting from unrestricted use of antibiotics, especially in poorer countries, has led to the publication of a World Health Organization document (WHO, 1983). This outlines measures for controlling the prevalence of antibiotic-resistant bacteria by two means: control of antibiotic use in hospitals and national and international surveillance of antibiotic resistance.

REFERENCES

British Medical Association (1989) *Infection Control: The BMA Guide*, London, Edward Arnold.

Brown EH, Spencer RC and Brown JMC (1990) The emergence of bacterial resistance in hospitals—a need for continuous surveillance. *J. Hosp. Inf.* **15** (Suppl. A): 35–39.

Drugs and Therapeutics Bulletin (1986) Broad-spectrum antibacterial regimens for the seriously ill. *Drugs Ther. Bull* **24**(9): 33–36.

Jawetz E, Brooks GF, Melnick JL, Butel JS, Adelberg EA and Ornston LN (1989) *Medical Microbiology*, 18th edn. London: Prentice-Hall.

Kunin CM (1981) Evaluation of antibiotic usage: a comprehensive look at alternative approaches. *Rev. Infect. Dis.* **3**: 745–753.

Moss F, McNichol MW, McSwiggan DA and Miller DL (1981) Survey of antibiotic prescribing in a district general hospital. *Lancet* **ii**: 349–352; 407–409; 461–462.

Roth JS (1989) *All about AIDS*. London: Harwood.

Shanson DC (1989) *Microbiology in Clinical Practice*, 2nd edn. Bristol: Wright.

Thomas CGA (1988) *Medical Microbiology*, 6th edn. London: Baillière Tindall.

UKCC (1984) The Code of Professional Conduct for the Nurse, Midwife and Health Visitor; Supplement, *Administration of Medicines* (1986).

Walters J (1989) How antibiotics work: the cell membrane. *Prof. Nurse* **4**(10): 508–510.

Wenzel RP ed. (1987) *Prevention and Control of Nosocomial Infections* Wilkins and Wilkins, Baltimore.

World Health Organisation (1983) Control of antibiotic-resistant bacteria. *Bull. WHO* **61**: 423–433.

FURTHER READING

Stone JW and Davies AJ (1986) New antimicrobials. *Br. J. Hosp. Med. Aug.*: 119–123.

Walters J (1988) How antibiotics work. *Prof. Nurse* **3**(7): 251–254.

Walters J (1990) How antibiotics work: nucleic acid synthesis. *Prof. Nurse* **5**(12): 641–643.

Wood MJ and Geddes AM (1987) Antiviral therapy. *Lancet* **Nov.**: pp 1189–1192.

6 Cleaning, disinfection and sterilisation

The intention of this chapter is to give the nurse an understanding of the meaning of the terms *cleaning*, *disinfection* and *sterilisation*, and to understand how the procedures involved are related to removal of microorganisms from human and inanimate surfaces to prevent transmission of infection. Brief descriptions of how the processes work are included but may be expanded by using the reference list at the end of the chapter. It is important to define the terms used.

Cleaning—the removal of contamination such as dirt.

Disinfection—the destruction or reduction in numbers of harmful microorganisms, not usually including bacterial spores.

Antiseptic—a particular type of chemical disinfectant that may be applied to the skin or living tissue to remove harmful microorganisms without causing tissue damage.

Sterilisation—the destruction or removal of all micro-organisms including spores.

The fundamental principle of disinfection and sterilisation is the prior **cleaning** *of an object or the skin. Without prior cleaning, methods of disinfection and sterilisation are almost bound to fail.*

It is also essential to understand the factors which will influence the action of whichever killing agent is chosen:

1. The susceptibility of the organism to be killed.
2. The number of organisms present.
3. The time necessary for action.
4. The optimum temperature.
5. The concentration of killing agent.
6. The optimum acidity or alkalinity for killing agent.
7. The physical state of the contaminated material involved; protein, blood, pus, mucus and dirt act as a protective coat for bacteria and limit the action of the killing agent.
8. Direct contact between all surfaces of the object and the killing agent. Air bubbles in tubing will protect bacteria from chemicals.
9. Substances which neutralise the activity of the killing agent.
10. Impurities diluting the agent.
11. Inactivation of the agent with time.

RISK ASSESSMENT AND CATEGORIES

Microbes are everywhere, and we need many of them—we cannot and should not try to destroy them all (Maurer, 1985; Collins, 1988). Within both the hospital and the home setting, we need to identify which situations have the highest risk for causing infection from the environment, equipment or skin, and then apply appropriate rigorous methods of microbe removal or destruction to those. This will avoid unnecessary and costly use of potentially toxic substances. Table 6.1 gives an accepted categorisation.

DEATH OF MICROORGANISMS

Contact between a sterilising agent and microorganisms effects a reduction in the number of organisms; most die,

Table 6.1 Risk categories for sterilisation and disinfection (based on categories described by Ayliffe et al, 1984)

High	Anything which penetrates the integument or comes into contact with a break in skin or mucous membranes (e.g. surgical instruments, cystoscopes, urinary or intravenous catheters). Usually requires sterilisation
Intermediate	Anything in direct or indirect contact with skin and mucous membranes (e.g. respiratory equipment, endoscopes, bedpans). Usually requires a combination of cleaning and disinfection
Low	Equipment or material which does not have close patient contact (e.g. walls, sinks, beds). Cleaning usually suffices

a few survive. If the survivors are exposed to continuous contact with the sterilising agent, virtually all of them will be killed in time. Only a minute percentage of very resistant organisms will survive, perhaps 1 in 10^6 with a marginally acceptable sterilising method, or only 1 in 10^{50} with an efficient method such as autoclaving. The percentage of surviving organisms and the time taken to kill them is dependent on:

1. the number of organisms originally present (hence the need to clean);
2. the efficiency and reliability of the sterilising method; and
3. the correct application of the method.

CLEANING

If the number of organisms present affects sterilising time and efficiency, it is crucial to *reduce* the numbers as far as possible before attempting to apply any method of sterilisation or disinfection. It is also essential to remove organic material which will protect bacteria against the action of physical or chemical agents.

Careful washing of skin, equipment or instruments with hot water and soap or detergent does not remove all bacteria, but it does remove grease and dirt which protect bacteria, and it does effectively reduce their numbers. Where there is a large quantity of equipment to be cleaned, e.g. central sterilising or central food service departments, automatic jet or deluge washing machines are used to give the most effective wash in a reasonable time.

The development of ultrasonic cleaning equipment has improved standards of cleaning delicate instruments with ridges and awkward crevices. The source of energy is very high frequency sound waves generated in the base of a tank of water to which detergent is added, and in which baskets or racks of instruments are submerged. The ensuing shock waves dislodge blood and dirt on the instruments which are subsequently rinsed and dried.

In addition to the need to aid disinfection or sterilisation processes, a basic standard of cleanliness needs to be maintained both for hygiene and confidence of all those using hospitals or other premises. Patients and visitors will not have confidence in a hospital's standards of care if cleaning is visibly badly done (Bromley, 1983; Ward, 1990). Nevertheless, this must not lead to use of disinfectants where cleaning is adequate; confusion still occurs about the benefits of a 'nice smell' given by a disinfectant when simple detergent and hot water would have sufficed.

Cleaning helps to maintain the appearance and efficiency of structures and equipment (Ayliffe et al, 1986), but this requires an understanding of how to use and maintain cleaning materials. Ward (1990) points out that incorrect methods will simply redistribute the dirt. Cleaning materials should be kept clean and dry between uses, and items such as mopheads should be launderable or withstand autoclaving. Maurer (1985) gives full information on the 'why and how' of hospital hygiene.

Persuading health-care workers of all disciplines that cleaning is often all that is needed and that disinfectants are worthless is no easy task (Thomlinson, 1990) (Figure 6.1). Central control is required; disinfectants should be kept off wards. Cleaning of floors with a detergent as

'Sister asked if you have finished with the Eusol,
as she is waiting to do the dressings'

Figure 6.1 Two abuses of a disinfectant!

opposed to a disinfectant over two 3-month periods on eight acute-care units (Danforth et al, 1987), showed no difference in floor contamination and the only ward with a lower infection rate was one using detergent. Similarly, Hambraeus and Bengstsson (1980) and Nystrom (1981) found no benefit in disinfection of toilets and bath/shower trolleys as opposed to cleaning with detergent. Cleaning *frequency* also needs consideration. Ayliffe et al (1966) showed that 80% of organisms were removed from a ward floor by use of a detergent, 95–99% by use of a disinfectant, but a return to the original numbers took place often within 2 h. Two-hourly cleaning is neither practical nor desirable.

Cleaning is a major part of the control of infection. Lack of hygienic practice has been responsible for outbreaks of infection such as bacterial infections from Ambu bags and breast milk pumps in special care baby units (SCBUs) (Stone and Das, 1985; Gransden et al, 1986). The nurse still has a major part to play in this field, mainly in knowing the most appropriate ways of decontamination, making sure that they are always followed, and spotting deficiencies which constitute a risk to patients.

DISINFECTION

Disinfection (see p. 119) is not so precise an activity as sterilisation. It should only be used for situations where an overall reduction of microorganisms is sufficient for safety of patients and staff. There are occasions when it is used to treat heat-sensitive items (such as endoscopes) as the nearest approach to sterility, but the difference must still be acknowledged.

Methods of disinfection are shown in Table 6.2.

Table 6.2 Methods of disinfection

Moist heat	Pasteurisation Boiling water Low-temperature (subatmospheric) steam
Chemical agents	*Halogens*: iodine and iodophors, e.g. Betadine; chlorine releasing agents, e.g. Milton, NaDCC *Phenolics*, e.g. Hycolin *Diguanides*, e.g. chlorhexidine *Quaternary ammonium compounds*, e.g. cetrimide *Alcohols*, e.g. 70% isopropyl alcohol *Aldehydes*, e.g. glutaraldehyde

Disinfection should always be preceded by thorough cleaning.

Moist heat

Heat is an excellent method of disinfection, being reliable, inexpensive and thorough. Examples include bedpan washers, anaesthetic apparatus washing machines and hot-water disinfectors (sometimes incorrectly referred to as boiling water 'sterilisers'), and cooking.

Hot water

Total immersion in hot water will kill all microbes except spores. Time must be allowed for the immersed objects themselves to reach the disinfecting temperature (100°C) for a full 5 min after the water returns to the boil. Ideally, machines should have a device to prevent opening during the process to remove or add instruments. If instruments are not properly cleaned before immersion higher temperatures and longer times may be required (Department of Health and Social Security (DHSS), 1987). Forceps (e.g. 'Cheatles') for removal of objects from the machine should be kept in sterile packets for single use only.

However, these conditions are often not complied with, the process blunts sharp instruments, and repeatedly immersed objects develop a 'fur' which makes further cleaning and disinfection inefficient. Sterilisation is always preferable to hot-water disinfection for instruments (such as vaginal speculae) and should replace disinfection wherever possible.

Low-temperature steam

This process is quite widely used for heat-sensitive items such as respiratory equipment which cannot be autoclaved and other equipment which will not breach the skin or mucosa.

Pasteurisation

This is the method of heat treatment of milk to make it safe for human consumption by removal of pathogenic bacteria. There are two methods:

1. the Holder process where milk is heated to 63–66°C, kept there for 30 min ('holder'), then cooled quickly to below 10°C; and
2. the flash method where milk is heated to 72°C for 15 s, followed by rapid cooling to below 10°C.

Chemical agents

There is a bewildering number of chemical preparations on the market. Too often the choice is a matter of current fashion which may result in unjustifiable expense and inefficient practice. It is essential that a Health Authority develops a disinfectant policy through the Control of Infection Committee which will include a qualified pharmacist. The aim should be to select efficient agents, limit the choice available in order to reduce confusion, and clearly define use dilutions and exposure times. The Control of Substances Hazardous to Health (COSHH) regulations should be applied and will ensure that all disinfectant usage is both necessary and safely conducted. All disinfectants are potentially harmful to a greater or lesser degree.

Guidelines for use should include the following reminders.

- Never use chemicals if more reliable methods (e.g. steam) are suitable.
- Cleaning is the first and most important step in disinfection.
- Total surface contact is essential.
- Recommended strengths for specific purposes must be known and adhered to.
- Recommended exposure times must also be followed.
- Equipment usually needs rinsing after immersion in a chemical.
- Many materials cause inactivation of chemical disinfectants.
- Antiseptic solutions and ointments may themselves become contaminated by incorrect use.

There are many examples of contamination of disinfectants which have led to outbreaks of infection (e.g. Burdon and Whitby, 1967; Bassett et al, 1970). Single-use preparations of ointments, small bottles of disinfectant instead of large containers which used to be 'decanted' and individual sachets of antiseptic solutions have helped to reduce the number of such avoidable disasters. The nurse must understand how a chemical works and what are its limitations in order to use it safely.

Table 6.3 gives examples of the major groups of disinfectants, their major advantages and disadvantages and the uses for which they are intended. A brief description of a few may help to clarify a subject which is a source of confusion to many.

Halogens

1. *Chlorine releasing agents—hypochlorites and dichloro-isocyanurates*. Both these agents are effective against bacteria, viruses, fungi and spores and are thus valuable disinfecting agents. *Hypochlorites* (bleach) include Milton, Domestos and others. They are used in two strengths (note that commercially available bleaches may vary widely in their concentration of free chlorine availability):
   (a) 1 in 10 dilution giving 10 000 parts per million (ppm) available chlorine for disinfecting blood spillages (but is corrosive to metal and will bleach fabrics at this strength);
   (b) 1 in 100 dilution giving 1000 ppm available chlorine for environmental decontamination and cleaning of food preparation surfaces (may still corrode and bleach).
   Sodium dichloroisocyanurate (NaDCC) is an alternative chlorine releasing agent which comes in tablet or powder/granule form, the latter being used now as an effective way of absorbing blood spillage. It has been found to be more active than hypochlorites and not so corrosive (Coates, 1988).
2. *Iodines and iodophors*. These substances are similar in many ways to hypochlorites but are more often used on the skin than environmentally. Some people

Table 6.3 Guide to disinfectants.

Agent	Advantages	Disadvantages
Environmental use *Chlorine-releasing agents* (halogens): including dichloroisocyanurates (NaDCC) e.g. Presept, HAZ-tabs and granules; and hypochlorites, e.g. Chloros, Milton, Domestos	Virucidal. Active against spores and tuberculosis Economical Fast-acting Stable while dry (tablets and granules) NaDCC products avoid dilutions	Corrosive to metals Unstable in solution Inactivated by protein (e.g. blood, pus) Irritant (avoid splashes and inhaling chlorine) Incompatible with some detergents
Phenolics (clear-soluble): e.g. Stericol, Hycolin, Clearsol	Active against tuberculosis Economical. Active in the presence of organic material	Not active against all viruses or spores Toxic, irritant to skin and mucous membranes Incompatible with some detergents Corrosive

Alcohols (see 'Skin disinfection'): used for clean surfaces, e.g. trolley tops

Table 6.3 Continued.

Agent	Advantages	Disadvantages
Skin disinfection		
Chlorhexidine (Diguanide): e.g. 0.5% in 70% alcohol, aqueous, undiluted, surgical scrub	Low toxicity	Limited range of microbial activity. Expensive. Aqueous preparation prone to contamination
Alcohols: e.g. ethanol (IMS), isopropanol	Active against tuberculosis and some viruses including HBV and HIV if surface clean. Evaporates rapidly	Does not penetrate organic matter. Flammable (especially ethyl alcohol)
Iodine and iodophors (halogens): e.g. Betadine, Disadine	Virucidal. Active against spores and tuberculosis	Relatively expensive. May cause allergy, and stains

Hexachlorophane:
e.g. Phisohex, Gamophen soap,
Ster-Zac powder; also Triclosan,
e.g. Manusept and Ster-Zac bath
concentrate

Retained well on skin.
Good action against
staphylococci

Concern remains over repeated
application of emulsions to
newborn infants

Instruments*

Aldehydes:
glutaraldehydes, e.g. Cidex,
Totacide, Asep

Wide range of activity.
Active in presence of organic
material.
Non-damaging to many
materials e.g. lens cement.
Non-corrosive

Slow-acting on spores and TB
especially.
Toxic, and irritant to skin, eyes
and respiratory mucosa.
Expensive.
Fixative

Chlorine-releasing agents (see 'Chlorine releasing agents' environmental use):
suitable for occasional rapid disinfection, e.g. tonometer heads

Alcohols (see 'Chlorhexidine'):
suitable for rapid disinfection

* Instruments should always be cleaned before disinfection, and disinfection should never be substituted for sterilisation
if the latter is required.
N.B. Control of Substances Hazardous to Health Regulations and the Health and Safety at Work Act should be taken
into account when planning any disinfection procedure.

are allergic to iodine and should always be patch tested before full use for signs of allergy. Iodophors have an added substance and are non-irritant and do not stain. They are used in pre-operative skin preparation in orthopaedics especially, for their activity against spore-bearing organisms such as *Clostridium tetani*.

Phenolics

These include the black fluids such as Jeyes fluid and white fluid such as Izal, and the *clear-soluble phenolics* such as Stericol and Hycolin. The former tend to be highly irritant and strong smelling and are rarely used now, but the latter are still used for surface decontamination at a concentration of 1–2%. They are active against many microbes, but not viruses or spores, so there is now a tendency to replace them with chlorine-releasing agents. There are specific areas where they can be useful, e.g. for cleaning beds and fomites after washing when a patient with MRSA has been discharged. They are less easily inactivated by organic matter than the chlorine releasers but are extremely toxic and irritant and should not come into skin contact.

Hexachlorophane is a chlorinated phenolic compound which can be mixed with some soaps and detergents and can be used as a preoperative skin preparation. As Ster-Zac powder it is used in routine umbilical care in neonates, but not in emulsion form because of concern over toxicity from cutaneous absorption. *Triclosan* (Cloxifenol) is a similar compound which has found favour in some quarters as a hand disinfection agent.

Alcohols

Alcohols are effective against most microbes (except spores and some viruses) but *only if the surface/equipment has had organic material removed first. Ethanol* (70%) and *isopropanol* (70%) are used extensively in health-care settings for clean surface disinfection such as trolley tops. They are also useful for skin disinfection, as in the form of an alcoholic hand rub for disinfection of hands between clean tasks (e.g. Hibisol, a combination of chlorhexidine, alcohol and glycerine solution). The property of evaporation avoids the need for rinsing and drying.

Diguanides

This group includes chlorhexidine preparations which are mainly active against Gram-positive organisms, fungi and some Gram-negative bacilli. It is less irritant and toxic than most disinfectants and is thus used as a skin-cleansing agent in alcoholic form and as a surgical scrub in operating theatres. Aqueous solutions are prone to contamination, e.g. with *Pseudomonas* spp., and should only be issued in single-use preparations (Thomas, 1988).

Savlon is a mixture of chlorhexidine and cetrimide but is very prone to contamination with pseudomonads and should only be used as a skin-cleansing agent where its added detergent properties are valuable, e.g. in dirty injuries such as road traffic accident victims. Cetrimide is not recommended for open wounds because of tissue toxicity.

Aldehydes

Glutaraldehydes are chemicals which are active against the whole range of microbes but are relatively slow-acting. They are useful for disinfecting heat-sensitive but 'high-risk' equipment such as endoscopes, and are the only chemicals which can 'sterilise' equipment given a sufficient immersion time (see Table 6.4). This approach is rarely needed and usually not quality controlled. Glutaraldehydes are toxic, allergenic, expensive and highly irritant (especially to eyes, skin and respiratory mucosa) and should only be used in a well-ventilated area using adequate protective clothing and preferably in an automated washing machine. They are also fixative and equipment must be properly cleaned before immersion. A nurse has recently received compensation for damage to health caused by exposure to glutaraldehyde (*Nursing Times*, 1989).

Formaldehyde is too irritant for use as a disinfectant, although active against more microbes. It is only used under carefully controlled conditions in combination with low-temperature steam.

Table 6.3 gives a guide for appropriate selection and use of disinfectants and antiseptics.

Responsibilities to other staff: maintenance and others

In 1987 the DHSS brought out a requirement for any equipment, linen or other surfaces contaminated with hepatitis B or HIV to be safely decontaminated before leaving the area of use (e.g. for repair). A notice to the effect that such action has been taken must be attached to the article, or else a warning that steps to protect the handler must be taken to prevent their contamination.

COSHH regulations and the Health and Safety at Work Act also reinforce the need for responsible use of all materials such as chemicals, and the need for adequate protection of all staff from potentially hazardous equipment or materials.

STERILISATION

The methods used for sterilisation are given in Table 6.4.

Heat

Heat resistance of organisms

Different species of microorganisms vary greatly in their ability to withstand heat. Some, such as the gonococcus, will be killed by a few minutes exposure at 47°C. A few which have the ability to form spores are very resistant. Since these spore-forming organisms are dangerous to a patient who has sustained an injury or surgery resulting in muscle tissue lacking an adequate oxygen supply, all hospital sterilisation procedures aim to kill spore-forming bacteria.

Table 6.4 Methods of sterilisation

Heat	*Moist*	Steam under pressure (autoclaves): 121°C for 15 min at 1.05 kg cm^{-1} (15 psi); 134°C for 3 min at 2.1 kg cm^{-1} (30 psi)
	Dry	Incineration (hot air oven): 160°C for 1 h
Chemicals	*Gases*	Low-temperature steam + formaldehyde (70–80°C). Ethylene oxide
	Liquids	Glutaraldehyde—2% solution for 3 h
Irradiation		
Filtration		

Time–temperature relationship

Destruction of microorganisms by heat is achieved by rapid coagulation of the cell protein by moist heat, or by a much slower process of oxidation with dry heat. If the temperature is raised, the exposure time can be decreased. For example, a standard time–temperature ratio for moist heat is 121°C for 15 min; if the temperature is raised to 134°C the time required for sterilisation is decreased to 3 min. This compares with 160°C for 1 h to achieve sterilisation by dry heat.

Moist heat

Steam under pressure

As used in autoclaves, pressurised steam has physical properties which allow rapid penetration of porous objects and fabrics as well as sterilisation of instruments and solid objects. Temperatures greater than the 121°C for 15 min required to kill spores can be readily obtained, and this is the commonest method of sterilising linen, instruments and equipment in hospitals.

The removal of air is critical, as

1. air + steam at a given pressure is at a lower temperature than steam alone; and
2. air insulates, and prevents condensation of steam onto inner surfaces of hollow instruments, etc.

Sterilising conditions in autoclaves (e.g. 121°C for 15 min or 134°C (for 3 min) are based on the probability of kill of a standard inoculum. This process would not be guaranteed to sterilise heavily contaminated substances (e.g. soil).

Autoclaves

These can vary from modified pressure cookers to complex, fully automated machines, each with a particular function for different types of load. They consist basically of a chamber with airtight doors, constructed to withstand high internal pressures and equipped with a safety valve, controlled steam inlet, chamber drain, thermometer in the outlet drain line, temperature and pressure recorders (see Figure 6.2).

Three types of autoclave are widely used in hospitals.

1. *High pressure pre-vacuum autoclaves* mainly used in the central sterile supply department (CSSD) and the theatre sterile supply unit (TSSU). These are complex, often automatically operated, jacketed autoclaves

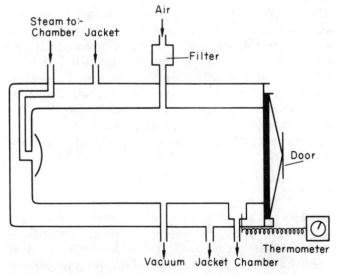

Figure 6.2 Diagrammatic representation of an autoclave.

designed for efficient, fast sterilisation of air-trapping loads such as packs of fabric, dressings and instruments, limited lengths of tubing and hollow equipment.

2. *Downward displacement autoclaves*. These should only be used for unwrapped instruments because air would be trapped in packs or tubing and thus prevent access by the steam, and fabrics or paper would be wet at the end of the cycle.

3. *'Pressure-cooker' type autoclaves* often used in laboratories. These operate on the same principle as the displacement type but can be adjusted to operate at a variety of steam pressures, thus allowing a wider range of temperature settings. They are less efficient.

Bench-top 'sterilisers'

These have come on the market in large numbers comparatively recently for use in clinics, health centres and other places without access to a central sterile supply department. A Health Equipment Information booklet (HEI 185) evaluates these models for use on unwrapped instruments and utensils. As with any equipment, they must be properly maintained and should only be used where operators are trained and able to perform the necessary checks to guarantee that they are working properly.

Dry heat

Dry heat is transferred from source to load by conduction or radiation. High temperatures and comparatively long exposure times are required. It is not a suitable sterilising agent for fabrics and dressings which are poor uneven conductors and ruined by excessive heat. It is, however, used for some pre-assembled glass syringes, other glass-ware and for sterilisation of some ophthalmic instruments liable to damage by moist heat. Dry heat is also used to sterilise oily pharmaceutical preparations and powders. Sterilising exposure time is always measured from the point at which the centre of the load attains the required sterilising (holding) temperature. This will vary according to the size of the load and the type of material being processed, and necessitates careful control and testing of the apparatus.

Incineration

This is the safest method of sterilising and disposing of infected dressings. Laboratory wire loops used for transferring bacteria and inoculating media are sterilised by heating to redness in a Bunsen burner flame.

Hot-air oven

The standard temperature/time ratio is 160°C for 60 min. The total cycle time is considerably longer since it includes the time required for the whole load to attain 160°C prior to exposure time, plus the time required for the load to cool down after sterilisation. Hot-air ovens used for sterilisation must contain a fan to ensure air circulation and thus an even temperature at all levels within the oven, and automatic door locks.

Chemicals

Low-temperature steam and formaldehyde

This is a method of killing all vegetative organisms and most spores present on heat-sensitive equipment such as endoscopes and electronic equipment. A high vacuum autoclave is modified to admit steam and formalin at subatmospheric pressure so that the temperature in the chamber does not rise above 80°C. Exposure times of 30 min to 2 h are recommended, according to the material to be processed. The formalin is neutralised by ammonia at the end of the cycle.

The disadvantages of the gas are that it has a pungent smell, is irritant to eyes, skin and mucous membranes, and has poor properties of penetration and diffusion into fabrics or narrow tubes such as catheters. Materials must also be packed in a way that allows vapour to penetrate. (See Hurrell (1987) for further information.)

Formaldehyde catheter 'sterilising' ovens are unreliable and unsatisfactory; they should not be used (DHSS recommendation 1969).

Ethylene oxide sterilisation

This is mostly confined to industry and a few large hospitals, not least because of the high capital outlay needed. The gas can be used at comparatively low temperatures (37–55°C), it does not corrode or damage a wide range of materials and it enables sterilisation of some equipment which would be ruined by heat or ionising radiation processes. However, it is toxic, potentially explosive, needs a prolonged aeration time and microbiological control. Further information is available from the Central Sterilising Club, *Working Report No. 2* (1986).

Glutaraldehyde

This chemical was discussed in the section on disinfection, but can also be used for sterilisation of heat-sensitive items (see p. 133 and Table 6.4).

Irradiation

Thermolabile (heat-sensitive) materials can be sterilised by irradiation. The size of the plant required, the cost of the source and the statutory safeguards for the handling of radioactive materials mean that the method is nationally and commercially organised, rather than hospital-centred.

Gamma irradiation from the radioisotope cobalt-60 is the chief method used, but high-energy electrons from a linear accelerator can also be used. In the UK, a radiation dose of 2.5 Mrad is used to sterilise medical disposable products, e.g. needles, syringes, suture material, arterial catheters, and prostheses. Only certain products can be sterilised by this method without causing changes in their composition and many cannot be safely re-sterilised by irradiation or any other method.

Filtration

Pharmaceutical fluids, fluids used in total parenteral nutrition and laboratory media would be damaged by other sterilisation methods and, therefore, are passed through fine filters to remove microorganisms. Bacterial filters vary in material and design, e.g. porous membranes such as glass fibre, various polymers and even cotton wool. Air filters must remain dry, or they will allow organisms to pass through. Some filters for liquid must remain wet. Filters are used to reduce microorganism load in some areas, e.g. in operating theatres, pharmaceutical clean rooms and units for the protection of patients at high risk of infection.

Cold

Freezing as a method of killing microorganisms is not satisfactory for ordinary use because the survival rate of organisms in low temperatures varies considerably. It is useful for killing parasites in fish and meat. Refrigeration is, however, an excellent method for preserving food, sera, etc., when the temperature is kept at about 4°C. Organisms are not killed by this method but they usually do not multiply. *Listeria* and some strains of *Salmonella* will grow, albeit slowly, at 4°C and most *Salmonella* will multiply at 8°C.

Perishable goods should be placed in the refrigerator immediately. If they are allowed to stay in a warm atmosphere for several hours the organisms present in them will have a chance of multiplying and refrigeration after this time will be useless. Preformed toxins are not destroyed by refrigeration and no amount of cooling after they have been formed will make the food safe to eat.

Drying

Many organisms are killed by drying and this factor limits the spread of many diseases. Spores, however, can withstand remaining dry for many months or even years and, as a practical method of killing bacteria, drying is unsatisfactory.

Ultraviolet light

Prolonged exposure to fresh air and sunlight is perhaps the oldest and most pleasant anti-infection measure. Ultraviolet rays reduce the number of airborne bacteria, but the practical value of an ultraviolet light installation as a means of killing bacteria in a hospital is minimal. Ultraviolet sources do not remain at the specified intensity for very long.

RE-USE OF DISPOSABLE EQUIPMENT

Problems arise in many health care areas when equipment is bought without sufficient consideration being given to how it can be dealt with between patient use. Any item of equipment which falls into a 'high-risk' category must be sterile. It must also be capable of withstanding a method of sterilisation possessed by the user if it is to be used again.

Articles which only require decontamination should also be capable of being safely and appropriately handled to reprocess. It is often the nurse in a department or clinic who is asked to reprocess equipment and he/she should be completely *au fait* with and confident of the safety and reliability of any method which he/she is asked to use.

Before reprocessing is carried out the following should be considered.

1. Can the item actually be reprocessed? (Did it come from a packet which said 'single-use only'?)
2. Is it cost-effective?
3. What are the risks to patients and staff?
4. What are the legal and ethical considerations?

Recent legislation about product liability suggests that items designated by the manufacturer as 'single-use only', become the responsibility of the organisation which processes and reuses the items. This would leave the user at fault from any subsequent problems associated with that equipment. Sterile articles packaged by the manufacturer and labelled 'single-use only' must not be reprocessed. A report by the Kings Fund discusses this issue in detail, as do Hunter (1987) and Simmons (1987). Both the Health and Safety at Work Act (1974) and the COSHH regulations must also be taken into account.

Perhaps the nurse must also be prepared to debate the

suitability of disposable equipment in many instances with a view both to unnecessary expense and production of waste, as environmental concerns become more acute (Daschner, 1989).

COMMUNITY DISINFECTION AND STERILISATION PRACTICES

Confusion concerning the meaning of the terms *cleaning*, *disinfection*, *antiseptic* and *sterilisation* are still widespread, and the appropriateness of their application is often in doubt. Three recent surveys of GP practices have shown most clearly that there is considerable, and worrying, variation in the methods used to decontaminate equipment and deal with spillages.

Morgan et al (1990) concluded that a detailed code of practice is required for primary health-care staff on control of infection, having identified poor knowledge of treatment of blood spills and finding that 22% of high-risk instruments were inadequately decontaminated. The BMA have issued a code of practice on instrument sterilisation aimed especially at primary health-care staff (British Medical Association, 1989). A smaller survey of 20 practices revealed that of 327 items examined, 100 were doubtfully decontaminated and 37 were considered totally unsatisfactorily processed (Hoffman et al, 1989). They also found much inappropriate use of disinfectants. Rogers (1989) identified lack of understanding of use, maintenance, storage and risk categories with regard to disinfectants, antiseptics, sterile instruments and machinery for sterilising. There is no reason to assume that hospitals would fare better in such surveys, and much education is needed to improve the situation and ensure safe standards of care.

REFERENCES

Ayliffe GAJ, Collins BJ and Lowbury EJL (1966) Cleaning and disinfection of hospital floors. *Br. Med. J.* **2**: 442.

Ayliffe GAJ, Coates D and Hoffman PN (1984) *Chemical Disinfection in Hospitals*. London: PHLS.

Ayliffe GAJ, Babb JR and Collins BJ (1986) Environmental hazards—real and imaginary. *Hlth Soc. Serv. J.* **26 Jun**: 3.

Bassett DCJ, Stokes KJ and Thomas WRG (1970) Wound infection with *Pseudomonas multivorans*: a water-borne contaminant of disinfectant solutions. *Lancet*, **i**: 1188.

British Medical Association (1989) *A code of practice for Sterilisation of Instruments and Control of Cross Infection*. London: BMA.

Bromley D (1983) Psychological factors in hospital infection. *Nursing Times*, *J. Inf. Control Nursing* **79**(23): 11–14.

Burdon DW and Whitby JL (1967) Contamination of hospital disinfectants with *Pseudomonas* species. *Br. Med. J.* **2**: 153.

Central Sterilising Club (1986) Washer/disinfection machines. *Working Party Report No. 1*. Obtainable from Hospital Infection Research Laboratory, Dudley Road Hospital, Birmingham.

Central Sterilising Club (1986) Sterilisation and disinfection of heat labile equipment. *Working Party Report No. 2*. Birmingham: Central Sterilising Club.

Coates D (1988) Comparison of sodium hypochlorite and sodium dichloroisocyanurate disinfectants: neutralisation by serum. *J. Hosp. Infect.* **11**: 60–67.

Collins BJ (1988) The hospital environment, how clean should a hospital be? *J. Hosp. Infect.* **11** (Suppl. A): 53–56.

Danforth D, Nicolle LE, Hume K, Alfieri N and Sims H (1987) Nosocomial infections on nursing units with floors cleaned with a disinfectant compared with detergent. *J. Hosp. Infect.* **10**(3): 229–235.

Daschner F (1989) Cost-effectiveness in hospital infection control—lessons for the 1990s. *J. Hosp. Infect.* **13**(4): 325–336.

DHSS (1987) *Decontamination of Health Care Equipment Prior to Inspection, Service or Repair*. Publication No. (87)22. London: HMSO.

DHSS (19/88) HEI 185 Evaluation of portable steam sterilisers for unwrapped instruments and utensils. London: HMSO.

Gransden WR, Webster M, French GL and Phillips I (1986) An outbreak of *Serratia marcescens* transmitted by contaminated breast pumps in a special care baby unit. *J. Hosp. Infection* **7**(2): 149–154.

Hambraeus A and Bengstsson AS (1980) Disinfection or cleaning of hospital toilets—an evaluation of different routines. *J. Hosp. Infect.* **1**: 159–163.

Hoffman PN, Cooke EM, Larkin DP, Southgate LJ, Mayon-White RT, Pether JVS, Wright AE and Keenlyside D (1988) Control of infection in general practice: a survey and recommendations. *Br. Med. J.* **297**: 34–36.

Hunter I (1987) Is re-use worth the risk? *Nursing Times* **83**(11): 29–30.

Hurrell DJ (1987) Low-temperature steam and formaldehyde (LTSF) sterilisation. Its effectiveness and merits. *J. Sterile Serv. Management* **5**: 40.

King Edwards Hospital Memorial Fund for London (1986) Re-use of sterile, single-use and disposable equipment in the NHS. *Conference Proceedings.* Kings Fund College: London.

Maurer IM (1985) *Hospital Hygiene*, 3rd edn. London: Edward Arnold.

Morgan DR, Lamont TJ, Dawson JD and Booth C (1990) Decontamination of instruments and control of cross-infection in general practice. *Br. Med. J.* **300**: 1379–1380.

Nursing Times (1989) Handle with care. **85**(37): 20–21.

Nystrom B (1981) The disinfection of baths and shower trolleys in hospitals. *J. Hosp. Infect.* **2**: 93–95.

Rogers J (1989) Sterilisation in GP surgeries. *Nursing Times, J. Inf. Control Nursing* **85**(9): 65–69.

Simmons B (1987) The case for re-use. *Nursing Times* **83**(11): 26–29.

Stone JW and Das BC (1985) Investigation of an outbreak of infection with *Acinetobacter calcoaceticus* in a special care baby unit. *J. Hosp. Infect.* **7**(1): 42–48.

Thomas CGA (1988) *Medical Microbiology*, 6th edn. London: Baillière Tindall.

Thomlinson D (1990) Time to dispense with the rituals. *Prof. Nurse* **May**: 421–425.

Ward K (1990) All that glisters . . . . *Nursing Times* **86**(24): 32–34.

FURTHER READING

Guide to Good Manufacturing Practice (1989) issued by Institute of Sterile Services Management to the National Health Service under cover of E.L 89(P)136.

Hanson PJV, Gor D, Jeffries DJ and Collins JV (1989) Chemical inactivation of HIV on surfaces. *Br. Med. J.* **298**: 862–864.

Rutala WA (1990) APIC guideline for selection and use of disinfectants. *Am. J. Inf. Control* **18**(2): 99–117.

Ward K (1985) Down the drain? *Nursing Times, J. Inf. Control Nursing* **81**(49): 60–62.

7 Diagnostic microbiology

Laboratory tests are ordered by the clinician in charge of a patient for various reasons. For example, the test may be to find out which particular organism is causing an obvious infection, or it may be to confirm or to eliminate a specific site or system as the focus of infection. The patient may apparently have recovered from an infection and the test prescribed is to check that he is free from the causative organism, or a specimen may be one of a series sent at regular intervals to monitor progress (rarely used now).

The clinician may consult with the microbiologist about the suitability of certain tests, for expert interpretation of laboratory findings or for advice on antibiotic therapy; he frequently delegates to the nursing staff the responsibility for obtaining appropriate specimens.

The laboratory staff can only examine the material and information presented to them, and the diagnosis, management, or treatment of patients may depend on the results which they report back to the clinician. Collecting specimens at the correct time, using the correct technique and despatching them without delay to the designated laboratory is therefore of critical importance. If the material presented to the laboratory is of poor quality then the result of the test reported back to the clinician will be unreliable.

COLLECTION OF SPECIMENS FOR BACTERIOLOGICAL EXAMINATION

The objectives are:

1. To collect an adequate amount of tissue or fluid uncontaminated by organisms from any outside source, but preserving any organisms which may be present.
2. To ensure that the specimen is correctly identified by labelling, and sent to the laboratory with an accurately completed request form.
3. To transport the specimen from the patient to the laboratory safely and with the minimum of delay.

Guidelines for appropriate specimen collection:

1. As a general rule the more material sent for examination, the greater the chance of isolating a causative organism. For example, it is preferable to send a few millilitres of pus aspirated with a sterile syringe and needle than to send a swab dipped in the pus.
2. Specimens are readily contaminated by poor techniques such as allowing urine to flow over the vulva before collecting it in the container, or by the use of unsterile equipment. Specimens should be collected in sterile laboratory containers, with the exception of faeces and sputum (clean containers).
3. Ideally, samples should be collected before the commencement of antibiotic therapy. When it is necessary to test during a course of antibiotic treatment, the specimen should be collected just before a dose is given.

Similarly if an antiseptic is used for cleaning or packing a wound or body cavity, a specimen should be collected at the commencement of the procedure as the presence of antibiotic or antiseptic in the specimen container may destroy organisms which are in fact active in the patient and this will affect laboratory tests. Such treatment should be noted on the request form accompanying the specimen.

It is important to ensure that every specimen is clearly identified by a label giving the name and location of the patient and the date. The accompanying request form should give any relevant data, e.g. a provisional diagnosis, pyrexia, wound infection, chemotherapy, as well as the patient's name, age, sex and location; it must be legible.

Specimen transport

The sooner specimens reach the laboratory the greater the chance of any organisms present surviving and being identified. With the exception of blood culture samples, which should be placed in a 37°C incubator, immediately if possible, specimens which cannot be sent to the laboratory within a short time should be placed in a specimen refrigerator at 4°C. Laboratories issue containers of sterile *transport medium* into which the swab stick is inserted. The purpose of transport medium is to preserve the organisms in the same condition and numbers as when present in the patient. It is effective for about 24 h and should not be refrigerated or incubated.

Any specimen may contain potentially pathogenic organisms. To avoid presenting a hazard to anyone in contact with the specimen, it is most important to avoid contamination of the outside of specimen containers and to ensure that they are securely closed and safely handled. Should a specimen container leak, not only are the porter and laboratory staff at risk but contaminating organisms may get into the container and a false result ensue. To ensure safety:

1. specimen containers are put in plastic bags which seal,
2. no staples or pins should be used, and
3. the specimen and request form are in separate compartments.

The 'Howie' Code of Practice (DHSS, 1978) described methods for the packing, handling and safe transport of specimens. This has now been updated and expanded to give guidance on safe working practices for clinical laboratories, rules for staff and visitors and also for post-mortem rooms (DOH, 1991).

Specimen containers must be 'robust and leak proof' and transported upright in designated trays or boxes which can be disinfected or autoclaved in case of breakage or spillage. Many hospitals now have trays with a bar to which specimen transport bags can be hooked (see Figure 7.1). These bags have two separate compartments to keep form and specimen apart.

There is also a document produced by the Advisory Committee on Dangerous Pathogens (1990), *Categorisation of Pathogens According to Hazard and Categories of Containment*, which is intended as guidance for laboratory staff.

The Control of Substances Hazardous to Health regulations (1988) also require that staff have documented procedures available concerning safe management of specimens and what to do in case of accidents. Nurses must play their part by ensuring that specimens are put safely into the appropriate container and present no hazard to the portering or laboratory staff. It is important to be familiar with the guidelines of the employing authority.

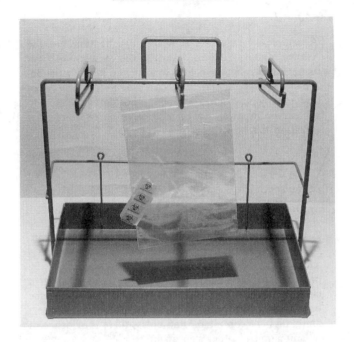

Figure 7.1 Specimen transport tray, two-compartment bag, and BIOHAZARD label.

Information and laboratory request forms

Although the initial request for laboratory investigations is usually made by medical staff, and should be signed by them, specimens are frequently collected by nursing staff. In addition to the importance of good, appropriate specimen collection, accompanying information must also be accurate and *relevant*. The range of tests available within the laboratory is wide and *if* relevant information is given the most appropriate test can be selected immediately.

Example 1

A sample of faeces is sent for investigation but the 'clinical details' section describes the long-stay patient as having chronic bronchitis and fails to identify the 36-h history of acute diarrhoea. Although identification of any pathogens should still be reported, a chance to be promptly aware of a potential hospital-acquired infection has been lost.

The suspected *site* of infection, and the history or origin of the specimen is very often omitted.

Example 2

A 'wound swab' is sent to the laboratory but fails to state the site. If it came from a post-operative site following a 'clean' operation (such as a knee replacement), any organism would require investigation. A swab from a chronic leg ulcer will yield many potentially pathogenic organisms which may only be colonising the ulcer: antibiotics are contraindicated unless there is evidence of inflammation or other sign of infection.

The *timing* of collection and transport are also important.

Example 3

A specimen of urine collected at 10 p.m. and left in the sluice overnight will almost certainly show a heavy growth of bacteria. These may represent overgrowth of a contaminant, or an organism which was present in the urine only in low numbers. If the culture is misinterpreted in the laboratory, this patient could eventually receive unwarranted or inappropriate antibiotic treatment. (Urine specimens should be repeated before antibiotics are given, to check the results.)

To obtain the best information from a laboratory for the benefit of the patient it is important for the nurse to ensure that, in addition to basic patient details, the following guidelines are observed.

- The specimen has been correctly collected at the appropriate time;
- The specimen has been securely contained;
- The specimen is accompanied by a form which shows:
  (a) time and date of collection,
  (b) any antibiotic therapy being given,
  (c) clinical information relevant to request, and
  (d) the site of the swab/specimen/infection.

(See Figures 7.2 and 7.3.)

Collection of swabs

Nasal swabs

The patient is placed facing a good light source, the procedure explained, and the swab taken from both nostrils according to the investigation required.

1. The area to the back of the nose will be sampled if the patient is being investigated for a purulent discharge. This requires tilting of the patient's head, and a gentle, twisting motion with the swab. The swab is replaced promptly in the container to avoid contamination.
2. When screening for staphylococcal carriage during an outbreak, samples are taken from the anterior nares. The swab is directed upwards in the tip of the nose and rotated five times towards the centre for each nostril (clockwise for the left nostril and anti-clockwise for the right nostril ensures minimal trauma to the septum). The normal, healthy nose is virtually

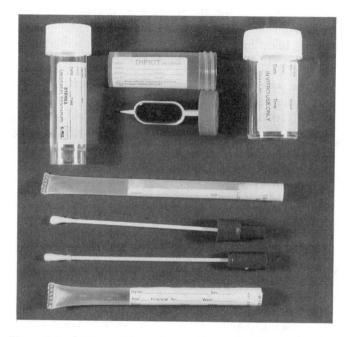

Figure 7.2 Some containers for specimen collection, and swabs with bacterial and viral transport media.

dry so the swab must be moistened with sterile distilled water or normal saline.

3. *Pernasal swabs* are taken in cases of suspected whooping cough. This is usually done by a paediatrician or microbiologist as it requires passing of a fine, flexible wire with cotton wool on the tip, into the nasopharynx. The child will automatically cough, and help and reassurance will be needed. The swab is either placed in charcoal transport medium or plated directly onto enriched charcoal agar at the bedside.

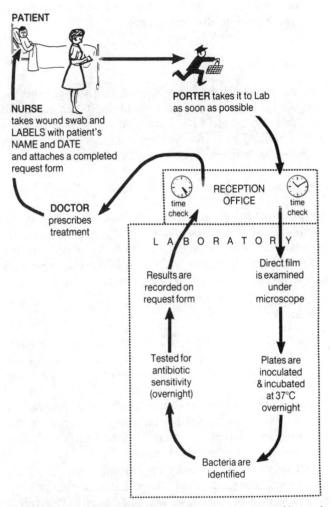

Figure 7.3 The sequence of laboratory identification of bacteria from infected material.

A *cough plate* held in front of the child is less traumatic but also less reliable.

Throat swabs

The patient is placed facing a good light source, and the tongue is depressed. Care should be taken to avoid touching the mouth or tongue, and the swab should be gently rubbed over the pillars of fauces and any area with visible inflammation, lesion or exudate.

Ear swabs

If otitis media is suspected, discharging pus may be sampled. An aural speculum will be needed. Care is necessary to avoid contamination of the swab from the external part of the ear which can be cleaned first with sterile normal saline or distilled water.

Eye swabs

Organisms commonly causing eye infections are delicate and chances of isolation are improved if samples are obtained using a wire loop to gently rub over the conjunctiva in the lower conjunctival sac, taking care to avoid contamination by touching the lids. These are plated directly onto blood or chocolate agar at the bedside, as lysozyme in tears is antibacterial. Medical staff usually perform this procedure.

Organisms causing 'sticky eye' problems in babies are usually staphylococci or coliforms, and a simple eye swab placed in transport medium will be adequate. If purulent conjunctivitis is present and gonococcal or chlamydial infection is suspected, special transport media must be used.

Swabs from the genital tract

To take high vaginal or cervical swabs, a speculum is required. Transport medium is essential for swabs from cervix, vagina or urethra. For investigation for suspected *Neisseria gonorrhoea*, *Chlamydia* or herpes simplex, the laboratory will supply special transport media.

Swabs from wound and pus exudates

Wound swabs should be taken before the area is cleaned, from the affected site not the surrounding tissue (which may be colonised with different organisms). The swab is gently rotated to collect as much pus or exudate as possible.

Collection of other specimens for laboratory investigation

Sputum

Care needs to be taken to ensure that a specimen is genuinely sputum and not saliva. The mouth and pharynx contain many commensal flora which are irrelevant to the investigation of suspected pulmonary infection. The help of a physiotherapist may be required to enable the patient to expectorate and an early morning specimen is likely to be most productive. Specimen containers need to be clean but not sterile.

Three early morning specimens taken on consecutive days are usually required for *Mycobacterium tuberculosis*. The organisms are rarely likely to be present in great numbers. Confirmation of the diagnosis may have to wait until culture results many weeks later.

Blood culture

Blood samples for direct isolation of pathogenic organisms in cases of septicaemia or other blood-borne infection are taken by medical staff after skin disinfection, and a fresh needle is used to inoculate each bottle of culture medium. (There is doubt about the effectiveness of this practice in reducing contamination, however, and danger in the additional need to handle the needles.) Either two or three bottles are usually used with 20 ml of blood distributed between them. Success or failure in isolating organisms depends upon careful collection to avoid skin contamination, and taking the specimen at the right time. The nurse can alert the medical staff when a patient has a sudden rise in temperature as this may reflect bacteraemia. The samples should not be refrigerated but promptly transported to the laboratory with the following information:

1. date and time of blood culture, and the patient's temperature at that time;
2. date of onset of illness;
3. any infective foci the patient may have, e.g. pneumonia, septic lesion, urinary tract infection, and the microbiology of these if known. Any underlying predisposing condition (e.g. HIV, leukaemia); and
4. any antibiotic therapy the patient is receiving and time of last dose.

Serum for antibodies. For this investigation, 10 ml of blood should be taken into a dry tube or bottle containing no anticoagulant, and allowed to clot.

Specific antibodies do not appear in the serum for several days. It is the usual procedure to take blood at the beginning of an infection and then again after 10 days; the specimens are examined together in the laboratory. An increase in the amount of antibodies in the second specimen will be an indication of continued stimulation by the organism which must therefore be present in the patient. By comparing two specimens more information is gained, although single samples are sometimes helpful. A single high-titre specimen may indicate old, not current, infection, or may be taken too early for antibodies to be detectable.

It is important that samples are accompanied by full details of:

1. the clinical history;
2. date of onset of illness;
3. any history of a previous attack of the infection, with dates;
4. any history of immunisation.

Cerebrospinal fluid and other body fluids

These fluids are collected by medical staff, and a strict aseptic technique coupled with safe transport is required to prevent contamination of the specimen. Cerebrospinal fluid (CSF) is collected in three sterile bottles, with the cell count being performed on the later sample which will be less likely to contain blood cells. Aspirations (pleuritic, joint, ascitic; 20–30 ml) and biopsy specimens should all be accompanied by as full a patient history as possible.

Urine

The best way to obtain a specimen of urine for laboratory investigation is to instruct the patient how to take a mid-stream sample of urine (MSU). The genital area should be washed with soap and water (antiseptics may confuse the findings), the first part of the stream passed into the toilet and the middle into a sterile container. In the male, the prepuce is retracted and the glans penis washed. In the female, careful explanation is needed and nursing supervision may be required as collection of an uncontaminated specimen is not easy. The vulval area is cleaned, with outer and then inner labia cleaned in a front to back direction to reduce perineal/perianal contamination. The patient micturates with the labia separated and the middle portion of the stream is collected.

In examination for tubercle bacilli, where the organisms are likely to be very scanty, the whole of the first specimen on three consecutive mornings should be sent.

Catheter specimen of urine. This is collected from the self-sealing sleeve of the drainage tubing with a sterile fine-bore needle and syringe. The sleeve should first be cleaned with alcohol and the needle inserted at an angle of 45°, ensuring that penetration of the far wall of the tubing does not occur. Samples should never be obtained by breaking the catheter–drainage bag junction. This will almost certainly lead to contamination of the system. Nor should samples be taken from the drainage bag as the inevitable multiplication of organisms in static urine will not represent the numbers present in the bladder.

Urine specimens should reach the laboratory within 1 h or be refrigerated at 4°C until transported so that the numbers and types of different bacteria can be accurately assessed. In the community or outlying hospitals where this may be difficult, 'dip slides' may be used; these are slides coated with a nutrient medium which can be incubated after insertion in a urine specimen, drainage, placing in the container and posting to the laboratory. An alternative is to preserve the urine with boric acid.

Faeces

Specimens of faeces may be sent for detection of bacteria, viruses, ova, cysts or parasites. They should be sent in clean, leak-proof containers, many of which contain a plastic spoon as an aid to collection. Most laboratories have a policy to reject leaking containers as a safeguard for laboratory staff and many specimens are wasted because of careless dispatch.

Detection of agents causing viral gastro-enteritis is only likely during the acute stage of the illness and thus prompt collection of samples is vital.

Specimens of stools for parasites. Segments of *tapeworm* can be seen with ease in any specimen of stool and the worm will continue to grow and shed segments unless the head is dislodged; it is therefore important to search for this in every specimen passed by the patient after treatment. Stool specimens should be strained through fine black material under a running tap, the tapeworm segments will be retained and can be sent to the laboratory for identification of the species and for confirmation of the presence of the head.

Many intestinal worms shed their *ova* into the faeces: they can only be seen microscopically and a fresh specimen of stool should be sent to the laboratory in a suitable container. Threadworms lay their ova on the perianal skin; swabs of this area should therefore be taken as the ova will not be seen in stool specimens. The sticky side of transparent Sellotape is used for this purpose and is pressed on to the skin of the perianal area, in the early morning and before defaecation. The Sellotape should then be placed adhesive side down on to a glass slide which is sent to the laboratory.

Specimens of stool for amoebae. The parasites of amoebic dysentery, *Entamoeba histolytica*, exist in a free-living motile form and in the form of non-motile cysts. Both forms are characteristic in their fresh state and a diagnosis of amoebic dysentery can be made from a fresh specimen of stool. The free-living form, however, becomes non-motile very easily in older specimens when the temperature has fallen, and both forms are more difficult to recognise when they are dead. It is therefore essential that specimens of stool for amoebae should be sent to the laboratory as soon as they are passed and should be examined immediately. It may be necessary to examine many specimens before the amoebae are seen. It is not necessary to keep the specimens hot, although 'hot stool' is the name given for specimens for amoebic trophozoites.

COLLECTION OF MATERIAL FOR FUNGAL INVESTIGATIONS

Many specimens for fungal investigation will be examined in the ways already described (e.g. vaginal swabs for detection of *Candida* spp.), but the following are examples of sampling techniques not yet described;

Hair

Samples of broken and infected hairs should be removed with forceps and sent to the laboratory in a clean sealed envelope or suitably dry specimen container so that the base of the hair can be examined and cultured. Some fungi fluoresce in ultraviolet light and a lamp may be used to identify infected hairs.

Nails

The whole thickness of the nail or deep scrapings should be sent in a dry container to the laboratory.

Skin lesions

The skin should be cleaned with alcohol. Epidermal scales scraped from the active edge of a lesion or the roof of any vesicles should be sent to the laboratory in a dry container.

Black paper aids identification of fungal samples. Commercial kits of paper with adhesive strip and self-sealing envelope can be obtained.

COLLECTION OF SPECIMENS FOR VIRAL INVESTIGATION

Viruses, with the exception of the poxviruses, do not survive drying and, therefore, are very labile outside the body and require special *viral transport media* (VTM) and prompt delivery to the laboratory. (VTM is isotonic buffered saline with protein to protect the virus and antibiotics to kill off the bacteria.) If in doubt, the virology department should be consulted before specimens are taken. In addition to the patient data sent with bacteriological specimens, the virologist will need to know:

1. the date of onset of illness;
2. history of blood transfusion or other blood product given within the past 6 months; and
3. the patient's immunisation history, particularly of any vaccine received within the previous month.

Specific investigations are mentioned alongside the appropriate virus in Chapter 9.

Serological tests are frequently used as a method of detecting viral infection and are described elsewhere in this chapter.

SUMMARY OF SPECIMEN COLLECTION GUIDELINES

- Always get specimens to the laboratory as soon as possible after collection. Refrigerate urine and sputum specimens if delay is unavoidable.
- Always use the appropriate transport medium.
- Never use a swab if faeces, fluid or pus is available.
- Complete the request form fully and use correct specimen bag. Only put one specimen in each bag.
- Do not send leaking specimens anywhere, discard them.
- If in doubt, *please consult the laboratory staff.*

LABORATORY ISOLATION OF ORGANISMS FROM SPECIMENS

The microbiologist processes material which is sent to him by a number of methods.

1. Macroscopic appearance of specimen.
2. Microscopy of specimen—identification using size, shape and staining properties.
3. Culture—according to the growth requirements.
4. Macroscopic appearance of colonial growth.
5. Biochemical tests to distinguish bacteria.
6. Resistance and sensitivity tests.
7. Serological tests (e.g. agglutination with specific antisera).
8. Bacterial typing (usually in support of outbreak investigation).
9. Pathogenicity tests in experimental animals.

Macroscopic appearance of specimen

This involves *direct examination* of the specimen. It may:

1. weed out unsuitable specimens, e.g. 'sputum', which is actually saliva;
2. speed diagnosis by alerting the laboratory staff as to which tests may be required, e.g. foul-smelling pus indicates possible anaerobic infection; or
3. confirm diagnosis by seeing, for example, a tapeworm segment.

Microscopy

This involves use of a microscope to examine the specimen and identify the morphology (e.g. round, spiral, or rod shaped) of any organisms present in the specimen; whether these are in pairs, chains or clusters and, if they are motile.

'Wet' films. These are unstained preparations where drops of liquid (CSF, urine and body fluids) are examined for organisms on a slide covered with a coverslip under a light microscope. It is possible to make direct examination of faeces when looking for cysts and ova; of skin, hair and nails when looking for some fungal infections; and of vaginal secretions for some infections including *Trichomonas vaginalis*.

Organisms in most specimens require *staining* with various dyes to make them readily visible. They are then examined with one of a variety of microscopes.

Transmitted light microscopy

This is the main diagnostic method used in bacteriology. It may even be life saving in terms of rapid identification (when organisms are identifiable in a specimen of CSF from a patient with suspected meningitis, or in some blood culture specimens from severely ill patients).

Dark ground illumination microscopy

Now used mainly to look at specimens from ulcers in patients with suspected syphilis, for the spirochaete *Treponema pallidum*.

Fluorescence microscopy

This involves using ultraviolet light on cells or bacteria stained with fluorescent dyes (e.g. auramine for myco-bacteria) or, alternatively, *immunofluorescence* using a combination of fluorescent microscopy and serology to allow identification of specific antigens by fluorescein labelled antibodies. Polyclonal or monoclonal antibodies may be used. The immunofluorescence procedure is used more in virology than bacteriology, e.g. detection of respiratory syncytial virus in infants, and is useful for the speed of identification which it allows in comparison with the time taken to culture the virus.

Phase contrast microscopy

Modifications to an ordinary light microscope allow the difference in light-wave phases to show up as differences in density. This shows up fine detail in unstained living organisms.

Electron microscopy

This is used to identify viruses in specimens. It uses electrons instead of light waves, thus enabling identification of minute details and differentiation between particles as little as 0.0001 μm apart.

Staining

The details of Gram and Ziehl–Neelsen staining techniques have already been described in Chapter 2. There are also special stains available for identifying various spores, mycobacteria, etc.

Culture

Bacteria can be grown artificially to allow further investigation and identification. They have different nutritional needs according to the organism involved. Viruses must be cultured in living cells (see p. 170).

Conditions of bacterial and fungal growth

It is usual when trying to isolate an organism, to put infected material into a sterile mixture of nutrients which will encourage its growth. Such mixtures are called *culture media*, and many have a nutrient broth like clear soup as a basis. This and other additions may be mixed with melted agar (a gel derived from seaweed), poured into flat Petri dishes or into slanted screw-topped bottles, and allowed to set. Infected material is spread on the surface of the agar using a swab and distributed or diluted using a loop in such a way that the load of organisms becomes progressively less (see Figure 7.4).

To encourage the growth of various organisms, specific substances can be added to the basic medium either to enrich it or to make it more selective.

Blood agar is used for identification of the majority of aerobic and facultatively anaerobic bacteria and also many fungi causing human infections. *Chocolate agar* (heated blood which may have added supplements) is used to detect fastidious organisms like *Neisseria* and *Haemophilus* spp. *MacConkey agar* is a selective medium used to culture Gram-negative enteric organisms including *Salmonella* spp. Amino acids, blood, proteins and vitamins may be used as *enrichments*.

Broth cultures which do not set are used for specimens

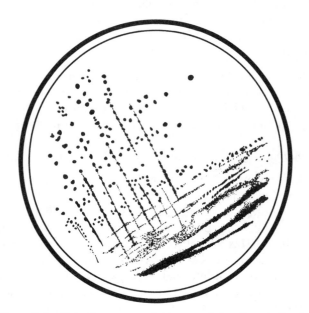

Figure 7.4 Colonies on a plate spread by the method of parallel streaks.

such as CSF, other body fluids and blood which are likely to have small numbers of organisms present.

Selective media are those which contain substances known to inhibit certain organisms or groups. They are also useful for the detection of pathogenic organisms in material such as faeces and throat secretions, normally full of organisms. They prevent overgrowth of pathogens by non-pathogens.

Cultural characteristics

As described above, infected material is introduced into suitable fluid or solid media. The inoculated media are then put into incubators adjusted to a constant temperature. In medical microbiology 37°C is the temperature of primary incubation, because the majority of human pathogens have this as their optimum temperature.

Many organisms, such as the staphylococcus or the diphtheria bacillus, grow best in an atmosphere containing oxygen; they grow well therefore in air and are said to be aerobic organisms. Some, such as the gonococcus, the organism causing gonorrhoea, grow best in an atmosphere containing carbon dioxide, and for isolation of this organism from an infected patient the inoculated plates are put into a jar which contains 5% carbon dioxide, and the jar is put in the incubator. Other organisms, such as *Clostridium tetani*, cannot grow where there is free oxygen, and to grow these organisms conditions must be made anaerobic by placing the plates in a jar, partially evacuating the air which is then replaced with hydrogen. The hydrogen is combined with the residual oxygen to produce completely anaerobic conditions. These are strictly anaerobic organisms, but there are some 'facultative anaerobes' which are equipped with enzymes which allow them to utilise either aerobic or anaerobic respiration.

It is usual to leave the plates undisturbed in the incubator overnight (18–24 h) before looking for growth. Some organisms grow slowly and often no growth is visible to the naked eye at this time. With other organisms, along the lines of inoculation there will be heaped colonies of growing organisms, ranging from 0.1 to 4 mm in diameter. These colonies, each containing many organisms, all of the same kind, have developed by division of the initial ones put on with the loop. Their size, shape, colour, consistency and effect on the surrounding medium are all of importance and characteristic of the species.

Instead of isolated colonies the organisms may have spread in a film all over the plate; organisms which do this are those which are highly motile, that is capable of movement in the thin film of water which covers the surface of the plate.

Viral culture

Viruses need living cells for growth. In the past, laboratory animals and embryonated hen's eggs were used to isolate viruses from pathological specimens but now *tissue culture* is the most important method of viral culture.

Cells can be used from almost every type of tissue from man and many animals. The tissue used is disrupted, e.g. with the enzyme trypsin (to break down the tissue into small clumps of intact cells). The cells are suspended in a nutrient medium containing antibiotics (to prevent the growth of bacteria) and allowed to settle onto glass or clear plastic surfaces in tubes or small flat bottles. The cells rapidly adhere to the surface and begin to grow. Soon they can be seen as a cell sheet with a low-power light microscope.

1. *Primary culture*—suitable for many viruses, using fresh tissue, but the culture cannot be sustained for more than 2–3 weeks and cannot be subcultured more than once, e.g. monkey kidney culture.
2. *Semi-continuous cell lines*—also suitable for many viruses and can be subcultured up to 40–50 times. The most common type of culture is of human embryo lung fibroblasts.
3. *Continuous cell lines*—these have made possible great advances as they can be indefinitely subcultured. The commonest of these lines is HeLa (derived from a human carcinoma of the cervix).

A small volume of the sample from the patient is

inoculated into the tissue-culture medium according to the type of specimen, e.g.

1. CSF—no preparation needed;
2. throat swab—viral transport medium (VTM) is centrifuged to remove gross bacterial contamination; and
3. stool—10% extract made in medium containing large amounts of antibiotics. (Most organisms which cause diarrhoea do not grow in tissue culture. However, enteroviruses found in the stool may cause meningitis or pleurisy.)

Viral growth is visualised in different ways according to the virus present.

1. *Cytopathic effect (CPE)*—the virus kills the cells which round up and fall of the glass (e.g. enterovirus, adenovirus or herpes simplex).
2. *Haemadsorption*—erythrocytes are added and stick to infected cell surfaces (e.g. mumps virus).
3. *Immunofluorescence antibody staining* (see p. 176)— e.g. cytomegalovirus.

Macroscopic appearance of colonial growth of bacteria

This involves the examination of the culture for characteristics of the *colony* (a group of cells visible to the naked eye on a solid medium). These include:

- size,
- shape,
- colour,
- haemolysis characteristics, e.g. is there a clear zone around the colony (*β-haemolysis*) where the red cells have disintegrated (lysis)?, and
- growth over the plate, e.g. swarming (typical of *Proteus* spp.).

From this the laboratory staff decide which colonies to identify further and also to test for antibiotic sensitivity.

Biochemical tests

Certain biochemical tests have been found useful to differentiate various bacteria. The majority of these tests are designed to detect the presence of enzymes in the organisms which bring about a specific chemical reaction. The *Shigella* group of organisms, those causing dysentery, are morphologically and culturally identical, but can be differentiated by the different carbohydrates which they can break down by enzyme action, to use them as a source of energy. If these organisms are grown in medium containing mannitol as a source of carbohydrate, certain of them can break this down, and the break-down products will be acid in reaction. If, therefore, an indicator is added which will show acid production by its change in colour, this change indicates the ability to ferment mannitol and tells the bacteriologist that this organism may be *Shigella sonnei*, or one of the *Shigella flexneri* organisms, if other reactions also fit in with what is known of these organisms.

Some organisms are soluble in bile; a *Pneumococcus* may be differentiated from a viridans type of *Streptococcus* by tests making use of this principle.

There are many other examples used diagnostically, all reflecting fundamental metabolic processes which have by experience been found useful in differentiating one organism from another.

A development of importance has been the production of miniaturised kits made of disposable plastic which contain materials for performing standard biochemical tests that are often used for the routine identification of organisms. One such is the API system, supplying 20 tests in a small space and using very small amounts of reagents; it allows rapid accurate bacterial identification even in laboratories with limited facilities (see Figure 7.5).

Resistance and sensitivity

The resistance of an organism to temperature, drying, acids, antiseptics, dyes, chemotherapeutic agents and antibodies is a help in diagnosis as well as in treatment and prevention of spread.

The sensitivity of various organisms to antibiotics may be of value in differentiating strains, particularly in investigation of outbreaks of hospital-acquired infection, but its major importance is as a guide to appropriate therapy.

The major method of testing for antibiotic sensitivity is that of *disc diffusion*. Paper discs impregnated with a range of antibiotics are placed on a Petri dish which has been inoculated with the organism being investigated.

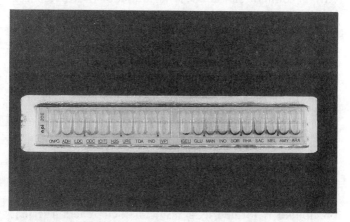

Figure 7.5 API kit.

Where the organism is resistant to the antibiotic, growth will occur up to the disc; where the organism is sensitive, a 'zone of inhibition' will occur around the disc (see Figure 5.1).

Serological tests

An organism isolated from infected material contains numerous antigens. Laboratories rely upon having a 'bank' of known specific antibodies and preparations of antigens (bacterial and viral) of known strengths. Serology (antigen–antibody reactions) is used both for identification of isolated organisms (bacteria or viruses) and for demonstration of antibodies either in diagnosis of illness or estimation of immunity.

Antigen–antibody reactions are now used less than previously in bacteriology. The union is often associated with an altered physical state of the mixture such as a clumping of bacterial cells, which allows the reaction to be visualised. This is known as *agglutination* (see Figure 7.6). A common simple use is agglutination of streptococci by different Lancefield antisera (see Chapter 8). Slide agglutinations are used in the Widal test, a test for patient's antibody to salmonellae in enteric fever, but it is unreliable and is now hardly used. Serum tests are also used for brucella, leptospiral and rickettsial investigations. All have serious drawbacks when applied to diagnosis.

Other types of agglutination tests also exist.

Precipitation

There are a variety of precipitation tests. All depend on mixing a soluble form of the antigen with the antibody in a tube or in a gel preparation after which a visible precipitate is formed as a result of their reaction if the antibody agglutinates the antigen.

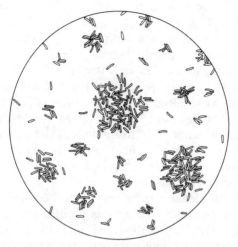

Figure 7.6 Agglutination as seen under the microscope.

Viral serology

This is a very important part of the diagnosis of illness caused by viruses. The presence of either antibody to a virus or of the virus itself can be demonstrated in the patient's serum, and similar serological techniques are used to identify virus isolated from other fluids or tissues. All of the many methods used depend on the ability to indicate the presence of a specific antigen–antibody reaction. The differences between the methods are simply variations in the 'indicator system' used.

Some of these indicators of antigen–antibody reactions are listed below.

1. Neutralisation of the cytopathic effect (CPE) of the virus in tissue culture by the presence of specific antibody. This may either be in prepared antisera or in the patient's serum, e.g. for the identification of

an isolated virus or for the estimation of immunity to poliovirus.

2. Inhibition of viral agglutination of erythrocytes by presence of specific antibody, e.g. estimation of immunity to measles and rubella.

3. Addition of complement (C′) which will be bound to any viral antigen–antibody complex if present. It will, therefore, not be available to lyse erythrocytes coated with anti-red-cell antibody. This reaction when carried out in the fluid phase is known as the *complement fixation test* and is used to measure antibodies to many viruses.

4. Various particles large enough to be visible to the naked eye can be coated with purified viral antigens. When specific antibody is added, the particles agglutinate. Examples are polystyrene 'latex' particles coated with cytomegalovirus antigens and gelatin particles coated with antigens derived from HIV.

5. Labelling anti-human-globulin antibodies or viral specific antibodies or in some cases the viral antigens with any of the following:

    (a) radioisotopes in *radioimmunoassay* (RIA);
    (b) colour-producing enzymes in *enzyme-linked immunosorbent assay (ELISA) and Western blot (WB) assays*;
    (c) fluorescent stains in *immunofluorescent assays* (IFA).

    Labelled antibodies (or antigens) are used to detect the patient's antibody reacting with specific antigens by coating these onto polystyrene wells or beads (RIA and ELISA) or nitrocellulose strips (WB). Viruses growing in tissue culture cells may also be detected by specific antibody labelled with a fluorescent stain (IFA), e.g. detection of cytomegalovirus, influenza, or respiratory syncytial virus (RSV) in pharyngeal aspirate.

Viral antibody reporting

Not only do different classes of antibody (IgM and IgG) appear at different stages of a viral illness, but antibodies to and different antigens of one particular virus appear at different times during the illness. Various serological assays can distinguish these and the results be used to assess how recently the patient caught the infection (e.g. rubella IgM antibody and the various antigens and antibodies of HBV) (see Chapter 9).

Viral antibody results may be reported as the 'titre' of antibody, i.e. the reciprocal of the *highest* dilution of serum at which antibody is demonstrable.

A significant rise (greater than four-fold) in titre over a 2–4 week period following onset of illness can indicate a recent infection, e.g.

anti-measles IgG titre 25/6/90 (week 1):   40
anti-measles IgG titre 6/7/90 (week 3): 256

suggests recent measles infection.

The immunological class of antibody detected may also be reported, e.g. rubella IgM detected suggests recent infection, and hepatitis A IgM positive suggests recent infection.

The interpretation of serological responses to viruses which remain latent in the body (e.g. the herpesvirus group or HIV) is difficult and a virologist should be consulted.

Bacterial typing

During outbreaks of infection with organisms such as *Staphylococcus aureus* or *Klebsiella* spp., it may be necessary to try and identify the source to confirm that the cases are indeed the result of cross-infection. Although *antibiograms* or antibiotic sensitivity patterns may reveal differences between organisms, if they are the same they are not usually definitive enough to call organisms indistinguishable. Also the antibiotic sensitivity patterns may change in the same organism by the acquisition and loss of plasmids. The bacteriologist has a number of methods available to differentiate organisms further. These are called *typing*.

Serotyping

This involves the recognition of different strains by differences in antigenic structure. Commonly used to identify *Salmonella* and *Shigella* spp., as already described. The technique is now used in hospital outbreak investigation with *Pseudomonas* and *Klebsiella* spp. Sometimes needs to be combined with bacteriophage typing.

Bacteriophage typing ('phage typing')

Phages were discussed in Chapter 2. Different strains of a species of bacteria will be lysed by different viruses. The viruses are derived from the strains of bacteria themselves. This method is used particularly in typing *Staphylococcus aureus*.

Biotyping

This involves identifying biochemical or cultural differences.

Bacteriocine typing

Bacteriocines are proteins similar to antibiotics produced by bacteria, which inhibit growth of other members of one species and so identify different strains.

Protein typing

The chromatography of, for example, outer membrane proteins reveals specific patterns.

DNA typing

1. Plasmids (short free strands of extrachromosomal DNA) can be extracted, divided by specific enzymes, and the fragments separated by chromatography. Patterns or fingerprints may be revealed.
2. DNA probes are specific chains of DNA usually labelled with a radioisotope or chemical marker. They will only bind to exactly complementary strands of DNA. Selection and design of the probes can increase or decrease the specificity of the test.

Pathogenicity tests in experimental animals

Some infectious agents cannot be cultured on artificial media, and their presence can only be detected by producing the disease in an experimental animal which is known to be suspectible. Tissues from the animal may show changes typical of the disease. The complicated laboratory techniques involved mean that this method is now less important, but is sometimes still needed. The definitive test for *Corynebacterium diphtheriae* toxin is to inject a guinea-pig with the organism and demonstrate adrenal haemorrhage.

Summary of investigations

All these methods are available to help the microbiologist identify organisms present in the material sent to him, but it will be obvious that this may take some time. In a few cases, a diagnosis can be made when organisms are seen in direct films. More commonly, 18 h are necessary for the organisms to be grown on media and only then can the differential tests be applied. A further delay may occur in the separation of a suspected pathogen for culture from a *mixed growth* of several different organisms from sites with a commensal flora, e.g. respiratory tract, bowel, vagina and skin.

THE LABORATORY REPORT

In addition to understanding why it is necessary to collect a correct and adequate specimen, and send it safely to the laboratory with an appropriately completed request form, the nurse needs to understand the report when it is returned to the clinical area.

When a report is received, a nurse may have to alert the medical staff or take action through the care plan. An obvious example is the need to 'source isolate' (see Chapter 14) the patient with methicillin-resistant *S. aureus* (MRSA). It is equally important to recognise when *not* to alert the medical staff or isolate the patient.

Many important results are phoned to the ward before a report is received. These pathology results must be recorded properly and written in the care plan and the patient's notes (see below). Handover of patient information *must* include a comment about pathology results and any consequent alteration to the care plan.

Example of communication problems

Mrs Smith was admitted to a medical ward with an exacerbation of chronic bronchitis. During the taking of her medical history, she mentioned having been jaundiced a few months earlier. A routine screening for evidence of hepatitis A or B infection was carried out. A staff nurse took a telephone call from the virology laboratory two days later and wrote down 'Hepatitis B Ag detected'. She promptly moved the patient to a single room and added to the distress of the patient who was already feeling extremely unwell. Precautions instituted included the wearing of gloves and aprons for anyone dealing with the patient's blood or excreta, and the bagging of linen as infected.

Later that day, the written report was received and found to state 'Hepatitis B Ag *not* detected'. The Ward Sister spent considerable time that evening reassuring Mrs Smith and apologising to her for the distress she had been caused. Although *some* of the precautions taken were perfectly correct for a patient with HBV infection (and, indeed, for dealing with blood from *anyone*) the fact that the patient had been suddenly and unnecessarily (see Chapters 9 and 14) moved to a single room had heightened the anxiety she was already feeling.

It is most important that telephone messages are accurately recorded and actions are only implemented in a careful and considerate fashion. The example above is similar to situations encountered by the author and colleagues. The problems of 'isolation' are discussed in more detail in later chapters, but accurate recording of information should be carried out by both medical and nursing staff.

The use of laboratory reports

Laboratory reports should only be interpreted with knowledge of the clinical condition of the patient.

The fact that a pathogen and antibiotic sensitivities are reported does not automatically imply that the patient must be given therapy:

- he may already be recovering from an infection; or
- the organism may only be colonising the site and not causing invasive infection (e.g. leg ulcer or pressure sores).

Failure to identify a pathogen, with a report stating 'no pathogens isolated' does not exclude the presence of infection; it could be the result of poor specimen collection or circulating antibiotics.

The microbiologist should always be consulted if there is any doubt over interpretation of the report or choice of an appropriate antibiotic. Several studies have revealed problems of communication and interpretation between laboratory and ward/surgery (e.g. Lee and McLean, 1977).

The nurse has a responsibility to the patient to be aware of how to use and cooperate with the laboratory and the clinician, and to incorporate the findings into the care plan for the patient.

Features described in the report

Macroscopy

The gross appearance of the specimen received by the laboratory may be important information to the clinician, e.g. a liquid, bloody, green stool will be of clinical significance, whereas a solid stool specimen suggests that the patient does not have a current clinical problem of diarrhoea-associated infection.

Microscopy

The presence of cells, casts, yeasts or fungi, parasites or their ova may be reported. This may give an immediate presumptive early diagnosis or help the clinician to assess significance of an organism isolated later, e.g. pus cells from a sputum specimen or wound swab suggest infection. Pus in faeces suggests enteritis.

Culture

1. The organism is named, e.g. *Streptococcus* (the family name or genus). This may be followed by the abbreviation sp. (or spp.) for *species* (singular or plural, respectively), or a further identification of a member of the family to genus and species, e.g. *S. pyogenes*, *S. pneumoniae* or *Enterococcus faecalis*.
2. The growth of the organism may be described in terms of *quantity*, e.g. heavy $(+++)$, moderate $(++)$ or light $(+)$. The numbers of organisms may be described more specifically, e.g. the number of bacteria per millilitre of urine, expressed as $> 10^5$/ml (i.e. more than 100 000 organisms per millilitre of urine).
3. The laboratory may report on the presence or absence of a particular organism as requested by the clinician, e.g. screening faeces for *Salmonella* spp. during an outbreak investigation.

Antibiotic sensitivity

The sensitivity of a pathogen to an appropriate range of antibiotics is reported for the clinician's guidance. Should the microbiologist consider that the organism may not be causing actual infection, the form may simply say 'Sensitivities available on request' or 'Please consult if treatment contemplated' or 'Query significant'. This helps the clinician to avoid unnecessary administration of antibiotics. Sensitivity is reported as:

S—fully sensitive (likely to be active *in vivo*);
R—resistant (and unlikely to be active); or
M—moderately sensitive (implying reduced sensitivity and, therefore, not a first choice for treatment).

Serum assay

The dosage of some antibiotics, e.g. gentamicin, is controlled in some patients by the estimation of serum levels of the drug. This is to ensure that therapeutic levels are maintained for effectiveness and excess levels which could lead to toxicity are avoided. Trough and peak concentrations are usually reported. *Trough* specimens are taken immediately before a dose of the drug is given and represent the lowest level reached by the drug. *Peak* levels represent maximum drug levels and are usually taken exactly 1 h after a dose of the drug has been administered. The timing is important for the interpretation of data. Blood must not be drawn through a line into which the drug has been given. For gentamicin, troughs of < 2 mg l^{-1} and peaks up to 8 mg l^{-1} are acceptable.

REFERENCES

Advisory Committee on Dangerous Pathogens (1990) *Categorisation of Pathogens According to Hazard and Categories of Containment.* London: HMSO.

DHSS (1978) *Code of Practice for the Prevention of Infection in Clinical Laboratories and Post-Mortem Rooms*. London: HMSO.

DOH (1991) 1. *Safe Working and the Prevention of Infection in Clinical Laboratories*; 2. *Safe Working and the Prevention of Infection in Clinical Laboratories—Model Rules for Staff and Visitors*; 3. *Safe Working and the Prevention of Infection in the Mortuary and Post-Mortem Room*. London: HMSO.

Lee A and McLean S (1977) The laboratory report: a problem in communication between clinician and microbiologist. *Med. J. Aust.* **2**: 858–860.

Statutory Instrument. *The Control of Substances Hazardous to Health Regulations* (1988) London: HMSO.

FURTHER READING

Ayton M (1982) Microbiological investigations. *Nursing* **2**(8): 226–230.

Health Service Advisory Committee (1986) *Safety in Health Service Laboratories: The Labelling, Transport and Reception of Specimens*. London: HMSO.

McFarlane A (1989) Using the laboratory in infection control. *Prof. Nurse* **4**(8): 393–397.

Shanson D (1989) *Microbiology in Clinical Practice*, 2nd edn. Bristol: Wright.

8 A guide to pathogenic bacteria

The aim of this chapter is to present some important facts about common organisms (and some less common ones) which the nurse may encounter in laboratory reports or clinical literature. References have been included so that the nurse can obtain further information in order to understand the importance of these organisms in the health-care setting. It is worth noting that many of these organisms are found as part of normal flora and only become pathogenic when transferred from their natural sites, or when the host is immuno-compromised in some way (see Chapters 3 and 4).

In addition to the information given in this chapter, a guide to sources, infectivity, transmission and care of patients infected with many of these organisms is given in the appendix to Chapter 14.

THE MAIN DIVISIONS OF BACTERIA

Clinically relevant bacteria can be divided conveniently, but artificially, into the following groups:

1. common cocci and bacilli which retain (Gram positive) or do not retain (Gram negative) Gram stain,
2. acid-fast bacilli,
3. spirochaetes, and
4. chlamydiae, rickettsiae and mycoplasmas.

Organisms are discussed below according to these groups, subdividing those in group 1 according to their shape and oxygen requirements. Tables 8.1 and 8.2 list the important organisms in this classification. Brief details of myco-plasmas, rickettsiae and chlamydiae are included at the end of this chapter.

GRAM-POSITIVE DIVISION

Aerobic gram-positive cocci

Staphylococcus

Spherical cocci in clusters like grapes (see Figure 8.1). They may be found as commensals on the skin and mucous membranes, but others may act as pathogens. *Staphylococcus aureus* is differentiated from other staphyl-ococci in that it produces an enzyme called *coagulase*. The coagulase test measures the ability of staphylococci to clot rabbit plasma.

S. aureus

Presence: it is found on the body, colonising the anterior nares of up to 50% of healthy people; less frequently found in the axilla, perineum, hair, vagina and mucous membranes.

Pathogenicity:

1. *superficial*—causing abscesses, carbuncles, paronychia, wound infections, impetigo;
2. *deep infections*—osteomyelitis, endocarditis, septi-caemia, pneumonia,
3. toxin-producing strains—*toxic shock syndrome* is caused by a toxin (TSST-1) from particular strains of *S. aureus*. In association with prolonged tampon use it can lead to rash with desquamation, diarrhoea and

Table 8.1 Summary of gram-positive bacteria.

Genus	Medically important species
Gram-positive cocci	
Aerobes	
Staphylococcus	*S. aureus*; *S. epidermidis*; *S. saprophyticus*
Streptococcus	β-Haemolytic: *S. pyogenes (group A); S. agalactiae (group B);* groups C, G, R and S
	α-Haemolytic: *S. pneumoniae* (pneumococcus); Viridans-type streptococci: *S. milleri* (group F); *S. mitis*; *S. mitior*; *S. sanguis*, etc.
Enterococcus	*E. faecalis*, *E. faecium* (mostly group D)
Anaerobes	
Peptostreptococcus	*P. anaerobius*
Gram-positive bacilli	
Aerobes	
Bacillus	*B. anthracis*; *B. cereus*; (*B. subtilis*)
Corynebacterium	*C. diphtheriae*; *C. ulcerans*; non-diphtheroid coryneforms
Listeria	*L. monocytogenes*
Erysipelothrix	*E. rhusiopathiae*
Nocardia	*N. asteroides*; *N. madurae*
Anaerobes	
Clostridium	*C. perfringens*; *C. tetani*; *C. botulinum*
Actinomyces	*A. israeli*
Propionibacterium	*P. acnes*
Lactobacillus	

hypotension. *Toxic staphylococcal food poisoning* from ingestion of food contaminated with strains which elaborate enterotoxins. *Toxic epidermal necrolysis (scalded skin syndrome)*: this has an onset of sudden toxaemia, with blistering skin lesions in neonates and young children. One phage type (71) is often involved and the disease can be rapidly fatal. In one UK maternity hospital outbreak in 1987, 82 out of 150 babies checked were found to be infected with one particular phage type with toxin production (East, 1990). The outbreak was costed at approximately £10 000 and a variety of hygienic practices were reviewed and altered.

Treatment: sensitive to: flucloxacillin, erythromycin, clindamycin, fusidic acid, gentamicin, rifampicin and vancomycin (but see Chapter 5).

Resistance: penicillin—the prevalence of resistance to penicillin in hospital and community is 85–95%. *Strains resistant to methicillin are often resistant to a wide range of other antibiotics and cause major problems in some hospitals* (Bateman, 1990). The care of these patients is discussed in Chapter 14.

S. epidermidis

Presence: it is a part of normal skin flora and usually harmless, but is now increasingly recognised as a cause of infection in association with foreign bodies/implants ranging from artificial hip joints to intravenous cannulae.

Treatment: this organism is often far more resistant to antibiotics than *S. aureus*. All strains so far remain sensitive to vancomycin.

Table 8.2 Summary of Gram-negative bacteria.

	Bacteria		Genus	Examples of medically important species
Cocci	Aerobes		*Neisseria*	*N. meningitidis; N. gonorrhoeae*
			Moraxella	*M. (Branhamella) catarrhalis*
	Anaerobes		*Veillonella*	
Bacilli	Aerobes	Glucose non-fermenters Enterobacteriaceae		
		Lactose fermenters	1. *Escherichia*	*E. coli*
			Klebsiella	*K. pneumoniae; K. aerogenes*
			Serratia	*S. marcescens*
			Enterobacter	*E. cloacae*
		Non-lactose fermenters	2. *Proteus*	*P. mirabilis*
			Morganella	
			Salmonella	*S. typhi; S. paratyphi;* non-typhoid salmonellae
			Shigella	*Sh. sonnei; Sh. dysenteriae; Sh. flexneri; Sh. boydii*

Glucose non-fermenters	3. Pseudomonas Aeromonas Xanthomonas Acinetobacter Alkaligenes	P. aeruginosa A. hydrophila
	4. Vibrio	V. cholerae; V. parahaemolyticus
	Campylobacter Helicobacter	C. jejuni; C. coli H. pylori
	5. Pasteurella Yersinia	P. multocida Y. enterocolitica; Y. pestis; Y. pseudotuberculosis
	Francisella	F. tularensis
Parvobacteria	6. Haemophilus Bordetella Brucella	H. influenzae; H. ducreyi B. pertussis B. abortus; B. melitensis; B. suis
	7. Legionella	L. pneumophila; L. micdadei
Anaerobes	Bacteroides Fusobacterium	B. fragilis F. necrophorum

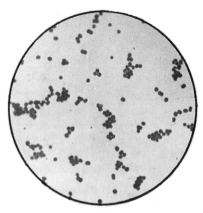

Figure 8.1 Culture smear of *Staphylococcus aureus* showing characteristic clumping (× 1000).

S. saprophyticus

This organism is found as normal skin flora but causes 10% of urinary tract infection in sexually active young women.

Streptococcus (including *Enterococcus* and *Pneumococcus*)

These are oval cocci found in pairs (*diplococci*), e.g. *S. pneumoniae*), or in chains (e.g. *S. pyogenes*). (See Figures 8.2 and 8.3.)

Presence: they may inhabit mucous membranes of man and animals, including mouth, upper respiratory tract, intestine and vagina. Most are harmless commensals, a few may cause serious pathogenic disease.

Classification: A complex group of organisms. Many are divided by Lancefield grouping according to their outer polysaccharide antigen structure. Also by haemolysis:

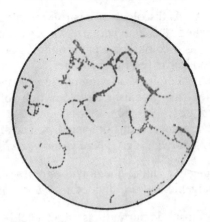

Figure 8.2 Culture smear of *Streptococcus pyogenes* showing the characteristic chain arrangement of streptococci (× 1000).

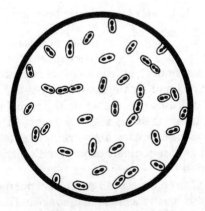

Figure 8.3 *Streptococcus pneumoniae* stained to show capsules.

1. Some kinds discolour or destroy red blood cells and are called *β-haemolytic streptococci*. This may be shown as a colourless zone around colonies growing on blood agar (e.g. *S. pyogenes*).

2. Partial haemolysis or denaturation of haemoglobin, showing as greenish discolouration of agar (*α-haemolysis*).

3. Some streptococci do not haemolyse and are therefore *non-haemolytic*, e.g. *Enterococcus faecalis*.

Pathogenicity: the β-haemolytic streptococci are the most pathogenic and are divided into *Lancefield groups*.

1. The most important is Lancefield group A (*S. pyogenes*) which used to be responsible for major outbreaks of puerperal sepsis with high mortality (see Chapter 1). Common diseases are acute tonsillitis and skin infections (erysipelas or impetigo). It can cause a septicaemia which is fatal in 50% of cases within 24–48 h if penicillin treatment is not started promptly.

Groups B, C, and G are also important.

2. Group B (*S. agalactiae*) is carried harmlessly in the vagina by up to 30% of women, but has been seen to be an important cause of occasional neonatal septicaemia and meningitis (Mayon-White, 1980). In these rare cases the mother does not make antibody to the strain in her vagina or cervix. The baby is therefore not protected by transplacental antibody but will almost certainly acquire the organism during parturition.

3. Group C streptococci can also cause puerperal fever. Meningitis, bacteraemia, pneumonia and endocarditis have all been associated with group C streptococci.

S. pneumoniae

S. pneumoniae (pneumococcus) is usually α-haemolytic and is often present in the nasopharynx as a commensal, but is also an important opportunist pathogen and can cause severe illness (see Table 8.3).

E. faecalis

E. faecalis and viridans-type streptococci may cause infective endocarditis (see Table 8.3). The infections caused are usually dependent on the connection between the normal site of the organism and its route of entry. *E. faecalis* is a normal inhabitant of the gut; other viridans-type streptococci inhabit the mouth, but entry to the blood stream or urinary tract can lead to infection.

Anaerobic Gram-positive cocci

Peptostreptococci

These may be found in a variety of wounds and deep abscesses (in brain or liver), usually as part of a mixed infection.

Aerobic Gram-positive bacilli

Bacillus

These are aerobic, Gram-positive organisms which form chains and spores, and may be found everywhere. They are mostly *saprophytic* (live on dead organic matter) but pathogens or potential pathogens include *B. anthracis*, *B. cereus* and *B. subtilis*.

Table 8.3   Illnesses caused by streptococci.

β-Haemolytic *S. pyogenes* (Group A)	Tonsillitis, scarlet fever, sinusitis, quinsy. Wound infections, cellulitis. Puerperal sepsis. Impetigo, erysipelas. Post-infectious complications include acute nephritis, acute rheumatic fever and Sydenham chorea, but strains associated with these diseases are now extremely rare in developed countries
S. agalactiae (Group B)	Neonatal septicaemia and meningitis. Puerperal and gynaecological sepsis
Groups C and G	Occasional cause of sore throats and other diseases similar to group A streptococci, but sequelae are now very important
Groups R and S (*S. suis*)	Found in pigs; rare cause of meningitis or endocarditis in farmers, butchers, etc.
α-Haemolytic *S. pneumoniae* (pneumococcus)	Sinusitis, otitis media, conjunctivitis. Pneumonia, meningitis, acute exacerbation of chronic bronchitis. Septicaemia
Viridans-type streptococci	Infective endocarditis after bloodstream invasion (e.g. dental surgery). One strain, group F (*S. milleri*), can cause deep abscesses and severe infections in association with anaerobes
Non-haemolytic *E. faecalis* (Group D)	Urinary tract and abdominal wound infection. Endocarditis (rare)
Anaerobic streptococci	May cause cellulitis, and deep infection of female genital tract. Cerebral abscesses

N.B. The haemolysis characteristics are not *always* absolute and depend a great deal on the media and environmental conditions used for culture, e.g. *Streptococcus viridans* may be β-haemolytic or non-haemolytic.

B. anthracis

Presence: the organism may be found in soil in relation to infected animal sources. Infection is still prevalent in Asia and some African countries but *almost unknown in Britain now* (Shanson, 1989) and is unlikely to be seen in hospital.

Pathogenesis: it causes *anthrax*. Spores are highly heat resistant and they can remain viable for years in animal products or soil.

1. Infection in humans is usually via the skin from infected animals or their products (*cutaneous anthrax*). Malignant pustule (a painless but inflamed lesion) forms locally with much oedema, and without treatment it may lead to septicaemia and death.
2. Anthrax may also be acquired through inhalation of spores from handling contaminated wool (*'wool-sorters' disease*); this causes *inhalation anthrax*. It is associated with high mortality.

Treatment: penicillin.

B. cereus

Presence: organisms are widely distributed in soil, air and dust.

Pathogenicity: it is associated with food poisoning, particularly in fried rice. Spores survive cooking and, if left at room temperature, may germinate, with multiplication and toxin production. Reheating, e.g. frying, may be too brief to kill all the organisms.

Two types of toxin are produced by individual strains; most infections are caused by the toxin which is associated only with growth on reheated (fried) rice. This causes acute vomiting 30 min to 2 h after eating. The second type is associated with soups and sauces and causes abdominal pain and diarrhoea after 6–16 h.

B. subtilis

Presence: found widely in the dry environment.

Pathogenicity: it is usually a harmless organism but sometimes causes contamination of blood cultures. It may cause occasional bacteraemia, e.g. via contaminated dialysis machines or by heavy aerosol contamination of air-supplying units with immunosuppressed patients.

Corynebacterium

Gram-positive bacillus, rod-shaped, found on the skin and mucous membranes, particularly those of the respiratory tract. There are several human species, some pathogenic, others commensals.

C. diphtheriae

This organism possesses characteristic 'club-shaped' swellings at one end. These are not spores.

Presence: organisms are found in the nose and throat, wounds, or skin of carriers or infected people.

Pathogenicity: chief pathogen of this family, and the cause of *diphtheria*. It is distinguished from harmless members of the group by biochemical tests and by exotoxin production (the marker of virulence). This may be demonstrated by guinea-pig inoculation or a gel-precipitation (Elek) test.

Clinical effects: usually the nose, larynx and pharynx are affected (but in areas of high prevalence skin ulcers or genital tract infection may occur). The toxin acts on mucous membranes to form a sticky membrane which may be in the tonsillar area or may involve the larynx. There is much swelling of the neck. Respiratory obstruction can occur and be fatal. The toxin particularly affects neurological and cardiovascular tissue. Since immunisation was widely introduced in the 1940s, both frequency of disease and mortality have fallen dramatically (DOH, 1990).

Treatment: sensitive to penicillin (first choice), erythromycin and others.

C. ulcerans

Distinguished from *C. diphtheriae* by biochemical tests. Causes similar throat lesions, but usually without the toxaemia. Some strains are, however, toxigenic. It is usually acquired from unpasteurised milk and is extremely rare.

Coryneforms

Poorly classified and rarely identified to species level. They include *C. hofmanii* and *C. xerosis* (conjunctiva) which may cause infection of prostheses of joints and heart valves.

C. minutissimum is a term used to cover several separate species which are found on the skin of feet and other moist areas associated with erythrasma, a scaling condition. The skin and organism fluoresces brick red under ultraviolet light.

Listeria

There are several species in this family but only one of human significance.

L. monocytogenes

These are short, motile, non-sporing rods which require Gram stain, motility and chemical tests to distinguish them from corynebacteria and β-haemolytic streptococci.

Presence: found in the faeces of animals, e.g. cattle

and pigs, in birds, rodents, colonised man, in soil and in food contaminated with animal faeces. The rind of certain cheeses is heavily contaminated.

Pathogenicity: transferred to humans by ingestion of contaminated foods (milk, soft cheeses, patés); vertical transmission may occur and cause amnionitis, fetal death (early) or precipitate labour.

Clinically: infection in man is thought to occur, not uncommonly, as a mild, often unrecognised, infection, but is a threat to:

1. *neonates*, acquired from unrecognised vaginal infection in the mother, causing stillbirth (early onset) or meningitis (late onset);
2. *pregnant women* are at risk of bacteraemia—the organism may cross the placenta causing amnionitis;
3. *adults* who are *immunocompromised* by underlying disease (e.g. lymphoma) or other condition (e.g. alcoholism) may develop sepsis leading to serious infection including meningo-encephalitis and pneumonia; and
4. cross-infection between newborn babies may occur.

Treatment: Ampicillin with gentamicin is the drug regime of choice; other antibiotics not properly evaluated.

During 1988 advice came from the Department of Health aimed particularly at pregnant women to avoid certain soft cheeses and patés (DHSS PL/CMO (89)3 and DOH Press Release 89/369). For cross-infection to occur, it appears that a sizeable inoculum of the organism is needed (McLauchlin, 1990), but staff hands and a rectal thermometer were implicated in one outbreak involving five neonates (Larsson *et al*, 1978). McLauchlin (1990) also stressed the high mortality rate with this infection, 46% in one series of British cases appearing between 1967 and 1985. A recent report (PHLS, 1990a) observes that human listeriosis reports (particularly of pregnancy-associated cases) had declined in 1989, and the reason for this is currently under investigation. Sensible food habits in pregnancy are essential (Holmes, 1989).

Nocardia

Presence: in the soil, especially in warmer climates.
Pathogenicity:

1. *N. madurae* is one of the many organisms involved in the tropical disease *Madura foot* which affects subcutaneous tissues and producing chronic sinus formation.
2. *N. asteroides* (star shaped) can causes abscesses in lungs, brain, kidneys or intestinally, especially in immunocompromised patients.

Treatment: many drugs are active *in vitro*, few in clinical practice. Sulphonamides and amikacin are useful. Treatment is given over a long period, as in the treatment of tuberculosis.

Anaerobic Gram-positive bacilli

Clostridium

This large group of spore-forming organisms, most of which are saprophytes, only grow under strictly anaerobic conditions and include these important pathogenic species:

C. perfringens (welchii)

The organism may be β-haemolytic or non-haemolytic. (See Figures 8.4 and 8.5.)
Presence: lives commensally in human faeces.
Pathogenicity:

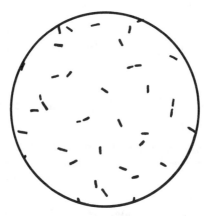

Figure 8.4 *Clostridium perfringens* (*welchii*) showing character-istic brick-shaped bacilli (× 1000).

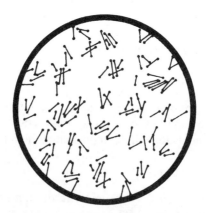

Figure 8.5 Diagram showing delicate rod-shaped *Clostridium tetani*, with many round terminal spores, characteristically drum shaped (× 1200).

1. This organism will only grow in tissue with poor blood supply because it is an obligate anaerobe. Traumatic wounds are usually involved (especially war injuries). Emphasis is, therefore, on removal of all dead tissue after traumatic injury. The organism and related species, e.g. *C. septicum*, *C. oedematiens* and *C. histolyticum*, reproduce locally, forming gas (hydrogen and nitrogen) leading to crepitus or gas gangrene. Dead tissue extends. Toxins produced particularly by *C. perfringens* may cause death.

2. Large numbers of *C. perfringens* taken in with food (usually cooked, reheated meat dishes) can lead to food poisoning (enterocolitis) from the production of enterotoxins in the gut. Acute diarrhoea occurs within 6–18 h. Outbreaks are common in institutions.

Treatment: Surgical excision and penicillin (gas gangrene). Supportive treatment alone is required for gastroenteritis.

C. tetani

Presence: found in the soil almost anywhere. Heavy colonisation is found in horse faeces. Spores can be found in old wall plaster made with horse hair.

Pathogenicity: When carried into deep cuts or wounds, including minor gardening injuries, it produces toxins. The toxin enters nerves local to the injury and travels up to the anterior horn cells of the spinal cord thus affecting the motor nerves. Disconnection from the cerebral control of motor nerves produces muscle spasm, resulting in the disease *lockjaw*.

Treatment: Surgical excision and anti-tetanus immuno-globulin and penicillin. There are now less than 100 cases annually in the UK (Shanson, 1989).

Prevention: immunisation with tetanus toxoid in the

first year of life with boosters every 5–10 years and, particularly, after trauma.

C. botulinum

Presence: found throughout the environment, spores may gain entry to canned or preserved foods. (Cans are placed in cold water after sealing. A vacuum is formed and water may be drawn into faulty cans. River water is often used and this may be sewage-contaminated.)

Pathogenicity: A *rare* cause of food poisoning, the organism produces an exotoxin which causes acute toxaemia characterised by paralysis of the cranial motor nerves and of the diaphragm which is known as *botulism*. Foods most commonly implicated are home-preserved and smoked foods. Sporadic cases are associated with canned salmon particularly. The disease can be rapidly fatal, and anti-toxin is needed urgently.

> An outbreak occurred in 1989 in Britain traced to hazelnut puree, which involved 27 patients, eight of whom needed mechanical ventilation (Acheson, 1989).

C. difficile

Presence: this is sometimes found in the faeces of 'normal' patients, particularly those who are hospitalised. Some strains produce enterotoxin. The organism is associated with the intestinal disease *pseudo-membranous colitis*. Colitis is associated with use of broad-spectrum antibiotics, especially clindamycin, cotrimoxazole and ampicillin, but almost any may be involved. Cross-infection has also been reported (see Appendix to Chapter 14). It may be fatal and treatment must be given.

Treatment: oral vancomycin or metronidazole (George, 1983).

Actinomyces

Presence: in the soil.

Pathogenicity: *Actinomyces israelii* is found in small numbers in the mouth. This causes granulomatous lesions of the jaw, caecum or appendix, or lungs. Infection may start after surgery or trauma to the related area, e.g. appendicectomy or tooth extraction. It is occasionally associated with intrauterine and more extensive pelvic inflammation related to intrauterine contraceptive devices (IUCDs).

Treatment: penicillin is the first choice; also sensitive to clindamycin, tetracycline or streptomycin.

Propionibacterium

Presence: human skin as part of the normal flora.

Pathogenicity: *P. acnes* appears to be associated with *acne vulgaris* (skin condition), and can also be a rare cause of infective endocarditis (infection in heart-valve surgery).

GRAM-NEGATIVE DIVISION

Again these may be divided into cocci and bacilli, and subdivided into aerobes and anaerobes (see Table 8.2).

Aerobic Gram-negative cocci

Neisseriaceae

These are kidney-shaped, oval diplococci (0.6–1.0 μm) often seen inside pus cells. They are found on mucous membranes, particularly of the upper respiratory tract, genitourinary tract and conjunctiva. Several commensal species are easy to culture, but two pathogenic ones require care—they die quickly outside the body and need appropriate culture media and prompt transport. Swabs for *Neisseria* should not be refrigerated.

N. meningitidis (meningococcus)

In the UK infection most commonly occurs in children and adolescents, in the first 3 months of the year. Epidemics are rare, usually involving crowded or residential situations. There are three predominant serological groups (A, B and C) which can be further subdivided. Group B causes most British infections. In Africa and South America, groups A and C cause severe epidemics.

> Twenty-three cases of group A infection occurred in pilgrims returning from Saudi Arabia to Britain in 1987 (DOH, 1990).

Presence: carried in the nasopharynx of 5–30% of healthy people. Infection occurs when organisms enter through mucous membranes and spread to the bloodstream and meninges.

Pathogenicity: meningitis may occur without septicaemia, or vice versa, although most cases show bacteraemia rapidly followed by meningitis. Mortality in acute meningococcal infection is approximately 10%. A typical haemorrhagic rash may occur with septicaemia and the disease may progress so rapidly that the victim dies before reaching hospital.

Treatment: prompt treatment on suspicion of meningococcal infection is vital, with intramuscular or intravenous benzylpenicillin, or chloramphenicol for patients allergic to penicillin.

Transmission: requires direct close contact and usually only the immediate family need prophylactic (preventative) treatment with rifampicin or ciprofloxacin.

(See Figures 8.6 and 8.7.)

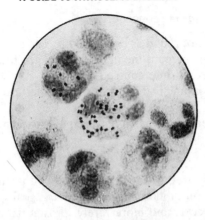

Figure 8.6 Direct smear of urethral discharge from a patient suffering from acute gonorrhoea. Note characteristic intracellular *Neissaeria gonorrhoea* and the close similarity to Figure 8.7 (× 1000).

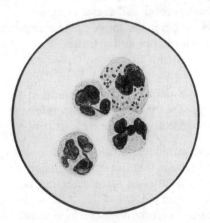

Figure 8.7 Smear of cerebrospinal fluid from a case of meningococcal meningitis. Note pus cells with characteristic intracellular *Neisseria meningitidis* (× 475).

N. gonorrhoeae (gonococcus)

Presence: not found as normal flora. The organism enters through the mucous membrane of the genitourinary tract during sexual intercourse. The eye may be infected through conjunctival inoculation and the throat following oral sex.

Pathogenicity: male and female presentations are different.

Men:

1. usually urethritis with dysuria and purulent discharge;
2. rectal (in homosexuals) and pharyngeal gonorrhoeae also occur, and more rarely, prostatitis, epidydymo-orchitis. Gonococcal arthritis may follow bacteraemia or may be an immune reaction after infection.

Women:

1. asymptomatic endocervical infection is the commonest, also urethral and rectal infection;
2. dysuria, vaginal discharge, pelvic inflammatory disease, bacteraemia and arthritis.

Neonates:

1. ophthalmia neonatorum beginning in the 48 h after delivery, the baby acquiring infection from the infected genital tract during parturition.

Treatment: penicillin (single high-dose amoxycillin with probenecid) always was the drug of choice, but penicillin-resistant strains are very common in the Tropics and occasionally occur in the UK. Alternative treatments (spectinomycin, cefuroxime, cotrimoxazole, tetracycline, and ciprofloxacin) are very effective, but single-dose treatment is often not so reliable.

Prevention: one attack does not protect against infection

with closely related strains. Contact tracing is an important part of the control of spread of the disease.

Moraxella (Branhamella) catarrhalis

Occasionally found as a commensal of the respiratory tract, but the organism can be involved as an additional pathogen in exacerbations of chronic bronchitis, in sinusitis and other respiratory tract infections.

Treatment: many strains are resistant to penicillin and ampicillin by production of β-lactamase. Tetracycline and cotrimoxazole are useful alternatives.

Anaerobic Gram-negative cocci

Veillonella

A commensal of the oropharynx, colon and female genital tract, but it can cause local sepsis in mixed infections with other anaerobic organisms such as *Bacteroides* spp.

Aerobic Gram-negative bacilli

Enterobacteria

This group (see Table 8.2) incorporates a great number of Gram-negative bacilli found in man, which are all aerobic or facultatively anaerobic (can grow with or without oxygen). They may be further subdivided according to their ability to ferment lactose. They are rod-shaped, sometimes motile, sometimes encapsulated, and are widely distributed in nature, in the intestinal tract of man and animals. Some species are pathogenic in the gut (e.g. *Salmonella* spp. and *Shigella* spp.); others (e.g. most strains of *E. coli*), are normal inhabitants of the gut, but may be pathogenic elsewhere. Others such as *Serratia* spp. are hospital 'opportunists' because they take advantage of diminished immune response and can cause infection. However, as with many commensal organisms, their presence in a site (e.g. a surgical wound) must not automatically be equated with pathogenicity, and the clinical situation must be fully assessed. *Salmonella* and *Shigella*, however, are usually pathogenic but may be carried asymptomatically in the gut, gallbladder and even the urinary tract.

Lactose fermenters
Escherichia

Escherichia coli (E. coli)

Presence: a normal inhabitant of the gut. Organisms are mostly motile, some are capsulated.

Pathogenicity: it is known as the commonest cause of urinary tract infections but may also cause wound infection, biliary tract infection and septicaemia. Specific virulent serotypes can cause neonatal meningitis, 'travellers' diarrhoea' and infantile gastroenteritis, and bloody diarrhoea seen in the haemolytic uraemic syndrome. Chest infections are also seen in immunocompromised patients who have altered respiratory tract flora because of antibiotic therapy. In the national prevalence study of 1980, *E. coli* was responsible for 26% of hospital acquired infection, mostly of the urinary tract (Meers et al, 1981). (See Figure 8.8)

Klebsiella spp., Enterobacter spp. and Serratia spp.

Presence: these are closely related genera and, like *E. coli*, are normal inhabitants of the gut. They thrive in moist environments.

Pathogenesis: a common cause of urinary tract infection,

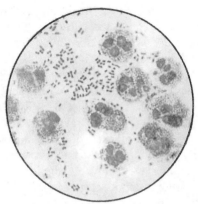

Figure 8.8 Deposit from infected urine showing pus cells and profuse *Escherichia coli* (× 1000).

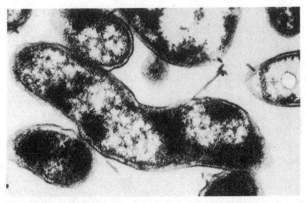

Figure 8.9 Scanning electronmicrograph of *Campylobacter* showing long, curved rods.

but they also cause wound and respiratory infections, septicaemia, meningitis (usually neonatal). The organisms are a problem in hospitals, especially on intensive-care units where extensive use of antibiotics suppresses normal flora and gives *Klebsiella* and other Gram-negative organisms the chance to flourish, e.g. in tracheostomy sites. They have a tendency to develop antibiotic resistance which can cause serious problems (Casewell et al, 1977; Mutton et al, 1981; Bullock et al, 1982; Braver et al, 1987). *K. pneumoniae*, particularly those with large mucoid capsules, are particularly virulent and cause about 2% of community-acquired pneumonia, especially in diabetics, alcoholics and other mildly immunosuppressed patients.

Non-lactose fermenters

Proteus spp. and Morganella spp.

Presence: these again are closely related organisms, normal flora of the intestines of man and animals.

Pathogenicity: there are several species of *Proteus*, but the one most commonly found in human infections is *P. mirabilis*. It commonly infects the urinary tract, and also occurs as a mixed growth in pressure sores, varicose ulcers and other chronic wounds. On culture it has a 'swarming' growth, tending to cover the media, and has a characteristic 'fishy' smell.

> A prolonged outbreak occurred in a newborn nursery in the USA involving 11 neonates of whom four died; *P. mirabilis* was the organism involved and epidemiological studies suggested that one carrier nurse transmitted the organism to these babies (Burke et al, 1971).

Salmonellae

Presence: found in the intestines of many animals which act as a source of human infection.

Pathogenicity: the organisms which cause 'enteric fever' (*S. typhi* and *S. paratyphi*) differ from the other 2000 or so 'food poisoning' species in that man is their only host. Organisms are cultured from faeces or blood and occasionally urine and further identification is by biochemical and serological (agglutination) tests. Organisms are usually fully identified and phage typed in reference laboratories. This enables very effective country-wide surveillance of salmonellae which may come from virtually any food source.

Some patients develop bacteraemia or septicaemia associated with non-typhoid *Salmonella* infections (notably *S. typhimurium*, *S. dublin* and *S. cholerasuis*). Following bacteraemia, some may develop bone, joint or meningitic infection. Osteomyelitis is common in those with sickle cell disease.

1. Enteric fever group. *S. typhi* (typhoid bacillus), *S. paratyphi* A, B and C. *S. paratyphi* A sometimes causes an illness like salmonella enteritis. *S. paratyphi* C is uncommon in the UK.

These organisms enter the intestine in food, milk or water contaminated by faeces of a human carrier. They then pass into the lymphatics, to the bloodstream and bone marrow, and reproduce over a relatively long period in the lymphoid tissue of the reticuloendothelial system. They are excreted in faeces and urine at various times during the illness. The gall bladder is often colonised.

The 'enteric fevers' differ clinically from the gastroenteritis food poisoning group below in several ways. The incubation period is 10–14 days, and symptoms include fever, headache, septicaemia, myalgia, constipation, and rose-coloured spots may be seen on the abdomen. Diarrhoea usually appears quite late in the illness, and intestinal perforation and haemorrhage may even occur.

Paratyphoid infection is usually milder. The majority of infection seen in the UK is seen in travellers returning from abroad.

2. Gastroenteritis food poisoning group. The second most common cause of food poisoning/gastroenteritis after *Campylobacter* spp. (PHLS, 1990b). *S. enteritidis* is now the commonest of the salmonellae, especially phage type 4 (DT4). Poultry has long been implicated but, in addition, eggs have emerged as an important source of infection. *S. enteritidis* can infect breeding flocks and the oviduct but the birds are not rendered sterile. *S. typhimurium* is the second most common species isolated and is also found in chicken carcasses, dairy products and meat.

In the routine laboratory, salmonellae are identified with biochemical reactions and by agglutination of 'O' and 'H' antigens.

Although food is the main source, outbreaks have occurred in hospitals from secondary, person-to-person spread in addition to hospital canteen-associated outbreaks.

The Stanley Royd Report (DHSS, 1986) documents a severe outbreak proved to be from poorly cooked meat involving several hundred cases and leading to 19 deaths in one large psychiatric hospital in 1984.

Incubation period: 6–72 h, usually 12–36 h.

Nursing care: this is discussed elsewhere, but chiefly consists of careful handling of excreta; 'source isolation' precautions are indicated but the necessity for single-room care will depend on the mental and physical state of the patient.

Treatment: the disease is best treated without antibiotics, except in septicaemic cases.

Shigellae

Organisms are rod-shaped and non-motile. They are distinguished from other intestinal organisms by biochemical and serological tests.

Presence: the intestinal tract of man and other animals.

Pathogenicity: highly infectious organisms, the cause of *bacillary dysentery* (diarrhoea with blood). The organisms produce their effect on mucous membranes of the large intestine, and infection is spread by human cases and carriers. It usually causes milder disease in the UK compared with the Tropics.

Sh. sonnei causes 90% of shigella infection in the UK, associated with outbreaks in the spring in nurseries, primary schools and hospitals for the mentally handicapped. It generally causes a mild illness.

Sh. dysenteriae (formerly *shiga*) is rare in the UK. It produces a virulent enterotoxin. It is usually brought in from abroad and causes the most severe form of infection.

Sh. flexneri (6 types) is fairly common in the UK, but is more severe in the tropics.

Sh. boydii (14 types) is rarely seen in the UK.

Aerobic Gram-negative bacilli—glucose non-fermenters

These Gram-negative rods are distinguished from enterobacteriaceae by their inability to utilise glucose alone and to reduce nitrate to nitrite. Common genera are *Pseudomonas*, *Aeromonas*, *Xanthomonas*, *Acinetobacter* and *Alkaligenes*.

Pseudomonads

These are motile, strictly aerobic rods with a characteristic smell and a blue–green pigment (pyocyanin) which may colour pus.

Presence: found in water and soil and can be found in the human and animal gut; hospital patients (especially those receiving broad-spectrum antibiotics) are more likely to be colonised than those in the community.

Pathogenicity; they can be found in moist sites in hospitals, e.g. standing water, ice from ice machines, ventilators, humidifiers, sink traps, and even contaminated antiseptic solutions from which outbreaks have occurred (see Chapter 6). However, most patient infections seem to be opportunistic and endogenous, and the role of sink traps and flower-vase water as common sources for outbreaks has probably been overstressed.

Pseudomonas aeruginosa (pyocyanea)

This is the principal species which causes hospital-acquired infection. It acts as an opportunistic pathogen, taking advantage of diminished resistance, e.g. intensive-care-unit patients with endotracheal tubes and tracheostomies, elderly patients with chronic wounds such as leg ulcers or pressure sores. The organism does not necessarily cause infection but simply colonises moist sites. It has also been implicated in equipment-associated outbreaks (Earnshaw et al, 1985; Brett and Vivier, 1985). Resistant to many antibiotics and able to further acquire resistance to ureidopenicillins (e.g. piperacillin) or cephalosporins when exposed to them.

Acinetobacter

A strictly aerobic but non-motile Gram-negative cocco-bacillus (oxidase negative) found widely in nature. It is the only Gram-negative organism which is a normal commensal of human skin, so it occasionally appears in blood cultures as a contaminant. Normally of low pathogenicity, it is increasingly recognised as a potential opportunistic pathogen in burns and intensive-care-unit patients and may be highly resistant to antibiotics (Stucke and Thompson, 1980; Holton, 1982; Gervich and Groot, 1985).

Vibrios and Campylobacter

Presence: these are curved or short spiral Gram-negative rods which are widespread in nature, vibrios particularly in water, and campylobacters in the gut of many animal species.

Vibrio

Vibrio cholerae is the cause of cholera and is found in faecally contaminated water; man is the definitive animal host. It has two distinct biotypes, 'classic' and 'El Tor', the latter now almost replacing the classic variety in many areas of the world and, being more easily transmitted and a better survivor, is a great international problem. However, the organisms are *rarely* imported into the UK. Sporadic cases still occur in mainland Europe.

Treatment: fluid replacement is critical, as diarrhoea is profuse and, if untreated, mortality due to dehydration can be 25–50% (Jawetz et al, 1989). Tetracycline is the drug of choice, although resistance is sometimes seen.

Vibrio parahaemolyticus is a cause of food poisoning associated with contaminated shellfish, especially from warm waters, e.g. South-East Asia and the USA. Cross-contamination from raw to cooked foods can occur.

Campylobacter

(See Figure 8.9.)

Presence: they are found in the faeces of many farm animals especially poultry, also in dogs and in raw (untreated) milk.

Pathogenicity: first recognised as recently as 1977 as an important human pathogen, it is now thought to be the most important cause of sporadic food poisoning in the UK. Some strains appear to produce enterotoxin. A summary of reports of gastrointestinal infection (PHLS, 1989b) states that *Campylobacter* infections have risen from 9453 in 1980 to 32 890 in 1989. This reflects a gradual increase in routine laboratories identifying the organisms.

C. jejuni is the main human pathogen in most countries and enteritis may (rarely) lead to bacteraemia. *C. coli* also causes enteritis. *C. laridis* is associated with seagulls and contamination of water reservoirs by seagull droppings, but is rarely isolated from man.

Helicobacter pylori used to be thought of as a campylobacter but has recently been reclassified. It is found in close relation to the mucosa and may be associated with gastritis and peptic ulceration, although its role in the pathogenesis of different types of ulceration remains unclear (*Nursing Times*, 1990). It has also been associated with iron deficiency anaemia in children in a UK study.

Pasteurella, Yersinia and Francisella

Pasteurella

These are small, ovoid bacilli, some with bipolar staining, sometimes capsulated.

Presence: found in the respiratory tract of many animals including cats and dogs.

Pathogenicity: human infection sometimes follows

scratches or bites, and apparently even from licking of a human wound by an animal (Shewring and Rushford, 1990). *P. multocida* (formerly *septica*) is the main human pathogen. Infected wounds are often slow to heal, and may be accompanied by lymphangitis and cellulitis. Rarely, meningitis can occur, and occasionally respiratory infection can follow inhalation of the organism.

Treatment: usually penicillin or tetracycline but the wound may also have anaerobic organisms such as *Bacteroides* involved; therefore it is wise to use additional metronidazole.

Yersinia

These are short rods that also show bipolar staining; they can be facultatively anaerobic.

Presence: commonly found in the intestines of many animals in Europe, and less frequently found as a cause of infection.

Pathogenicity: three varieties cause disease in humans. *Yersinia* infections commonly infect thalassaemics who have iron overload and are treated with iron chelators.

Y. enterocolitica causes gastroenteritis, especially in Europe. It may also cause septicaemia, and mesenteric adenitis mimicking acute appendicitis. Reactive arthritis is not uncommon.

Y. pseudotuberculosis causes abdominal pain, but rarely diarrhoea, and is often the cause of mesenteric adenitis. Both these species cause syndromes indistinguishable from acute appendicitis and may also cause acute intussusception in young babies.

Y. pestis (formerly classified as a pasteurella species). The cause of *bubonic plague*, carried by the rat and spreading to humans via rat fleas. Lymph glands become swollen and may discharge (called 'buboes'). *Pneumonic* plague results from inhalation of organisms often from another infected patient. Septicaemia and death will follow if untreated. Rare in Europe, it is still occasionally found in the USA and the Tropics.

Neal (1989) describes a case study of a patient in Riyadh who developed bubonic plague. A report by the WHO (1990) describes an outbreak of plague in Madagascar with 217 suspected cases and 20 deaths.

Treatment: streptomycin and tetracycline remain the first choice for plague. Newer antibiotics have never been clinically evaluated.

Francisella

Francisella tularensis

Presence: this organism is found in many rodents and other animals and transmitted to humans by tick bites, or contact with the animal tissue, by ingestion of contaminated food or water, or by inhalation.

Pathogenicity: It is *not common* but occurs in North America, and also in Scandinavia, and the organism is extremely infectious.

Clinical signs: infection usually starts with skin ulceration, lymphadenopathy, pyrexia, headache and hepato-splenomegaly.

Treatment: Streptomycin or gentamicin.

Parvobacteria

These are small, non-sporing, non-motile coccobacilli which sometimes need specially enriched media to grow.

Presence: the mucous membranes of man and animals.

Pathogens: these include *Haemophilus* spp., *Bordetella* spp., and *Brucella* spp.

Haemophilus spp.

Presence: they are found as normal flora in the respiratory tract but some strains cause infection.

H. influenzae is the main pathogen—the capsulate strain 'b' is virulent, but tends to affect only children under 5 years of age. It causes conjunctivitis, pneumonia and may pass via the bloodstream into the central nervous system to cause meningitis*. Other strains are normal commensals of the posterior nasopharynx of some adults. The organism is often found in patients with exacerbations of chronic bronchitis which are usually precipitated by viral infection. The pathogenic role of the organism in this situation is controversial.

Treatment: for *H. influenzae* meningitis, chloramphenicol is the first choice. Ampicillin is the first choice for respiratory tract infections but increasing numbers of strains are now resistant. Tetracycline may be a useful substitute for treating respiratory infection in adults. β-Lactamase producing strains still remain sensitive to second- and third-generation cephalosporins such as cefuroxime and cefotaxime.

Pathogenicity: *H. ducreyi* causes *chancroid* or *soft sore*, a sexually transmitted disease characterised by genital ulceration. The organism is supposed to enter by minor trauma to the mucous membrane of the genital tract.

Treatment: sulphonamides, tetracycline or erythromycin.

Bordetella

These are fragile organisms which need specially enriched culture material to grow.

---

* From October 1992 a vaccine to protect the under 5s from strain 'b' (Hib) has become part of the DOH immunisation programme.

Pathogenicity: of the three species, only one usually causes serious infection. *B. pertussis* causes *whooping cough*, a chronic cough characterised by paroxysms followed by a whoop of respiratory inspiration. It enters by the respiratory tract and *spread* is by respiratory droplets or by direct close contact between children. The disease is most infectious in the early stages. It can progress to bronchopneumonia, or cause convulsions at the end of a paroxysm of coughing. Most severe in children under 12 months of age. Since the introduction of vaccination in the 1950s, annual notifications have dropped from over 100 000 to 5027 in 1988 (DOH, 1990). Special media must be used to select for *B. pertussis*, cough plates or pernasal swabs are required.

Treatment: erythromycin may be used, although there are doubts about its effectiveness. The cough will last for 3 months and the condition is complicated by severe strain on the parents.

Brucella

Presence: parasites of animals and man, especially cattle, goats, sheep and swine.

Pathogenicity: it causes brucellosis in man which can be acute, subacute or chronic and after an initial acute phase can be a debilitating illness lasting months or years. The presentation is usually pyrexia of unknown origin (PUO) sometimes with acute soft tissue or joint infection with osteomyelitis. Now rarely acquired in the UK.

B. suis typically affects swine, and causes most infection in the USA.

B. melitensis mainly affects sheep or goats, and causes human infection in the Mediterranean and Middle East. This is the commonest species seen in imported infections in the UK.

B. abortus is found in cattle, in which it causes abortion fever. It is the main, but extremely unusual, source of brucellosis in the UK.

Spread: can be by contact with infected animal tissues, especially placental products; by ingestion of unpasteurised milk or milk products; through skin abrasions or, most rarely, through inhalation of organisms by laboratory workers.

Treatment: it requires long-term therapy, usually with tetracycline for months. Some recommend adding streptomycin for the initial month but this is toxic and rifampicin is a good alternative.

Legionella

These are non-sporing, non-acid-fast, strictly aerobic coccobacilli; they are slow growing except on special media.

Presence: widespread in moist environments, including air-conditioning systems and domestic water supplies. They are particularly associated with blue–green algae colonisation within water supply systems.

Pathogenicity: there are a number of species, but one main human pathogen.

L. pneumophila   (See Figure 8.10.)

This pathogen was recognised (and named) after an outbreak of severe atypical pneumonia affecting members attending a convention of the Pennsylvania branch of the American Legion in Philadelphia in 1976. It has since been recognised in many countries as a cause of sporadic or epidemic atypical pneumonia generally affecting elderly and mildly immunocompromised people, particularly men. Individual cases in the UK are often travellers returning from abroad (e.g. Spain and Portugal) who

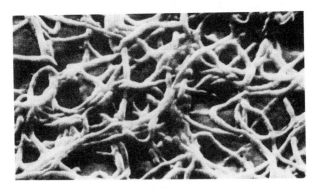

Figure 8.10 Scanning electronmicrograph of *Legionella pneumophila*.

have been exposed to sources of contaminated air-conditioning systems and piped hot and cold water supply in hotels. Older male patients who smoke and drink to excess seem to be more vulnerable to *L. pneumophila* aerosols.

> One severe outbreak associated with hospital air conditioning occurred at Stafford District Hospital in 1985 and caused 28 deaths. More recently, in April 1988 an outbreak associated with BBC Broadcasting House in Portland Place led to 70 confirmed cases, 25 suspected and 3 deaths (HSIB, 1990).

Clinical signs: the illness presents with influenza-like symptoms with a dry cough, and extensive pneumonia is found on chest X-ray. Case-to-case transmission has *not* been confirmed.

Treatment: erythromycin, with added rifampicin if there is no quick response, and treatment for at least 3 weeks.

Other species can cause pneumonia, e.g. *L. micdadei*, *L. bozemanii* and *L. dumoffii*.

L. pneumophila may also cause a milder infection known as *Pontiac fever*. This affects young fit people, has a high attack rate and is associated with exposure to intense aerosols. The illness is indistinguishable from severe influenza and chest X-ray is normal. Recurrence is common on re-exposure.

Anaerobic Gram-negative bacilli

Bacteroides

Presence: this large group of non-sporing, non-motile anaerobes are present in vast numbers in faeces but are also found in the mouth and genital tract.

Pathogenesis: most infection is caused by *B. fragilis* presenting as post-operative abdominal or gynaecological sepsis. It is often seen in association with other organisms such as *E. coli* or streptococci as a result of gut content contamination during surgery. Wound infections with *Bacteroides* spp. are likely to be slower to develop than most other organisms. It is frequently associated with the presence of foul-smelling pus, and is the most common anaerobic bacterium identified from human infection.

Treatment: metronidazole (see Chapter 5).

Fusobacterium

Presence: another anaerobic Gram-negative bacillary group which are commensals of the mouth and female genital tract.

Pathogenicity: they can combine with other organisms to cause infection, e.g. with spirochaetes to cause *Vincent's angina*, or with *Bacteroides* in gynaecological wound infection. *F. necrophorum* may cause severe sore throat with sepsis and abscess formation.

ACID-FAST BACILLI

Mycobacteria

These organisms are slender rods, enveloped with wax which makes them hard to stain by Gram's method. After staining by hot carbol fuchsin, the organisms are stain fast, resisting decolorisation with alcohols and strong mineral acids.

Presence: non-pathogenic forms are widely distributed in nature.

Pathogenesis: *M. tuberculosis* causes infection in man, as does *M. bovis* (or 'bovine' type). Other mycobacteria may cause opportunistic infection in man.

M. tuberculosis (human type)

This usually infects the lungs (*pulmonary tuberculosis*) but may also involve any organ and tissue (e.g. bone, joints or kidneys), except hair and nails. It is a slow-growing organism. If present in sufficiently large numbers it may be seen on direct microscopy, but more often before laboratory diagnosis can be confirmed or eliminated it must be grown on a special culture medium. Firm exclusion of positive culture takes 12 weeks. The bacilli are transmitted from open cases of tuberculosis in droplet nuclei by coughing, and inhalation of the organisms by susceptible individuals.

Treatment: 'first-line' drugs include rifampicin, izoniazid, ethambutol and pyrazinamide. Alternatives are used only if there is a problem of resistance, which is comparatively rare in the UK. The first two drugs are usually used for 6 months and the second two for only the first 2 months. The combination is used to accelerate healing (i.e. reduction of total course from, say, 9 to 6 months) and to prevent the emergence of drug-resistant strains. 'Second-line' drugs are toxic and unpleasant to take and courses must be much longer to guarantee cure. (See Figure 8.11.)

Tuberculosis is still a cause of major morbidity and mortality in developing countries but the prevalence in Europe and the USA had progressively fallen until the recent emergence of AIDS. Infection in patients with HIV may arise early in the course of the disease before AIDS is diagnosed as a reactivation of past endogenous infection in a highly exposed population such as Haitians in the USA (Rieder et al, 1989; Selwyn et al, 1989). However, outbreaks in AIDS units in the USA are now well described. Nursing care and management of infected patients is discussed later.

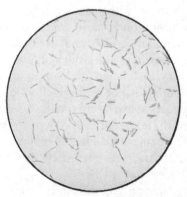

Figure 8.11 Culture smear of *Mycobacterium tuberculosis* (× 1500). Note the characteristic, slightly curved, delicate bacilli.

M. bovis (bovine type)

Infection in humans is by ingestion of milk from infected cattle. It is now very rare in the UK because herds are free from tuberculosis. Most disease seen now is in older patients who had primary disease as children. It involves cervical, small bowel and mesenteric lymph nodes.

Treatment: as for *M. tuberculosis*, but the organism is resistant to pyrazinamide.

M. leprae

This is the cause of leprosy which is diagnosed microscopically from skin scrapings or biopsies of skin or thickened nerves. It is not particularly infectious, requiring prolonged close contact for transmission. Only *lepromatous* patients are infectious; they transmit disease via respiratory secretions. Disease may occur as *tuberculoid leprosy* which shows anaesthetic skin lesions lacking pigment; *lepromatous leprosy* with nasal discharge, secondary infection and ulceration to nose and face (with possible collapse of the nasal septum and even blindness); and *borderline leprosy* where lesions in skin and nerve tissues are more severe and liable to lead to injury. Severe deformity in leprosy is not a direct effect of the leprosy bacillus but occurs because of trauma to anaesthetised regions (especially extremities). A leprosy patient will, therefore, easily damage his feet, or may burn his fingers on cigarettes. Contractures may occur because of nerve damage.

Treatment: dapsone and rifampicin, in combination. This is a major disease in the Third World, it is difficult to detect in the majority and treatment is expensive.

Atypical *mycobacteria*

There are many mycobacteria which have little pathogenicity for man under normal circumstances but occasionally cause disease.

M. kansasii causes pulmonary infection and is the most often found of the atypical or opportunistic mycobacteria, as in miners with already damaged lung tissue, e.g. pneumoconiosis (Shanson, 1989).

M. xenopi is also associated with chronic lung disease, particularly bronchopulmonary aspergillosis.

M. avium-intracellulare (MAI) also causes pulmonary infection and has been increasingly recognised as a cause of opportunistic infection in patients with late AIDS. One-third of AIDS patients who die have MAI in many sites. The organism often causes gut disease and is frequently isolated from blood culture.

M. marinum causes local granulomas on the hands of fish-tank handlers.

M. ulcerans causes tropical skin ulcers. Both are very rare in the UK.

SPIROCHAETES

These are a group of motile, spiral (helical) organisms which sometimes stain poorly or not at all, and move by flexing and cork-screw motion. Most of them are non-pathogenic, anaerobic and are found in the mouth, on gums and the genitalia.

The three main genera which include pathogenic strains are *Treponema*, *Leptospira* and *Borrelia*.

Treponema

These are very delicate regular coils. There are three species.

T. pallidum is the cause of *syphilis*. Organisms die rapidly outside the body. They enter through minor trauma to mucous membranes of the genitourinary tract, mouth or other direct contact site.

Clinically there are several stages: an initial local lesion ('chancre'); a secondary stage when bloodstream invasion (or central nervous system) occurs and rashes and enlarged lymph nodes may be found; and a tertiary stage which may occur after a latent period of years, involving chronic lesions (*gummas*) of many body systems, e.g. brain and also bones. (See Figure 8.12.)

T. pertenue is the cause of *yaws*, a chronic, endemic, relapsing disease of the tropics. Infection is spread by direct contact with organisms from skin lesions which are characteristically ulcerative.

T. carateum is the cause of *pinta*, a disease of Central and South America and the West Indies; this also is transmitted by direct skin contact with the infectious

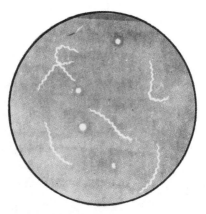

Figure 8.12 *Trepenoma pallidum* from a primary syphilitic lesion (× 1000).

lesions, which eventually become thickened and depigmented.

The main treatment for all three is penicillin.

Leptospira

These are very tightly coiled, cork-screw-shaped spirals with hooked ends.

Presence: there are two distinct species. *L. biflexa* is found in pools, streams and other wet, natural sites and *L. interrogans* is found in the kidneys of rodents and domestic animals. *L. interrogans* has at least 20 serogroups.

1. *L. canicola* can affect children from the urine of puppies; no cases have been seen in Britain since 1985.
2. *L. icterohaemorrhagiae* is carried by rats, is excreted in the urine into the environment and can infect sewer workers through damaged skin or mucous membranes.
3. *L. hardjo* is associated with cattle and accounted for 52% of human infection in England and Wales between 1985 and 1989 (PHLS, 1990).

Leptospira cause *leptospirosis*, with symptoms of fever and 'flu-like' illness initially, jaundice and nephritis sometimes with meningitis (*Weil's disease*) only occurring in a small proportion of cases. Cases have remained at a steady number for the last few years, despite increased public awareness. Some cases are associated with recreational water sports such as canoeing.

Treatment: penicillin, but it is probably ineffective.

Borrelia

These are large organisms with irregular worm-like spirals.

Presence and pathogenicity: *B. recurrentis* and *B. duttoni* are carried by lice and ticks, respectively, to human hosts who develop *relapsing fever* in tropical countries.

B. vincentii accompanied by *Fusobacterium* spp. are found in the ulcerative mouth and gum condition of *Vincent's angina*.

B. burgdorferi is also tick-borne. The definitive host is deer. It causes *Lyme disease*, notably on the north-eastern coast of the USA and in sandy heathland in the UK (e.g. New Forest). This is characterised first by a skin rash at the site of the bite (erythema migrans) and then by neurological, cardiac or arthritic sequelae (MMWR, 1988). Since the isolation of the cause and development of serological tests, it is now increasingly recognised in the UK, notably in areas where deer are numerous (Muhlemann and Wright, 1987) and also in Australia.

Treatment: penicillin or tetracycline.

MYCOPLASMAS

These are bacteria which have no cell wall and, therefore, are of indefinite shape and size. They are the smallest independent organisms, are aerobic, difficult to grow, and occur naturally. They were formerly known as pleuropneumonia-like organisms (PPLO).

Pathogenicity: the three mycoplasmas most commonly seen as human pathogens are:

M. pneumoniae is the commonest cause of atypical pneumonia (especially in children and young adults) and some milder respiratory diseases. This appears to have a cyclical pattern with epidemics every 4 years in temperate climates (PHLS, 1990c).

M. hominis colonises the vagina, causes 10% of pelvic inflammatory disease (PID) and has been recognised recently as an important cause of post-partum pyrexia.

Ureoplasma urealyticum (T-strain mycoplasma) is found without evidence of infection in genital tracts, but is thought to be involved in non-specific urethritis in man.

RICKETTSIAE

These are a group of obligate, intracellular parasites which contain both RNA and DNA. They can be seen with a light microscope.

There are two genera of rickettsiae: *Rickettsiae* and *Coxiellae*. The group includes the following, although they are not found in the UK:

1. *R. prowazekii*—typhus fever (body lice)
2. *R. mooseri*—murine typhus (fleas)
3. *R. tsutsugamushi*—tsutsugamushi fever (mites)
4. *R. rickettsii*—Rocky Mountain spotted fever and other tick-borne fevers
5. *C. burnetii*—Q fever

R. conorii is perhaps the only species regularly imported into the UK. It causes tick-borne fever with rash in Africa, India and Mediterranean countries.

Spread: usually from ticks, lice or fleas as appropriate, but sometimes a rodent itself is the source. There is *no* recognised person-to-person spread.

Pathogenesis: *epidemic typhus fever* is the most important, and it is associated with poor, overcrowded living conditions; it is transmitted by the victim scratching infected louse faeces into the skin. It is an epidemic disease; control measures are directed towards eliminating lice. A vaccine is available for this and for Rocky Mountain spotted fever.

Rickettsial infections tend to be severe, including lymphadenopathy and haemorrhagic complications, with a fatality rate of up to 20%. Recurrent illness is often seen.

Treatment: tetracycline or chloramphenicol is successful if started early. Sulphonamides are contraindicated.

Coxiella burnetii is found world-wide, but is relatively rarely seen in Britain. It is primarily a disease of large domestic animals, transmitted to man in the milk of infected cows or sheep and by inhalation of dust from straw and chaff contaminated by placentae, fetal membranes and fluid after the birth of a calf or lamb to an infected animal. The patient will have a 'flu-like' illness followed in about 50% of cases by atypical pneumonia and, very occasionally, subacute endocarditis if the heart valves are already damaged.

A recent outbreak at East Birmingham Hospital involved over 100 patients and is thought to have been spread by contaminated dust at lambing time (Smith, 1989).

Treatment: tetracycline or chloramphenicol. If endocarditis occurs, replacement of the affected valve may be necessary.

CHLAMYDIAE

These organisms are also obligate intracellular parasites, containing both RNA and DNA, and are closely related to Gram-negative bacteria, but they do not have a peptidoglycan cell wall and are resistant to β-lactams.

Presence: they occur naturally in human and animal populations.

Pathogenicity: there are three important species.

C. trachomatis

C. trachomatis, whose host is man, has a number of different serogroups which cause a variety of disease.

1. Non-specific urethritis and cervicitis—this is sexually transmitted and is increasing continually in Britain. It can also cause salpingitis in pelvic inflammatory disease.
2. Eye infections—neonatal ophthalmia (acquired at birth); and trachoma (chronic inclusion conjunctivitis with fibrosis and entropion which causes much blindness in the tropics). A milder form of inclusion conjunctivitis, usually effectively treated before fibrosis can occur, is seen in temperate climates such as the UK in outbreaks related to swimming pools.
3. Pneumonia—in neonates.
4. Lymphogranuloma venereum—a common sexually transmitted disease of the Tropics, usually commencing with a painless ulcer on the penis.

Treatment: most *C. trachomatis* diseases are treated with tetracycline or erythromycin. (Oral tetracycline in pregnant women and children up to 6 years of age will cause staining of the teeth.)

C. psittaci

This infects many animals, but birds are the most important reservoir for transmission to humans. Transmission involves inhalation of dust from infected birds (mostly budgerigars and parrots) or by direct contact.

The organism causes *psittacosis* in humans, usually presenting as atypical pneumonia after a 'flu-like' illness. Rarely, it causes infective endocarditis, myocarditis, renal complications and even disseminated intravascular coagulation.

N.B. Infection can spread from person-to-person, and instances of spread to nursing staff have been recorded.

In Louisiana in 1943, there were 19 infections and 8 deaths among staff in one outbreak (Sanford, 1986). It is important, therefore, to care for patients in single rooms during the acute febrile stage of the illness.

Cases of chlamydiosis in pregnancy causing sepsis associated with *ovine* (sheep) origin have been recorded (CDS, 1985; Bloodworth et al, 1987) and pregnant women are advised to avoid contact with sheep at lambing time.

Treatment: tetracycline (but not in pregnancy).

C. pneumoniae

C. pneumoniae is the Taiwanese adult respiratory agent (TWAR). Recently this has been recognised as a cause of mild pneumonic respiratory infection in man, who appears to be the only host. Outbreaks occur in schools.

REFERENCES

Acheson ED (1989) Botulism and hazelnut yoghourt. *Health Trends* **21**: 66.

Bateman W (1990) Imported organisms. *Nursing Times, J. Inf. Control N. Suppl.* **86**(26): 73–75.

Bloodworth DL, Howard AJ, Davies A and Mutton KJ (1987) Infection in pregnancy caused by *Chlamydia psittaci* of ovine origin. *Communicable Disease Report* **10**: 3–4. Internal publication of the Public Health Laboratory Service.

Braver DJ, Hauser GJ, Berns L, *et al* (1987) Control of a *Serratia marcescens* outbreak in a maternity hospital. *J. Hosp. Inf.* **10**: 129–137.

Brett J and du Vivier A (1985) *Pseudomonas aeruginosa* and whirlpools. *Br. Med. J.* **290**: 1024–1025.

Bullock DW, Bidwell JL, Reeves DS, *et al* (1982) Outbreaks of hospital infection in southwest England caused by gentamicin-resistant *Serratia marcescens*. *J. Hosp. Inf.* **3**: 263–73.

Burke JP, Ingall D, Klein JO, *et al* (1971) *Proteus mirabilis* infections in a hospital nursery traced to a human carrier. *N. Engl. J. Med.* **284**(3): 115–121.

Casewell MW, Dalton MT, Webster M and Phillips I (1977) Gentamicin-resistant *Klebsiella aerogenes* in a urological ward. *Lancet* ii: 444–446.

CDS (1985) Severe sepsis in pregnancy due to *Chlamydia psittaci* infection. *Communicable Diseases Scotland Weekly Report* 85/44.

DHSS (Department of Health and Social Security) (1986) *The Report of the Committee of Inquiry into an Outbreak of Food Poisoning at Stanley Royd Hospital*. London: HMSO.

DOH (Department of Health) (1988) *ML/CMO (89)3* and *Press Release 89/369*—statements of advice on listeria and food.

DOH (Department of Health, Welsh Office, Scottish Home and Health Department) (1990) *Immunisation Against Infectious Disease*. London: HMSO.

Earnshaw JJ, Clark AW and Thomb T (1985) Outbreak of *Pseudomonas aeruginosa* following endoscopic retrograde cholangiopancreatography. *J. Hosp. Infect.* 6: 95–97.

East J (1990) Staphylococcal scalded skin outbreak in a maternity unit. *Proceedings of 1989 I.C.N.A. Conf. (I.C. Yearbook)*. Cambridge, CMA Medical Data Ltd.

Gervich DH and Grout CS (1985) An outbreak of nosocomial *Acinetobacter* infections from humidifiers. *Am. J. Infect. Control* 13(5): 210–215.

George RH (1983) *Clostridium difficile* and the gut. *Proceedings of 14th Annual Symposium of ICNA*, pp. 37–38.

HSIB (1990) Preventing legionellosis, *Health and Safety Information Bulletin* 69: 5–8.

Holmes S (1989) Careful food handling reduces the risk of listeria. *Prof. Nurse* 4(7): 322–324.

Holton J (1982) A report of a further hospital outbreak caused by a multi-resistant *Acinetobacter anitratus*. *J. Hosp. Infect.* 3: 305–309.

Jawetz E, Brooks GF, Melnick JL, *et al* (1989) *Medical Microbiology*, 18th edn. London: Prentice-Hall.

Larsson S, Cedarberg A, *et al* (1978) *Listeria monocytogenes* causing hospital-acquired enterocolitis and meningitis in newborn infants. *Br. Med. J.* ii: 473–474.

McLauchlin J (1990) Listeriosis. *Proceedings of ICNA Conf. 1989*, pp. 165–173. Cambridge, CMA Medical Data Ltd.

Mayon-White RT (1980) Neonatal group B streptococcal infections. *Proceedings of 11th Annual Symposium of ICNA*.

Meers PD, Ayliffe GAJ, Emmerson AM, *et al* (1981) Report on the National Survey of Infection in Hospitals, 1980. *J. Hosp. Inf.* 2 (Suppl.).

MMWR (1988) Lyme disease—Connecticut. *Morb. Mortal. Weekly Rep.* 37(1): 1–3. U.S. Public Health Service.

Muhlemann MF and Wright DJM (1987) Emerging pattern of Lyme disease in the United Kingdom and Irish Republic. *Lancet* i: 260–262.

Mutton KJ, Brady LM, Harkness JL (1981) Serratia cross-infection in an intensive therapy unit. *J. Hosp. Inf.* 2: 85–91.

Neal A (1989) Ring-a-ring o'roses. *Nursing Times* 85(5): 49–50.

Nursing Times (1990) Ulcers linked to *H. pylori*. Clinical upate. **86**(2): 10.

PHLS Leptospira Reference Laboratory Hereford (1990) *Leptospirosis Update: 1985–89.*

PHLS (1989a) Salmonella in eggs. *PHLS Microbiol. Digest* **6**(1): 1–9.

PHLS (1989b) Surveillance of gastrointestinal infections 1980–89. *Communicable Disease Report* **52:1**. Internal publication of the Public Health Laboratory Service.

PHLS (1990a) Surveillance of listeriosis. *Communicable Disease Report* **21: 3**. Internal publication of the Public Health Laboratory Service.

PHLS (1990b) Gastrointestinal disease surveillance: England and Wales, 1989. *Communicable Disease Report* **19:1**. Internal publication of the Public Health Laboratory Service.

PHLS (1990c) *Mycoplasma pneumoniae* infections in England and Wales. *Communicable Disease Report* **18:1**. Internal publication of the Public Health Laboratory Service.

Reider HL, Cauthen GM, Bloch AB, *et al* (1989) Tuberculosis and acquired immunodeficiency syndrome: Florida. *Arch. Intern. Med.* **149**: 1268–1273.

Sanford JP (1986) in *Hospital Infections* (eds Bennett JV and Brachman PS), 2nd edn, Chap. 26, p. 416. Boston, MA: Little, Brown & Co.

Selwyn PA, Hartel D, Lewis VA, *et al* (1989) A prospective study of the risk of tuberculosis among intravenous drug users with human immunodeficiency virus infection. *N. Engl. J. Med.* **320**: 545–550.

Shanson DC (1989) *Microbiology in Clinical Practice*, 2nd edn. London: Wright.

Shewring DJ and Rushforth GF (1990) A bizarre post-operative wound infection. *Br. Med. J.* **300**: 1557.

Smith G (1989) Q fever outbreak in Birmingham UK. *Lancet* **ii**: 557.

Stucke VA and Thompson REM (1980) Infection transfer by respiratory condensate during positive pressure ventilation. *Nursing Times, J. Infect. Control N. Suppl.* **76**(9): 3–4.

WHO (1990) *Report on Plague in Madagascar.*

9 A guide to viruses

INFECTION

Many infections are known to be due to viruses; others are believed to be when no bacterial source of infection can be demonstrated in an obviously transmissible disease. Virus infections are common and most are mild (e.g. colds). Some are 'silent' and the virus multiplies in the body, usually without causing disease (e.g. cytomegalovirus), some cause latent infection (e.g. herpes simplex virus), a few cause very severe or fatal illness (e.g. rabies virus).

Many viruses enter the body by inhalation (e.g. influenza and measles), others gain entry by ingestion (e.g. poliomyelitis), or inoculation (e.g. hepatitis B), all spread locally directly to the tissues and some are disseminated widely via the blood stream. Viruses invade living cells and 'take over' the cell metabolic processes to reproduce themselves; the cell usually dies and releases the virus particles but it may survive and carry the virus as in latent infections. Viruses, unlike some bacteria, do not produce toxins. Certain viruses can induce changes in the genetic material of cells causing them to undergo malignant transformation.

DEFENCE MECHANISMS

Cells invaded and infected by a virus produce a protein substance, *interferon*, in the acute stage of the disease. This is released and temporarily protects other cells which take it up, from infection. Viral antigens stimulate the production of antibodies which are carried in the patient's serum and neutralise any subsequent invasion by the same virus, i.e. the patient becomes immune to that virus. Specific immunity, of which circulating antibody is one manifestation, often lasts a lifetime, but with some infections it may gradually decrease to a level where the patient is again susceptible or partially susceptible to infection. For example, herpes zoster (shingles) occurring in an adult is due to the same virus which caused his/her childhood attack of varicella (chickenpox); the recrudescent infection occurs when the immunity level has decreased.

DESTRUCTION OF VIRUSES

Viruses, with the exception of certain virus-like agents (see p. 279) are killed by exposure to heat such as boiling for a few minutes, but survive storage at temperatures as low as $-70°C$. Their ability to withstand drying is very variable but all are thought to be sensitive to ultraviolet light. In general terms, many viruses can be destroyed by the action of aldehydes, chlorine, iodine and some alcohols; some are completely resistant to the phenolics; chlorine-releasing agents are commonly used for disinfection purposes (see Chapter 6). The advice of a virologist should be taken in outbreaks of infection since different viruses vary in their reaction to chemicals. All such advice will have to be in line with the Control of Substances Hazardous to Health (COSHH) regulations.

Only certain viruses contain lipid and the fact that lipid-containing viruses are inactivated by ether or chloroform is used in the laboratory identification and classification of viruses.

CLASSIFICATION

Viruses may be grouped according to their nucleic acid, size, symmetry, structure and by the diseases that they cause. For the purposes of this nursing textbook, viruses have been grouped according to the systems of the body which are affected and the routes by which infection may be transmitted. Whilst it is not possible to categorise every virus in this way, it is intended to reinforce the relevance of the scientific details to the actual nursing care of the affected patient. Table 9.1 gives the groupings.

LABORATORY IDENTIFICATION AND INVESTIGATIONS

Details of the investigations undertaken for diagnosis of viral infections have been covered in Chapter 7. The appropriate investigations for each virus are therefore only named against that organism in this chapter.

STRUCTURE

This has been described in Chapter 2, with explanation of terms such as 'icosahedral' and 'naked'.

INFECTIVITY, SOURCES, TRANSMISSION ROUTES AND CARE

Although these are mentioned in the text for a large number of viral infections, they are summarised, along with information on many bacterial infections, in the Appendix to Chapter 14.

Table 9.1 Grouping of viruses.

Respiratory group
Adenoviruses
Orthomyxoviruses (influenza viruses)
Paramyxoviruses (including mumps, measles and respiratory
  syncytial virus)
Rhinoviruses
Coronaviruses
Rubella virus
Gastroenteric group
Picornaviruses (mainly enteroviruses including poliovirus,
  echovirus, coxsackie viruses)
Reoviruses including rotavirus
Norwalk agent, caliciviruses, astroviruses, small round viruses
  (SRV) and small, round structured viruses (SRSV)
Hepatitis A and E
Blood-borne viruses
Hepatitis B, C and D
Retroviruses (including HIV 1 and 2, HTLV)
Herpesviruses
Herpes simplex virus types 1 and 2
Varicella–zoster virus
Cytomegalovirus
Epstein–Barr virus
Human herpesvirus 6 (HHV6)
Arthropod-borne viruses
Flaviviruses (including yellow fever)
Togaviruses (including alphaviruses such as equine
  encephalitis viruses)
Bunyaviridae (e.g. Rift valley fever virus)
Reoviridae (including orbiviruses such as Colorado tick fever)
Zoonoses
Rhabdoviruses (including rabies virus)
Arenaviruses (including Lassa fever)
Filoviruses (Marburg and Ebola diseases)
Other viruses
Poxviruses
Papovaviruses
Parvoviruses
Unconventional virus-like agents
Spongiform encephalopathy agents (Creutzfeldt–Jakob disease
  and Kuru in man; bovine spongiform encephalopathy in
  cattle; scrapie in sheep)

RESPIRATORY GROUP

These are viruses which affect the respiratory tract. They are principally *spread* by droplets containing the virus in coughs and sneezes, but may also be spread on droplet-contaminated hands (or, more rarely, inanimate objects) to a susceptible person. It includes the viruses causing colds and influenza and also many of the childhood infectious diseases.

Adenoviruses

These are DNA viruses. They are naked, icosahedral, and 70–90 nm in size.

Diagnostic material: throat swabs, faeces, conjunctival swabs (in eye disease), clotted blood.

Identification method: tissue culture; fluorescent antibody, radioimmunoassay (RIA) and enzyme-linked immunosorbent assay (ELISA).

A model of an adenovirus showing its 'antennae' is shown in Figure 9.1.

Effects:

1. pharyngitis;
2. conjunctivitis;
3. epidemic keratoconjunctivitis ('shipyard eye'), sometimes seen in factories or hospitals, and associated with dust particles or eye instruments and trauma; and
4. pneumonia: rare but occasionally seen, especially in immunocompromised patients, especially children; it may be fatal.

Occasional epidemics occur in schools or army camps and hospital-acquired infection has been reported (Straube et al, 1983). (See also the section on enteric group viruses, p. 253).

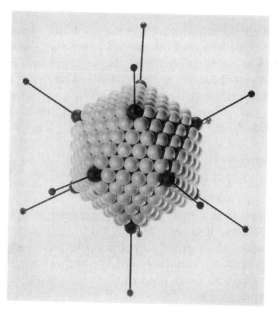

Figure 9.1   Model of adenovirus showing its 'antennae'.

Orthomyxoviruses (influenza viruses)

These are RNA viruses. They are helical, enveloped, and 80–120 nm in size.

Diagnostic material: throat swab, clotted blood.

Investigations: isolation of virus in tissue culture. Complement fixation tests and haemagglutination inhibition (paired sera required; see Chapter 7). Also immunofluorescence.

Unique among viruses, human influenza viruses undergo *antigenic changes* where, as the name implies, alterations occur in some (H and N) antigens. These may be complete (known as *antigenic shift*) when new subtypes occur, or only partial (*antigenic drift*) when only smaller antigenic changes have occurred. Pandemics occur (see below) because immunity from previous attacks is not protective against the new subtype.

Influenza A virus

This is the principal cause of epidemic influenza. Pandemics occur approximately every 10–12 years, the most recent being:

1957 —'Asian flu' (H2N2),
1968 —'Hong Kong flu' (H3N2), and
1977 —'Red flu' (H1N1)

the last two strains are still circulating (see also p. 246).

Influenza B virus

This causes smaller epidemics and outbreaks which may have a wide geographic distribution. It may undergo *antigenic drift*, leaving some people with residual protective immunity from previous infection. Widespread outbreaks occurred in 1973 (Hong Kong) and 1979 (Singapore) and the present strains are closest to the 1979 variety.

Both viruses attack and desquamate the epithelium of the respiratory tract leaving it susceptible to secondary bacterial invasion, e.g. staphylococcal infection.

Influenza C virus

This rarely causes clinical infection.

Spread
The viruses spread by the respiratory route in droplets and droplet nuclei; the incubation period is only 2–3

days. They may cause a problem in hospitals because of acute reduction in staff numbers during epidemics.

Influenza virus vaccines

These give considerable protection, although they are not always effective because of the multiplicity of strains. Influenza A in particular develops antigenic shift as already described. The speed of spread of a new strain often makes it difficult to prepare a new vaccine fast enough for all. Therefore it is important to ensure protection, as early as possible, particularly to susceptible individuals, e.g. the elderly and people with chronic respiratory disease. Antibodies are not formed immediately, so vaccine must be given before an epidemic starts, although the modern vaccines appear to take effect within a week. Attempts are being made to ensure this is carried out more effectively. During the winter of 1989–1990, 26 000 people in the UK died of influenza A (H3N2 strain mainly) or secondary infections, despite the availability of an effective vaccine (Reilly, 1990).

Reye's syndrome

This is an acute encephalopathy of children and young adolescents with a high mortality rate of 10–40% (Jawetz et al, 1989). It is seen as a complication of influenza A or B, varicella–zoster and other viral infections. An association between viral infection and the use of aspirin leading to Reye's syndrome is under investigation.

Paramyxoviruses

These are RNA viruses. They are helical, enveloped, and 100–250 nm in size.

Parainfluenzae (4 types)

Diagnostic material: throat swabs, clotted blood.

Identification: isolation of virus in tissue culture and look for haemadsorption, or immunofluorescence. Serology.

Effects: febrile cold; croup; bronchiolitis (and pneumonia). It occurs most commonly in children under 5.

Respiratory syncytial virus (RSV)

Diagnostic material: nasopharyngeal secretions.

Identification: direct demonstration of virus in nasopharyngeal aspirate by immunofluorescence, or serology (complement-fixation test (CFT)).

Effects: colds, but it is an important cause of bronchiolitis (and pneumonia) in children under 1 year of age.

Mumps

Diagnostic material: cerebrospinal fluid, throat swab, clotted blood.

Identification: isolation of virus in tissue culture; serology (CFT).

Effects: fever and inflammation of salivary glands with swelling (initially usually of only one parotid gland); it can also cause mumps, meningitis, orchitis and more rarely pancreatitis or oophoritis.

Incubation period: 12–25 days. Most infectious about 48 h before the onset of illness.

(See Figure 9.2.)

Measles (rubeola)

Diagnostic material: nasopharyngeal aspirates, clotted blood.

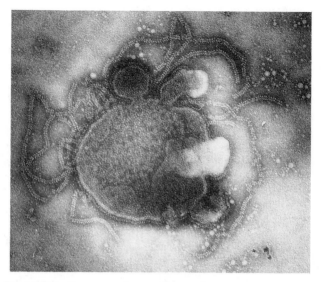

Figure 9.2 Paramyxovirus: a disrupted mumps particle showing fragments of internal nucleocapsid (× 60 000).

Identification: direct demonstration by immunofluorescence; also serology (CFT, ELISA or haemagglutination inhibition).

Effects: mild disease usually in the UK with fever and rash (facial first), but it is a serious and frequently fatal infection in countries where living conditions and nutrition are poor. Not uncommon with measles are complications of the respiratory tract (bronchitis, otitis media, pneumonia) and the central nervous system (encephalitis occurs in a small number of cases) and *very rarely* subacute sclerosing panencephalitis can occur years later (Bingham, 1987). When a child develops measles after admission to a nursery or hospital ward it is usual to protect susceptible contacts by administering γ-globulin.

Incubation period: about 10 days, but can be 7–18 days.

Rhinoviruses

These are RNA viruses. They are icosahedral, naked, and 20–30 nm in size.

Laboratory diagnosis is rarely carried out.

Effects: upper respiratory tract infections including the common cold. Unlike other *picornaviruses* these are respiratorily spread, and may also be transmitted by contact.

Coronaviruses

These are RNA viruses. They are enveloped and 80–160 nm in size.

Identification: difficult, seldom attempted.

Effects: upper respiratory tract infections, generally mild.

Rubella virus (German measles)

This is a RNA virus. It is helical, enveloped, and approximately 60 nm in size. It is a *togavirus*, but is not arthropod-borne as the others are.

Diagnostic material: blood.

Identification: serology (ELISA or RIA).

Effects: a mild febrile illness with a macular rash and some pharyngitis, but if the disease is transmitted to a pregnant woman during the first 4 months of pregnancy it may cause congenital defects in the fetus, e.g. deafness, cataract, heart defects. In the UK since 1988, rubella virus vaccine has been given to both sexes in the second year of life to reduce the amount of circulating rubella in the population. As yet there is no plan to discontinue the vaccination of girls aged 10–14 years without documented evidence of previous measles–mumps–rubella (MMR) vaccination (clinical diagnosis is notoriously unreliable, a stated history of infection is not enough).

Post-partum vaccination may also be offered to pregnant women shown by serological tests to be non-immune. Pregnancy should be avoided for 3 months after vaccination to ensure that there is no possibility of fetal infection due to the attenuated virus. According to Shanson (1989), the risk of multiple defects from infection in the first month of pregnancy is 60–80% and becomes progressively less in months 2, 3 and 4.

VIRUSES INVOLVING THE GASTROINTESTINAL SYSTEM

These include, among others, the picornaviruses, reoviruses, and hepatitis A and E.

Picornaviruses

These are RNA viruses. They are icosahedral, naked, and 20–30 nm in size (pico = small).

Diagnostic material: faeces, throat swabs, cerebrospinal fluid, nasal secretions (depending on clinical symptoms).

Enteroviruses

These include polioviruses, coxsackie viruses (groups A and B), echo viruses, and hepatitis A (see p. 253). They are ingested, multiply in the alimentary tract and pharynx and spread from the gut to tissues and organs via the bloodstream. Virus is excreted in the faeces.

Spread: faecal–oral route mainly, but respiratory spread by droplets is thought to be implicated with some enteroviruses. As neonates are particularly at risk, a history of recent febrile illness in any admission to maternity units should lead to initial single-room care (Isaacs et al, 1989).

Prevention: careful handling of faeces and secretions at all times should be the rule.

Poliovirus causes paralytic poliomyelitis, but symptomless intestinal infections are more common. There are three serological types of poliovirus. Type 1 virus causes most epidemics and most cases of paralysis which results from damage to the anterior horn of the spinal cord, causing lower motor neurone lesions. Live attenuated strains of each type are incorporated in trivalent oral poliovaccine. The use of vaccine has virtually eliminated poliomyelitis in many countries. Immunisation with poliovaccine should be given in childhood, but the vaccine should also be given to adults who may be exposed to the virus, e.g. when travelling to countries where poliomyelitis is still common. Live oral poliovaccine still leads to a very occasional case of paralytic poliomyelitis. Safer inactivated vaccine requires a large proportion of the population (in excess of 90%) to be immunised to achieve effective herd immunity and is not yet the rule in the UK (Beale, 1990).

Incubation period: 7–14 days in paralytic cases, but can be longer.

Coxsackie viruses cause 'hand, foot and mouth disease', herpangina (coxsackie A virus), Bornholm disease (epidemic myalgia or pleurodynia), myocarditis and pericarditis (coxsackie B virus).

(*Enterovirus 70* has caused outbreaks of acute haemorrhagic conjunctivitis around the world. The disease is thought to spread from eye discharges and the virus is *not* found in the faeces.)

Echoviruses are the commonest enteroviruses to cause meningitis and also occasionally cause skin rashes. Like other enteroviruses they are most common in spring and summer.

Reoviruses

These are RNA viruses. They are double stranded, icosahedral, naked, and 60–80 nm in size.

Rotavirus

This is wheel-shaped in appearance (see Figure 9.3).

Diagnostic material: faeces.

Identification: electron microscopy; ELISA to detect virus in 10% faecal suspension.

Effects: increasingly identified since the 1970s in outbreaks of gastroenteritis and febrile diarrhoea in

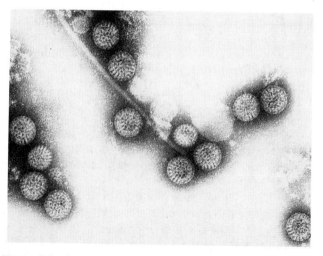

Figure 9.3 Rotavirus particles in a partially purified faecal suspension ($\times$ 100 000).

infants and young children (Chrystie et al, 1975) and also in homes for the elderly. It is often accompanied by 'flu-like' respiratory symptoms.

Incubation period: approximately 24–72 h.

Other infant viral gastroenteritis

Other infant viral gastroenteritis has been recorded, and sometimes in adults too, caused by adenoviruses, astroviruses, caliciviruses, Norwalk virus, small round viruses (SRVs) and small round structured viruses (SRSVs). These may cause outbreaks in schools, families and hospitals. They can only be demonstrated by electron microscopy, and stool samples taken during the first 48 h of illness are needed for identification. All these agents require conscientious care in terms of handwashing, careful disposal of excreta and, preferably, single-room care in hospitals, especially in paediatric and neonatal units, in order to prevent spread to other patients (Dowsett, 1988).

Hepatitis A virus

This is a RNA virus. It is single stranded and 28 nm in size.

Diagnostic material: blood.

Identification: blood for serology (RIA or ELISA).

Spread: hepatitis A virus (infectious hepatitis) is transmitted by the faecal–oral route from person to person or by faecally contaminated food or water. Sewage-contaminated shellfish have been responsible for several outbreaks (O'Mahony et al, 1983), as have raspberries (Reid and Robinson, 1987). Hepatitis A occurs world-wide but is becoming less common in the UK. It spreads fairly readily in close-contact situations, e.g. nursery schools, families. A formaldehyde inactivated hepatitis

A virus vaccine is now replacing human normal immuno-globulin which had previously been given for short-term passive immunity (3–6 months) for travellers to highly endemic areas. This is only licensed for adults as yet.

Incubation period: 2–6 weeks, average 28–30 days. Nursing care: infectivity is at its peak during the 10 days before symptoms, including jaundice, appear and for the next few days. Care in contact with faeces or faecally contaminated equipment is the basic preventive measure, and patients rarely require isolating in single rooms.

Hepatitis E virus

This is a RNA virus. It is naked, single stranded, spherical, and 27–34 nm in size. It is probably a *calicivirus*.

Diagnostic material: no diagnostic tests are yet available (under development).

Effects: epidemic and sporadic infection clinically similar to hepatitis A, often including fever and arthralgia. Infection occurs in many parts of the world, notably the Soviet Union, India, Nepal, Japan and several African countries. It appears to spread via sewage-contaminated water and person-to-person. Some outbreaks have affec-ted mostly young/middle-aged adults and a high mortality rate has been reported in pregnant women (Lever, 1988; Zuckerman, 1990).

Incubation period: 2–6 weeks.

There may be other enteric forms of *non-A non-B hepatitis* (the term used for all other types of hepatitis before they were separately identified) still to be ident-ified.

Table 9.2 shows some characteristics of the different types of viral hepatitis.

Table 9.2 Some characteristics of the different types of viral hepatitis.

Type	Transmission route	Incubation period (weeks)	Carrier state	Mortality	Serology available
A	Faecal–oral	2–6	No	Low	Yes
B	Parenteral	6–26	Yes	Can be high	Yes
C	Parenteral	5–10	Yes	Moderate	Yes
D	Parenteral (with HBV)	As HBV	Yes	High	Yes
E	Faecal–oral	2–6	Unknown	High in pregnancy	Being developed

HBV, hepatitis B virus.

BLOOD-BORNE VIRUSES

Hepatitis B virus (HBV; hepatitis B–serum hepatitis)

This is a DNA virus. It is partially double-stranded, double-shelled, and is 42 nm in size (the Dane particle). It consists of a 27 nm nucleocapsid core, containing hepatitis B core antigen (HBcAg) surrounded by an outer lipoprotein coat containing surface antigen (HBsAg). Another antigen associated with the core is HBeAg, the presence of which in the blood suggests high infectivity. The detection of these different antigens and their antibodies, i.e. to core antigen (anti-HBcAg), surface antigen (anti HBsAg) and 'e' antigen (anti-HBeAg), are used as markers of infectivity (see Table 9.3). (See Figures 9.4 and 9.5.)

Diagnostic material: blood.

Identification: RIA or ELISA are used to detect all the above HBV markers.

Incubation period: 40–180 days.

Transmission: the virus may be found in most body substances but transmission is usually by blood or blood products or via semen and vaginal fluids. It can also be transmitted perinatally. Groups with a higher risk of carrying HBV include intravenous drug users (from sharing of contaminated needles and syringes), people with multiple sexual partners, especially prostitutes and promiscuous male homosexuals, patients receiving multiple transfusions of blood and blood products (the risk is minimal in the UK since donors are screened for HBsAg), and those from parts of the world where the infection is endemic, e.g. Africa and South-East Asia.

In the UK, from 1985 to 1988 the annual incidence of acute HBV was 4 per 100 000 males and 2 per 100 000 adult females (DOH, 1990b). Most carriers of the virus give no history of illness and remain healthy, but a few

Table 9.3 Guide to hepatitis B serology.

HBsAg	The viral antigen found in acute hepatitis B and in chronic HBV carriers
HBeAg	This antigen is present in acute hepatitis B and also in chronic HBV carriers during the initial phase which generally lasts 5–10 years or longer. It is associated with high infectivity
anti-HBs	This antibody usually develops after resolved HBV infection and is protective. It is the antibody induced by vaccination
anti-HBc	Appears early in an acute infection, initially as IgM. High levels are found in HBV carriers. Sometimes found in the absence of HBsAg or anti-HBs indicating a past HBV infection and possible residual infectivity, but only at a level which is important in donated blood. The best marker for past HBV infection
anti-HBe	This antibody appears during recovery from acute HBV and in the second phase of chronic HBV infection. If present with HBsAg it indicates low infectivity. Chiefly of importance in donated blood

develop chronic active hepatitis and cirrhosis after carrying the virus for many years. 5–10% of adults infected in the UK go on to become chronic carriers. In the UK these are predominantly male, but in South East Asia where roughly 15% of the population are carriers of HBV, mothers transmit the virus to their newborn infants who in turn become carriers. This *vertical transmission* from infected mother to baby, occurring during the perinatal period, is thus a major cause of long-term illness. It is now possible to prevent the acquisition of the virus by a newborn baby by treatment with hepatitis B immunoglob-

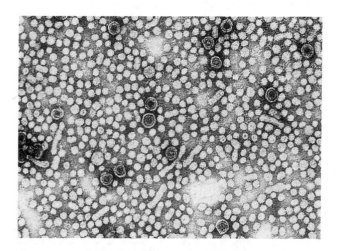

Figure 9.4 Hepatitis B surface antigen (HBsAg) purified from the blood of a carrier. The large particles with an inner core are complete infectious virions (× 60 000).

ulin, preferably within 12 h of birth, accompanied by active immunisation with hepatitis B vaccine.

Prevention of transmission in health-care settings is based on careful handling of blood and blood-stained body fluids, and education in safe handling of all contaminated and sharp instruments. Prompt action is vital when a 'needlestick' or 'sharps' injury occurs (see also Chapter 12).

The Department of Health publication referred to above (DOH, 1990b) details the action to be taken in the event of accidental exposure to HBV, including passive immunisation with specific hepatitis B immunoglobulin (HBIg) and immunisation with hepatitis B vaccine (a genetically engineered preparation now widely available and recommended to health-care workers). A course of

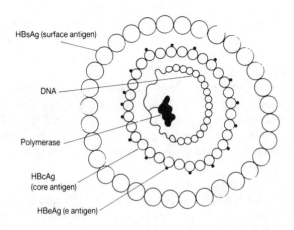

Figure 9.5 Diagrammatic representation of hepatitis B virion (Dane particle).

three injections at 0, 1 and 6 months is required, with testing to check for antibody response, and a booster dose given if indicated*. The vaccine appears to be effective in about 90% of those vaccinated (increasing the amount of antigen in the vaccine could improve on this and reduce the necessity for widespread serological checks (D. S. Dane, personal communication).

Hepatitis D virus (HDV; delta virus)

This is a defective RNA virus. It is enveloped, circular, single stranded, and 35–37 nm in size. It requires the presence of HBV to replicate. HBsAg forms the outer coat of HDV.

Diagnostic material: blood.

* New guidelines on HBV prophylaxis following exposure have been issued by the PHLS in September 1992.

Identification: ELISA for Ag and Ab.

HDV can exist as a *coinfection* in someone with acute HBV infection resulting in a more severe infection; or *superinfection* when HDV infection occurs in someone who already has chronic HBV infection; this can result in very severe or fulminant hepatitis (Frosner, 1988).

If infection with HDV becomes chronic, the outlook is poor. It is found most frequently in the Middle East, Africa and South America and the highest risk groups are intravenous drug abusers and people receiving multiple transfusions.

Nursing care: as for HBV, with emphasis on safe handling of blood, blood-stained body fluids and contaminated instruments. As pointed out by Hart (1990), vaccination against hepatitis B will also prevent acquisition of hepatitis D.

Hepatitis C virus (HCV)

This is a RNA virus. It is single-stranded.

Diagnostic material: blood.

Investigation: serology (ELISA and recombinant immunoblot assay (RIBA)).

At least 90% of transfusion-associated hepatitis now appears to be caused by hepatitis C virus (HCV; formerly one of the non-A non-B forms of viral hepatitis) in the USA and some other countries (Choo et al, 1990). Diagnosis has been by elimination of the alternatives, i.e. by not finding serological markers for HAV or HBV, but several tests for anti-HCV have recently been developed and, although not completely evaluated, are now available for diagnostic use and for screening blood donations. The illness is similar to acute HBV, but is generally milder. Asymptomatic chronic hepatitis frequently, perhaps nearly always, follows acute infections and this may eventually lead to cirrhosis.

Incubation period: 5–10 weeks.

Retroviruses

These are RNA viruses. They are enveloped, helical, and 100–120 nm in size.

They contain an enzyme (*reverse transcriptase*) which converts the virus RNA into DNA which is then integrated into the host cell and is thus ensured continuation as the cells reproduce.

Retroviruses can cause sarcomas or leukaemias in many animal species. Retroviruses which infect humans include HTLV and HIV.

HTLV

These are human T-cell lymphotropic viruses associated with leukaemia and lymphoma. HTLV-1 is found most often in Japan and the Caribbean, and also causes tropical spastic paralysis (TSP).

HIV 1 and 2 (human immunodeficiency viruses)

HIV attacks T-cells, particularly the T4 helper lymphocytes, by binding to the CD4 receptor site and allowing the virus entry into the cell (see Chapter 4). Slowly the number of T4 cells is depleted, because the new viruses which escape from the infected T4 cells by 'budding' cause death of the helper cell. The ratio of T4 (helper) to T8 (suppressor) cells is slowly reversed and opportunistic infections such as *Pneumocystis carinii* pneumonia or *toxoplasmosis* can take advantage of the altered host defence. The time from initial infection (often accompanied by a glandular fever-like or 'flu-like' illness) to the onset of acquired immune deficiency syndrome (AIDS) varies from between 2 and about 16 years, with a mean incubation of about 9 years. Between the initial attack and this stage many patients develop persistent generalised lymphadenopathy (PGL) or AIDS-related complex (ARC) involving weight loss, fever, and generalised weakness. Care of patients who are HIV-positive, or suffering from frank AIDS is discussed elsewhere, and detailed guidance and information on the subject is contained in the Guidance for Clinical Health Care Workers (DOH, 1990b) and the Advisory Committee on Dangerous Pathogens (HMSO, 1990) (See Figure 9.6.)

HERPESVIRUSES

These are DNA viruses. They are icosahedral, capsid, enveloped, and 100 nm in size.

There are six herpesviruses which are common in man; HSV 1 and 2, VZV, CMV, EBV and human herpesvirus 6 (HHV-6), often causing symptomless and latent infections (e.g. most adults have antibodies to both herpes simplex, HHV-6, EBV and cytomegalovirus without symptoms or history of infection).

Herpes simplex virus

Types 1 and 2 herpes simplex virus

Effects: vesicular lesions. The illnesses caused can be split into *primary* and *reactivated* forms. Primary HSV 1 infection is often symptomless but can produce herpetic whitlows, gingivostomatitis or conjunctivitis. Primary infections with HSV 2 may also be silent or cause *herpes genitalis* (sexually transmitted), whitlow from contact during nursing care, and severe generalised neonatal infection (high mortality) which may be acquired at birth.

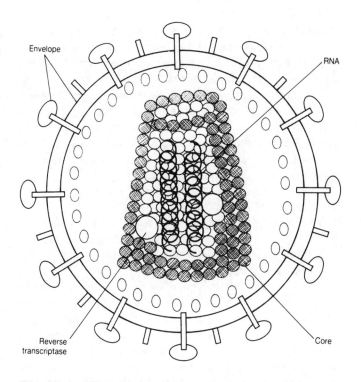

Figure 9.6 Diagrammatic representation of the human immuno-deficiency virus (HIV).

Aseptic meningitis is a rare complication of primary herpes simplex (usually HSV 2) infection. Encephalitis can also occur, in both immunocompromised and apparently healthy individuals, either at the time of primary infection or in the previously infected. Often occurring in a severe haemorrhagic form with high mortality, it requires prompt antiviral therapy to be effective.

Reactivated latent infection can occur. 'Cold sores' are common recrudescent episodes of infection; the virus is thought to remain latent in the trigeminal nerve ganglion between attacks and to be reactivated by non-specific stimuli, e.g. sun, colds. Recurrent infections of the eye cause dendritic corneal ulcers.

Diagnostic material: vesicle fluid and scrape, blood.

Identification: demonstration of virus by electron-microscopy and growth on tissue culture; serology (CFT) for primary infections, and ELISA and RIA. In cases of suspected herpes encephalitis it is *not* usual to wait for laboratory diagnosis before starting treatment.

Spread: close contact, e.g. kissing (HSV 1) or sexual intercourse (HSV 2).

Treatment: acyclovir, orally or systemically for encephalitis, severe or genital herpes, and topically for cold sores and some genital lesions; idoxuridine, topically for skin, whitlows and keratitis.

Nursing care: all evidence to date suggests that the virus is transmitted by direct contact with the lesions. *Staff* with active herpes simplex lesions which are uncovered should not look after immunocompromised or newborn patients, or patients with eczema, and those with herpetic whitlows should not have any patient contact. When dealing with *patients* with active herpes simplex lesions gloves should be worn for direct contact with lesions and correct handwashing by attendant staff is most important. Mothers with active genital lesions may well have elective caesarean section to minimise risk to the baby. The mother and baby should be cared for in a single room, and staff should wear aprons and gloves for contact with the mother's vaginal discharges, and contain pads, etc., as infected. The mother must be reminded of the importance of careful personal hygiene before caring for her baby, and the baby must be carefully observed for any signs of illness (Valenti and Wehrle, 1986).

Varicella–zoster virus (VZV)

Varicella

Varicella (chickenpox) is the primary infection. (See Figure 9.7.)

Diagnostic material: vesicle fluid and scrape; blood.

Identification: electronmicroscopy and tissue culture. Serology (CFT and ELISA).

Effects: a mild fever and rash progressing from maculopapular to vesicular to pustular stages, occurring in 'crops' and starting on face or trunk and then spreading to the limbs. Complications are unusual but include encephalitis, severe varicella pneumonia, disseminated

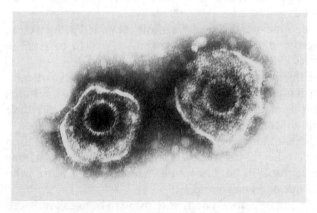

Figure 9.7 Two herpesvirus particles from a vesicle of a patient suffering from chickenpox ($\times$ 60 000).

lesions (more likely in immunosuppressed or immuno-deficient patients) and secondary bacterial infection (in children, from scratching).

Spread: droplet infection and contact with vesicle fluid. Leclair et al (1980) document an epidemic of chickenpox in a paediatric hospital where the airborne route appears to have been important.

Nursing care: it is important that patients with chicken-pox are nursed in single rooms with the doors closed, and gloves and aprons should be worn for contact with the lesions or contaminated articles. Attending staff should be immune to chickenpox.

Incubation period: 2–3 weeks, usually 13–17 days.

Zoster

Zoster (shingles) is the reactivated infection from the latest virus in sensory nerve ganglia; when the level of immunity decreases the virus may be reactivated, resulting in an attack of *zoster*.

Diagnostic material: vesicle fluid, scrape and swab; blood.

Identification: clinical diagnosis combined with electron microscopy is quickest, followed by growth of virus in tissue culture; serology (CFT).

Effects: painful vesicles corresponding to particular dermatomes, e.g. thoracic. Infection may leave a residual neuralgia. Seen in AIDS patients because of their immunocompromised state.

Spread: an *autogenous* infection, zoster is not acquired from other cases of zoster or of varicella, but it may cause varicella in susceptible people, i.e. a nurse who has not had chickenpox.

Treatment: intravenous acyclovir can be used for severe infections, especially for the immunocompromised.

Nursing care: if the lesions can be covered and there

are no immunocompromised patients on the ward and
no non-immune staff, the patient may stay in an open
ward, but these criteria can rarely be guaranteed and
single-room care with use of aprons and gloves when
coming into contact with lesions are usually observed.
Individual circumstances must always be assessed.

*Patients undergoing immunosuppresive therapy are par-
ticularly susceptible to varicella–zoster virus (VZV) in
whom it can be a life-threatening infection.* It is therefore
advisable for the hospital Occupational Health Service to
screen all staff who have 'hands-on' contact with patients
for evidence of past varicella infection.

Cytomegalovirus (CMV)

Diagnostic material: urine, throat swab, blood.
Identification: detection of early antigen fluorescent foci
(DEAFF) in tissue culture. (Serology is generally of
doubtful value.)
   Effects: in later life infection is often inapparent or
may cause a glandular-fever-like illness. A high proportion
of the population have antibody to CMV, indicating past
infection. Serious forms of the disease present when
infection occurs perinatally, after congenital or acquired
infection. In older children, hepatitis may occur (rarely).

Congenital infections

These are generally symptomless, but can later be found
to have caused deafness or mental deficiency (Glyn
Owen, 1989). It may lead to death *in utero*, or severely
affected neonates may have generalised infection with
microcephaly, jaundice, blood disorders and a high degree
of resulting retardation.

Generalised infection

This may occur when immunity is impaired by immunosuppressive drugs (as in transplant patients), or severe disease (e.g. neoplasia) or, more recently, in AIDS patients, causing pneumonitis, retinitis or hepatitis.

Spread: direct contact with body fluids, and *sexual transmission*. Despite concern about the risk to health-care workers, it appears that as long as good hygienic hand washing is practised, there is no increased risk even in paediatric wards (Dworsky et al, 1983).

Nursing care: good hand washing.

Epstein–Barr virus (EBV)

Diagnostic material: blood.

Identification: serologically: 'monospot' test or Paul Bunnell test with differential absorption; or by immunofluorescent antibody test.

Effects: a symptomless infection in the majority of people, it is more likely to cause disease in adults, as glandular fever (infectious mononucleosis). This is characterised by sore throat, lymphadenopathy, pyrexia, general malaise and extreme tiredness. Probably also causes *Burkitt lymphoma*, a malignant tumour seen in African children.

Spread: close/intimate contact, such as kissing.

Incubation period: 4–6 weeks.

Human herpesvirus 6 (HHV-6)

Diagnostic material: blood.

Identification: not yet routine, but serologically (immunofluorescence).

Effects: although knowledge of the structure and

relationship to other herpesviruses has increased considerably since first identification of this 'new' herpesvirus in 1986, less is known about its disease association. Possibly the only clinical manifestation is *roseola infantum*, when a child experiences sudden high fever for several days which is followed by a characteristic macular, rosy-pink rash. Most infections appear to be very mild, and many may be inapparent. Other possible disease links are under investigation (Briggs et al, 1990).

Spread: probably from mother to infant so that secondary cases in family or ward are unlikely.

ARTHROPOD-BORNE VIRUSES

Some viruses from several different families are spread by the bite of infected insects from one host to another and are known collectively as the 'arthropod-borne viruses'. They include the following.

1. *Flaviviridae*—mosquito-borne causing, for example, Yellow fever, Japanese B encephalitis, dengue and the tick-borne encephalitis viruses.
2. *Togaviridae*—equine encephalitis viruses are the most important.
3. *Bunyaviridae*—Californian encephalitis, Rift valley fever and others, causing severe haemorrhagic fevers.
4. *Reoviridae*—Colorado tick fever is the most important for humans.

Diagnostic material: blood.

Identification: serological (haemagglutination inhibition by antibody).

Effects: two major types of disease: *encephalitis*, a world-wide problem but in Britain only sheep ticks cause louping-ill in man; or *febrile disease* which may, or may not, be accompanied by a haemorrhagic rash.

Hosts: birds and mammals, only occasionally man.

Yellow fever

This is endemic to Central and South America and much of tropical Africa. It causes a febrile, 'flu-like' illness followed by haemorrhagic symptoms and, as the name implies, jaundice. Yellow fever vaccine is highly effective and is required by travellers to endemic areas.

Dengue fever

This is the most widely distributed arthropod-borne viral infection, causing a febrile illness with a rash and joint pains, but it is rarely fatal. A rarer form is dengue haemorrhagic fever which follows reinfection with dengue virus and causes high mortality in young people, and is an important cause of morbidity and mortality in children in South-East Asia.

Encephalitis caused by arthropod-borne viruses

This occurs world-wide causing fever, headache, neck stiffness, nausea and vomiting with possible convulsions, neurological complications and coma (see above). Epidemics are usually seasonal, mostly in summer and autumn (Timbury, 1986; Thomas, 1989).

Nursing care: is aimed at alleviation of symptoms and avoidance of vector access to the patient. Family and close contacts of patients developing yellow fever should be vaccinated if this has not already been done.

ZOONOSES

Rhabdoviruses

These are RNA viruses. They are bullet shaped, enveloped, helical, and 70–80 nm in size.

Diagnostic material: saliva, cerebrospinal fluid, urine.

Investigations: rapidly by immunofluorescence of tissues directly (brain, corneal or skin tissue). Serologically by detection of antibodies (immunofluorescence or complement fixation).

Rabies virus

This is transmitted from infected dogs, cats, bats, or carnivorous wild animals in the saliva, usually by biting, but infection can occur through mucous membranes contaminated by the saliva of an infected animal. Rabies occurs world-wide except in a few countries like the UK, Japan and Australia where it has been eradicated and island status helps this position to be maintained. The virus spreads from the wound to the central nervous system via nerve tissue and the disease is almost always fatal.

Effects: an illness which may develop from pain, malaise and fever to hydrophobia, hallucinations and ultimately paralysis, convulsions and death. Two cases of human-to-human transmission have occurred via corneal transplants.

Treatment/prevention: the long incubation period (usually 2–8 weeks but may be much longer) makes prophylactic active immunisation possible. A combination of human diploid cell vaccine (HDCV) (*active* immunisation) with heterologous antirabies serum or human antirabies immunoglobulin (*passive* immunisation) is usually given. Modern vaccines prepared from tissue-culture grown virus are potent and safe in contrast with the Semple vaccine, still used in the Far East and Africa, which may have severe neurological side-effects (DOH, 1990b; Benenson, 1990).

Nursing care: strict isolation will be needed for patients with proven or suspected rabies.

The WHO has been co-ordinating research into immunising wildlife against rabies and several European countries are having encouraging results in their antirabies campaigns (BMA, 1989).

Arenaviruses

These are RNA viruses. They are enveloped, helical, and 50–300 nm in size.

Diagnostic material: blood, throat swabs, cerebrospinal fluid.

Reservoir: mice or rats.

Effects: important diseases include Lassa fever, lymphocytic choriomeningitis, and South American haemorrhagic fevers.

Lassa fever

This is an acute haemorrhagic virus disease with a high mortality. Cases of mild febrile disease are also seen in endemic areas. It was first recognised in West Africa in 1969 and has also occurred in some parts of central Africa. In endemic areas the virus is transmitted to man by contact with the urine or saliva of an infected rat (*Mastomys natalensis*). Person-to-person transmission can occur by direct contact with the blood, pharyngeal secretions or urine of an infected patient.

Treatment: Immune plasma has been used in treatment as has the antiviral agent *Ribavirin*.

Nursing care: patients are nursed in strict isolation in special units (see Marburg and Ebola viruses, below).*

* Recent evidence from the USA suggests that precautions taken with blood and body fluids should prevent spread. DHSS (1986) advice is still followed in UK to date.

Lymphocytic choriomeningitis

This rarely causes viral meningitis in man, being transmitted from infected mouse excreta in dust inhaled by humans. It may present as a mild systemic (usually unrecognised) illness or a severe fatal systemic disease or severe encephalomyelitis.

Argentinian and Bolivian haemorrhagic fevers (Junin and Machupo)

These are severe illnesses with renal and cardiovascular complications in addition to haemorrhage, again acquired from infected mouse excreta.

Filoviruses (Marburg and Ebola viruses)

These are RNA viruses. They are rod shaped, variable in length, and 80 nm in diameter.

Diagnostic material: blood.

Identification: isolation of virus in laboratory animals (guinea-pigs) or tissue culture.

Reservoir: uncertain, but a recent report from the USA (Jahrling et al, 1990) suggests the cynomolgus (Macaque) monkey may be a natural reservoir.

Marburg virus disease was first seen in 1967 when seven laboratory workers died after handling African vervet monkeys, and there have been occasional cases reported since. *Ebola* caused severe outbreaks in Zaire and the Sudan in 1976.

These viruses cause severe illnesses with characteristic rash and headache progressing to diarrhoea, vomiting, haemorrhage and renal complications. Case fatality rate is high.

Person-to-person transmission can occur via infected blood, semen, secretions and, possibly, the respiratory route.

Nursing care: patients in the UK are nursed in three designated high-security infectious-disease units (London, Liverpool and Glasgow), with strict isolation techniques and total containment facilities. (Further information can be found in DHSS (1986), DOH (1989), Vella (1977).)

OTHER VIRUSES

Poxviruses

These are DNA viruses. They are enveloped, brick shaped, complex in structure, and 200–300 nm in size.

Diagnostic material: vesicle fluid, crusts, scrapings from maculopapules.

This virus group includes: variola (now extinct), vaccinia, monkeypox, orf and molluscum contagiosum.

Variola

Variola, which causes smallpox, is one of the most dreaded of all infectious diseases. After a world-wide eradication campaign by the WHO, the disease was declared extinct in 1980. The virus is now stored in only two laboratories in the world, one in Atlanta, USA, and one in Moscow.

Vaccinia

Strains of the virus are passaged in animals for use in human vaccination (now only recommended for a few specific workers at 'identifiable risk') (DOH, 1990a).

Monkeypox

This produces a disease not unlike smallpox in monkeys which is very occasionally transmitted to humans. It is not thought to spread between humans.

Orf

This causes contagious pustular dermatitis in workers in contact with infected sheep. A single lesion usually occurs on the fingers or hands, sometimes with fever and local lymphadenopathy. There is now an effective vaccine to prevent orf in sheep (Shanson, 1989).

Mollusucum contagiosum

This is a not uncommon, mild, localised infection in children especially, causing papules in the epidermal skin layer, especially on the trunk or axilla. It is spread by scratching and close contact and resolves spontaneously. There is increasing evidence of sexual transmission (Baxby, 1990).

Papovaviruses

These are DNA viruses. They are naked, icosahedral, and 45–55 nm in size.

This virus group comprises papilloma, polyoma and vacuolating viruses; apart from the human wart virus they are mainly animal viruses, but those affecting humans are described briefly below.

Human warts

Human plantar and genital warts are caused by human papillomavirus (HPV). It appears that some types of HPV (16 and 18) are connected with development of cervical cancer, 6 and 11 with laryngeal papillomas, and others with rare skin cancers (WHO, 1987). (See Figure 9.8.)

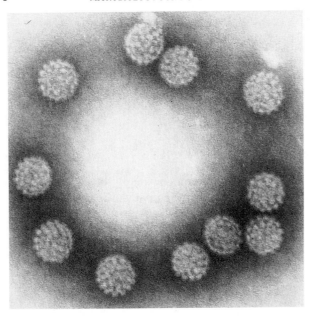

Figure 9.8 Wart virus particles (× 150 000) from a plantar wart.

JC virus

This is a human polyoma virus which causes the slow virus disease progressive multifocal leucoencephalopathy in patients with immunosuppressive diseases or treatments.

BK virus

This is another human polyma virus which appears to reactivate in immunodeficient patients.

Parvoviruses

These are DNA viruses. They are naked, icosahedral, single stranded, and 20 nm in size (parvo = small).

Diagnostic material: blood.

Identification: serologically for IgM. Detection of virus by DNA hybridisation techniques or countercurrent immunoelectrophoresis.

Effects: *erythema infectiosum* ('slapped cheek syndrome' or 'fifth disease') is caused by one parvovirus (B19). It consists of a febrile illness lasting 2 or 3 days, followed about a week later by a typical maculopapular facial rash in children especially. Arthralgia can occur, usually in adults, ranging from a very mild involvement to full arthritis.

More recently it has been observed that serious complications of B19 infection may occur (Anderson, 1990). Infection in pregnant women may lead to fetal death. Individuals suffering from chronic haemolytic anaemia may suffer transient aplastic crisis (TAP); these patients usually require hospitalisation and transfusion, but only a few individuals are likely to be this severely affected, notably those with sickle-cell anaemia.

Nursing care: The virus is spread by the respiratory route, but isolation of these patients is not necessary as they are no longer infectious by the time the rash has appeared. However, patients with transient aplastic crisis, or immunodeficient patients with chronic B19 infection should be cared for in single rooms as there is a potential for nosocomial transmission.

Unconventional virus-like agents

There is a group of diseases with unknown but lengthy incubation periods, which have progressive central nervous system involvement and are often ultimately fatal.

They may be subdivided into those due to common viruses, and those due to as yet undetermined agents.

Common virus origin

1. *Measles*—can rarely lead to *subacute sclerosing panencephalitis* (SSPE) (see measles, p. 247).
2. *Rubella*—after congenital infection, SSPE can sometimes develop.
3. *JC virus*—involved in *progressive multifocal leucoencephalopathy* (PML) (see papovaviruses, p. 276).

Diseases characterised by spongiform encephalopathy, which are probably caused by unconventional virus-like agents

1. *Kuru*—a fatal disease confined to New Guinea, which is disappearing now that ritual cannibalism has ceased.
2. *Creutzfeld–Jakob disease* (CJD)—a rare disease involving progressive dementia and ataxia, and usually fatal within a year of onset of symptoms. Human transmission has been reported from a corneal transplant (Duffy 1974), neurosurgical electrodes (Benoulli 1977) and human growth hormone.
3. *Scrapie*—a neurological disease affecting sheep for over 200 years in Britain, with many other countries also affected. Symptoms are very similar to CJD and both show spongiform degeneration of the brain, but there is no evidence that scrapie is transmitted to humans. Other animals have similar infections, including mink.
4. *Bovine spongiform encephalopathy*—the latest disease in this group to be identified in Britain in cattle, with symptoms very similar to CJD and scrapie.

Although CJD is neither a communicable nor a contagious disease, transmission in humans is well documented under certain circumstances (see above) and extreme care to avoid injury or implantation with blood or body fluids (especially cerebrospinal fluid) and brain tissue, directly or via contaminated instruments, is imperative. The agent for CJD is particularly resistant to disinfection and sterilisation procedures and the Department of Health and Social Security has issued special advice following advice from the Medical Advisory Committee (DHSS, 1984).

REFERENCES

Advisory Committee on Dangerous Pathogens (1990) *HIV—The Causative Agent of AIDS and Related Conditions*, 2nd edn. London: HMSO.

Anderson MJ (1990) Human parvoviruses. In *Principles and Practice of Clinical Virology* (eds Zuckerman AJ *et al*), 2nd edn. Chichester: Wiley.

Baxby D (1990) Poxviruses. In *Principles and Practice of Clinical Virology* (eds Zuckerman *et al*) 2nd edn. Chichester: Wiley.

Beale AJ (1990) Polio vaccines, time for a change in immunisation policy (Review). *Lancet* 225: 839–842.

Benoulli C, Siegfried J, Baumgartner G, *et al* (1977) Danger of accidental patient-to-patient transmission of Creutzfeldt–Jakob disease by surgery. *Lancet* i: 478–479.

Benenson AS (1990) *Control of Communicable Diseases in Man*, 15th edn. Washington: American Public Health Association.

Bingham E (1987) Subacute sclerosing panencephalitis. *Nursing Times* 83(35): 45–47.

BMA (British Medical Association) (1989) *Infection Control*. London: Edward Arnold.

Briggs EM, Fox JD and Tedder RS (1990) Human herpesvirus 6. In *Principles and Practice of Clinical Virology* (eds Zuckerman AJ *et al*), 2nd edn. Chichester: Wiley.

Choo QL, Weiner AJ, Overby LR, Kuo G, Houghton M and Bradley DW (1990) Hepatitis C virus: the major causative agent of viral non-A non-B hepatitis. *Br. Med. Bull.* 46(2): 423–441.

Chrystie IL, Totterdel B, Baker MJ *et al* (1975) Rotavirus infections in a maternity unit. *Lancet* ii: 79.

DHSS (1984) Management of patients with spongiform encephalopathy (Creutzfeld–Jakob disease (CJD)). *DHSS Circular* DA (84) 16.

DHSS (Department of Health and Social Security) (1986) *Memorandum on the Control of Viral Haemorrhagic Fevers*. London: HMSO.

DOH (Department of Health) (1989) *Letter EL (89) P/133*. London: HMSO.

DOH (Department of Health, Welsh Office and Scottish Home and Health Department (1990a) *Immunisation against Infectious Disease*. London: HMSO.

DOH (Department of Health, UK Health Departments) (1990b) *Guidance for Clinical Health Care Workers: Protection Against Infection with HIV and Hepatitis Viruses*. London: HMSO.

Dowsett EG (1988) Human enteroviral infections. *J. Hosp. Infect.* **11**: 103–115.

Duffy P, Wolf, J, Collins G, DeVoe AG, *et al* (1974) Possible person-to-person transmission of Creutzfeldt–Jakob disease (letter). *N. Engl. J. Med.* **290**: 692.

Dworsky ME, Welch K, Cassady G and Stagno S (1983) Occupational risk for primary cytomegalovirus infection among pediatric health-care workers. *N. Engl. J. Med.* **309**(16): 950–953.

Frosner GG (1988) Hepatitis delta virus. *J. Hosp. Inf.* **11**(Suppl. A): 161–165.

Glynn Owen O (1989) Hidden hazard. *Nursing Times* **85**(16): 16–17.

Hart S (1990) Guidelines for infection control. *N. Standard* **4**(45): 24–27.

Health and Safety Commission (1988) *Control of Substances Hazardous to Health Regulations*. London: HMSO.

Isaacs D, Wilkinson AR, Eglin R, Dobson SRM, Hope PL and Moxon ER (1989) Conservative management of an echovirus 11 outbreak in a neonatal unit. *Lancet* **ii**: 543–545.

Jahrling PB, Geisbert T, Dalgard D, *et al* (1990) Preliminary report: isolation of Ebola virus from monkeys imported to USA. *Lancet* **335**: 502–505.

Jawetz E, Brooks GF, Melnick JL, Butel JS, Adelberg EA and Nicholas Ornston L (1989) *Medical Microbiology*, 18th edn. Connecticut: Appleton and Lange.

Leclair JM, Zaia JA, Levin MJ, Congdon RG, Goldmann DA (1980) Airborne transmission of chickenpox in a hospital. *N. Engl. J. Med.* **302**(8): 450–453.

Lever AML (1988) Non A/non B hepatitis. *J. Hosp. Inf.* **11** (Suppl. A): 150–160.

O'Mahony MC, Gooch CD, Smyth DA, Thrussell AJ, Bartlett CLR and Noah ND (1983) Epidemic hepatitis A from cockles. *Lancet* **i**: 518–520.

Reid TMS and Robinson HG (1987) Frozen raspberries and hepatitis A. *Epidem. Inf.* **98**: 109–112.

Reilly H (1990) High risk groups are not getting their flu vaccine. *General Practitioner* **28 Sep.**: 26.

Shanson DC (1989) *Microbiology in Clinical Practice*, 2nd edn. London: Wright.

Straube RC, Thompson MA, Van Dyke RB, *et al* (1983) Adenovirus type 7b in a childrens hospital. *J. Inf. Dis.* **147**(5): 814–819.

Thomas CGA (1989) *Medical Microbiology*, 6th edn. London: Baillière Tindall.

Timbury MC (1986) *Notes on Medical Virology*, 8th edn. London: Churchill Livingstone.

Valenti WM and Wehrle PF (1986), in *Hospital Infections* (eds Bennett JV and Brachman PS), 2nd edn. Boston, MA: Little, Brown and Co.

Vella EE (1977) Marburg disease. *Nursing Times* **27 Jan.**: 120–122.

WHO (1987) Genital human papillomavirus infections and cancer. Memorandum from a WHO meeting. *Bull. WHO* **65**: 817.

Zuckerman AJ (1990) Hepatitis E virus. *Br. Med. J.* **300**: 1475–1476.

FURTHER READING

Bowell E (1986) Nursing the isolated patient: Lassa fever. *Nursing Times, J. Inf. Control Nursing* **33**: 72, 74, 79, 81.

Sadler C (1988) Hepatitis—an occupational hazard? *Nursing Times* **84**(24): 19.

Symington I (1987) Hepatitis B—an avoidable hazard. *Nursing Times* **14 Jan.**: 50–51.

Weber DJ and Rutala WA (1989) Hepatitis B immunisation update. *Inf. Control Hosp. Epidemiol.* **10**(12): 541–546.

Wright SG (1978) Rare virus infections from the tropics. *Nursing Times* **12 Jan.**: 74–76.

Zuckerman AJ, Banatvala JE and Pattison JR (1990) *Principles and Practice of Clinical Virology*, 2nd edn. Chichester: Wiley.

10 A guide to fungi, protozoa, helminths and ectoparasites

FUNGI

The frequency of fungal infections in hospitalised patients, although not extensively documented, has increased considerably over the last 20 years. Systemic fungal infection is now associated with almost as many deaths as bacterial infection in leukaemic patients (Bodey, 1988). This is because it has proved possible to immunosuppress patients further and to treat effectively the bacterial infections they subsequently acquire. Fungi are also seen in other immunocompromised patients, the most notable group being patients with HIV who may develop infections with *Candida*, *Cryptococcus*, *Histoplasma* or *Tinea* spp.

Infections with *Candida* spp. are also increasingly seen in patients with in-dwelling vascular devices who are treated with broad-spectrum antibiotics. These are organisms which the nurse needs to know about in order to care for highly susceptible patients.

Fungi may be divided into four groups (see Chapter 2) and the diseases which they cause may be further subdivided into those causing *superficial* or *deep/systemic* infections (see Table 10.1).

Table 10.1 Fungal infections.

Fungus type	Superficial	Deep
Yeast/yeast-like	*Candida*	*Candida*
		Cryptococcus
Filamentous	Dermatophytes *(tinea)*	*Aspergillus*
		*Mucor**
	Aspergillus	*Rhizopus**
Dimorphic		*Histoplasma*
		Blastomyces
		Coccidioides
		Paracoccidioides
		Sporothrix

* Zygomycetes.

Yeasts and yeast-like fungi

Cryptococcus

Presence: found in soil, especially in bird droppings.

Pathogenicity: *Cryptococcus neoformans* is the only pathogenic species. Inhalation leads to lung colonisation or infection which may lead to meningitis. It is an exceedingly rare cause of infection in healthy people but quite common in people with AIDS. It has also been associated with outbreaks of infection in renal transplant patients (Brooks and Remington, 1986).

Spread: by inhalation of contaminated dust.

Treatment: amphotericin plus 5-fluorocytosine, or fluconazole.

Nursing care: the patients with central nervous system (CNS) involvement will require skilled care, in addition to drug treatment, to alleviate the symptoms of meningeal infection such as severe headache and photophobia.

Candida

Candida albicans is the cause of most *Candida* infections.

Presence: normal flora of mucous membranes of the mouth, intestinal tract and vagina.

Pathogenicity: it may cause local infection (mucosites) or, less frequently, widespread systemic infection usually seen in immunosuppressed individuals; mucosites may also be seen in those with diabetes, general debility, those receiving long-term broad-spectrum antibiotics, or those with in-dwelling devices such as urinary catheters. Pregnancy is also a predisposing factor for overgrowth of *Candida*.

Superficial infections—'thrush': infections of mouth and vagina, may pass from mother to baby and be a potential source of cross-infection, e.g. in maternity units. In patients with AIDS, oral candidiasis may extend to include the oesophagus and even the stomach; it may occur at any stage of the gastrointestinal tract.

Candida may also affect skin, especially moist areas, and also nail beds.

Severe mucocutaneous infections occur in T-cell deficient children.

Deep infections—these occur more rarely and mainly affect the lungs, but may also affect the heart, kidneys and meninges. A particular predisposing feature is jejunal or duodenal surgery.

Treatment: Topical—nystatin or amphotericin, and miconazole and other azoles; systemic—amphotericin B with flucytosine, and ketoconazole (hepatotoxic) or fluconazole.

Nursing care: good hygienic practice (maternity units

especially); care with oral hygiene for all patients and good handwashing (see Burnie et al (1985) and Burnie (1986) describing an intensive-therapy-unit outbreak). Patients with AIDS or leukaemia will require frequent, careful and gentle maintenance of oral hygiene.

Filamentous fungi

Dermatophytes (ringworm or tinea *fungi)*

Presence: soil and/or animals acting as a source of infection.

Pathogenicity: these infect the skin, nail or hair, but rarely invade tissue. Three genera cause infection: *Microsporum* (hair and skin, e.g. *T. capitis* which gives scalp ringworm); *Trichophyton* (skin, hair and nails, e.g. *T. pedis* or 'athlete's foot'); and *Epidermophyton* (skin and nails, e.g. *T. cruris* affecting groin and perineum).

Treatment: topical imidazole for mild infections; griseo-fulvin (for a prolonged period) for severe infections. Oral itraconazole is a new alternative to griseofulvin and may be less toxic.

Aspergillus

Presence: in soil and dust everywhere.

Pathogenicity: the main pathogen is *A. fumigatus* but *A. niger* and *A. flavus* also cause infection. The following types can occur.

1. Pulmonary aspergillosis in response to inhalation of spores as:
    (a) an *aspergilloma* where it grows as a fungal ball in an existing old tuberculous cavity,
    (b) an allergic form where the spores create a hypersensitivity reaction, and

    (c) *invasive aspergillosis* where lung infection may spread to other organs. This usually occurs in severely immunocompromised individuals; bone marrow and renal transplant patients are particularly susceptible. Recent infections in susceptible medical patients have been attributed to local building work (Hopkins et al, 1989; Dewhurst et al, 1990).

2. *Superficial* infections have been seen in ears, burns and surgical wounds.

Zygomycetes

Presence: soil, spores in air and dust.

Pathogenicity: two species cause infection (*Mucor* and *Rhizopus*) causing invasive *zygomycosis* in lungs, sinuses and brain. Immunocompromised patients, diabetics and those on long-term antibiotic therapy have been affected. Infection may be fatal but has responded to amphotericin B combined with surgical excision (Thomas, 1988).

Dimorphic fungi

These grow as yeasts or filaments, and cause systemic infections.

Presence: soil, with some being specific to certain geographic regions.

Pathogenicity: entrance is via the respiratory tract, mostly causing initial pulmonary disease followed by generalised infection or localised granulomatous lesions. The major dimorphic fungi are described below.

Histoplasma capsulatum

Causes *histoplasmosis* (Tropics), from inhalation of spores, causing initial pulmonary disease which may resolve, but in immunocompromised, old or very young patients may cause severe pneumonia and disseminated infection. This is most often seen in the USA, and infection may reactivate years after an individual leaves the endemic area.

Treatment: amphotericin B.

Blastomyces dermatitidis

Causes *blastomycosis*, which may cause pulmonary or generalised granuloma including skin lesions. It appears to be acquired by inhalation, and is found in dogs and other animals also, especially in the USA, Canada, Central America and Africa.

Coccidioides immitis

Causes *coccidioidomycosis* which is acquired through spore inhalation and usually produces a mild 'flu-like' illness, sometimes with hypersensitivity reaction shortly afterwards. A few may develop the disseminated disease which has a high fatality rate. Found particularly in focal areas in south-west USA and Latin America.

Paracoccidioides brasiliensis

Causes *paracoccidioidomycosis* which is also acquired by inhalation and produces lung lesions followed by others, frequently involving nose, mouth and local lymph nodes. Mainly in South America.

Sporothrix schenki

Causes *sporotrichosis*, found rarely but world-wide, and differs from the others in that it results from implantation of the fungus into the skin through cuts or injury. Causes a local lesion with some spread via lymphatics.

Nursing care: person-to-person spread does not occur in these infections.

PROTOZOA

These unicellular members of the animal kingdom cause widespread disease in tropical areas especially, but some are seen in the UK, mainly in returning travellers. As with some fungal infections, an increase in some protozoal infections has occurred recently in the susceptible group of immunocompromised people such as those with AIDS, e.g. increased recognition of pneumonia due to *Pneumocystis carinii* infection.

Some protozoa are true parasites in that they require living hosts; some may exist in cyst form outside the host body for some time (e.g. *Entamoeba histolytica* causing *amoebic dysentery*), while others have a complex cycle requiring man and arthropod (e.g. *Plasmodia* spp. using mosquito and man for the successive stages of its life cycle).

Some of the major protozoal infections are described briefly. Because foreign travel is so much easier than it used to be, some protozoal infections may appear anywhere and at any time. It is necessary to be aware of this possibility. Every year patients die of malaria in Britain because doctors fail to think of this possible diagnosis.

Plasmodium

Causes probably the best-known protozoal infection, *malaria*. Although this is basically a disease of tropical countries, where it is a major cause of death in children especially, many patients do arrive in Britain with, or subsequently develop, malaria. Four species are pathogenic to man:

1. *P. falciparum*—causes malignant tertian (fever every second day) malaria;
2. *P. vivax*—the most widespread, benign tertian form;
3. *P. ovale*—less common cause of benign tertian form; and
4. *P. malariae*—quartan (fever every third day) malaria.

All four species have life cycles involving man and the *anophelene* mosquito, with an asexual cycle in man and a sexual one in the mosquito. The mosquito introduces the parasite into man by biting and sporozoites are injected with saliva, enter the bloodstream to reach the liver and reproduce. Development continues through several stages including growth in red blood cells. Gametes are eventually acquired by another *female* mosquito sucking the blood of the infected human. Male and female forms unite in this mosquito stomach and replicate in the lining of the stomach to produce sporozoites. These eventually reach the salivary glands from where they can infect a new victim (for further details see Thomas, 1988; Jawetz et al, 1989; Shanson 1989).

The disease is characterized by shaking fevers (rigors) and headaches which occur in cycles a few days apart— the interval depending on the agent involved—and may involve relapses over many years. *P. falciparum* malaria requires urgent diagnosis and treatment because it may result in severe CNS complications, coma and death. Deaths have occurred in Britain due to delay in recognition of the possible cause of symptoms. Infection is not transmitted from person to person except by contaminated blood products and congenitally.

The World Health Organization (WHO) malaria eradication campaign broke down under a combination of pressures including the development of insect resistance to DDT (an insecticide used to reduce the number of mosquitoes) and parasite resistance to antimalarial drugs. It is necessary to check before travelling to any affected area in order to have up-to-date advice on appropriate chemoprophylaxis.

The protozoa described below cause infections acquired in Britain.

Giardia intestinalis (lamblia)

Causes *giardiasis* which is a common cause of diarrhoea world-wide and is usually acquired through ingestion of cysts (which have matured from the active *trophozoite* form) in contaminated water or food (see Figure 10.1). Cysts may be transmitted by hands or on fomites so good hygiene and careful disposal of faeces is needed. It is not uncommon in Britain, although it is usually acquired abroad (see Tomkins, 1977).

Treatment: metronidazole.

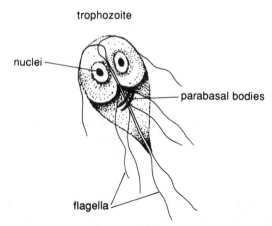

Figure 10.1 *Giardia intestinalis (lamblia)* trophozoite.

Trichomonas vaginalis

Causes *trichomoniasis* as vaginitis in women, characterised by intense irritation and a yellowish discharge. Men are infected asymptomatically and the infection is usually sexually transmitted. It can also be transmitted from mother to baby and via contaminated equipment, so scrupulous hygiene is needed.

Treatment: metronidazole.

Entamoeba

Entamoeba histolytica is the cause of *amoebic dysentery*, a widespread cause of intestinal infection in the tropics. It exists in two forms: a motile trophozoite, and a non-motile cyst which is the form that transmits infection (see Figure 10.2). Disease ranges from asymptomatic or very mild, to an acute dysentery, involving frequent stools full of blood and mucus. Rarely, this may progress to an ulcerative colitis-type infection with possible peritonitis and death, particularly if steroids are used. Chronic abscess formation may also occur, usually in the liver. Man is the reservoir and infection is acquired through contaminated food or water.

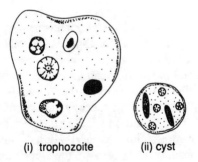

(i) trophozoite   (ii) cyst

Figure 10.2   *Entamoeba histolytica.*

Toxoplasma

The definitive host of *T. gondii* is the cat. *Toxoplasmosis* is a disease of many mammals. The organism is transmitted to humans by ingestion of cat faeces, or undercooked meat (pork or mutton, rarely beef) containing cysts. It exists world-wide. Most primary infections are asymptomatic or run a mild, febrile course with lymphadenopathy. Latent infection is reactivated in immunocompromised patients (e.g. those with AIDS), causing large brain lesions or retinitis. Congenital infection occurs when a non-immune mother has a primary infection during pregnancy (PHLS, 1989; Turnbull, 1989). Infection in early pregnancy may cause abortion. Later in pregnancy, disease is more likely to occur and a variety of effects including microcephaly, hydrocephalus and meningoencephalitis, jaundice and hepatosplenomegaly may be seen at birth. Signs of mental deficiency or choroidoretinitis may develop as late effects of intrauterine infection. Patients with HIV showing signs of focal disturbance may have a cerebral abscess caused by *T. gondii*.

Cryptosporidia

These cause *cryptosporidiosis* which is usually a mild self-limiting acute diarrhoea in children. Severe, persistent diarrhoea occurs in the immunocompromised (mainly AIDS patients) in whom it can be life threatening. Found in many rodents, cattle and other animals, it may be acquired by humans from faecally contaminated food or water. It is recognized more often now as a cause of diarrhoea in both children and adults, but the overt effects are usually restricted to the very young or old, and patients with HIV.

Babesia

Babesia are protozoa which, like malaria, affect the red cells of a variety of animals and rarely cause human infection from ticks. Only patients who have had splenectomies develop infection and they may develop fatal haemolytic anaemia.

Pneumocystis carinii

The cause of a form of severe *pneumonia* (*Pneumocystis carinii pneumonia*) (PCP) seen increasingly in patients with AIDS, although asymptomatic colonisation is common. The route of infection is uncertain, but is probably inhalation of cysts from water. *P. carinii* pneumonia used to be the cause of more than 50% of deaths in AIDS patients in the USA (Jawetz et al, 1989). Recent treatment has improved survival from this infection. Other immunocompromised individuals may also be affected. Infection in these cases may be reactivation of latent infection or be newly acquired (Benenson, 1990).

The following protozoa, although rarely seen in patients in Britain, are a serious cause of disease in many areas.

Leishmania

There are several pathogenic species of Leishmania all with animal reservoirs and transmitted by sandflies.

L. donovani causes *visceral leishmaniasis* (kala-azar) in India, Africa, Asia, the Middle East and South America. The organism multiplies in the reticuloendothelial cells, especially in the liver and spleen, and can be fatal.

L. tropica (Middle East) and *L. braziliensis* (South America) cause *cutaneous leishmaniasis* ('Delhi boil', etc.) and *mucocutaneous* or *nasopharyngeal leishmaniasis*, which is a slow but extensive granulomatous form of the disease.

Trypanosoma

Two main types of disease are caused by these protozoa.

T. rhodesiense and *T. gambiense* in central and eastern Africa, spread by a tsetse fly and causing *sleeping sickness*. Febrile illness follows the initial lesion which progresses to CNS involvement and is generally fatal.

T. cruzi occurs in central and South America causing *Chaga's disease*. The organism is spread by a large bug (not by a bite, but through the faeces being scratched into broken skin or conjunctivae). It causes an initial febrile illness, but may go on to chronic infection involving the autonomic nerve supply to heart or gut.

HELMINTHS

Illness caused by multicellular parasitic animals (helminths or 'worms') is not a major problem in the UK, but is a major cause of morbidity in many tropical and subtropical countries. *Ascaris lumbricoides*, one of the three helminths which are commonly seen in the UK, affects over 1 billion people world-wide; hookworms (see Table 10.2) affect 600–800 million; and hundreds of millions are affected by pinworms and filarial worms (Jawetz et al, 1989). Table 10.2 lists some of the major helminths affecting man, and shows their geographical location, the intermediate hosts (where applicable), the site where they are found in man, and their mode of transmission. There are many more helminths than those listed.

There are three classes of helminths, comprising the *nematodes* (or roundworms), the *cestodes* (or tapeworms) and the *trematodes* (or flukes) (the last two classes being flatworms).

Nematodes (roundworms)

Nematodes are a highly efficient group of unsegmented parasites which invade almost all animal and insect species and are free living at some stage in soil and water also. They may infect humans via food, water or soil contamination, and may infect at a variety of different developmental stages. For example, *Ascaris lumbricoides* infestation occurs by ingestion of eggs from contaminated soil where they can survive for long periods. *Enterobius vermicularis* (pinworms/threadworms) are passed from human to human in a very direct and short cycle as the female lays eggs on the perianal skin and the infected person will scratch and then pass on the eggs via hands, food or clothing to infect others. Others are only passed on by the larval form in cysts, such as *Trichinella spiralis* which is acquired by eating undercooked pork with encysted forms in the muscle tissue. Yet others are transmitted by an intermediate host, e.g. *Wuchereria bancrofti* which is transmitted by mosquitoes. Hookworms which live in the small intestine are transmitted by a series of stages. The ova are passed in faeces, developing into larvae which infect man through the skin (walking on contaminated soil), passing to the lungs and finally back to the small intestine to mature.

Ascaris lumbricoides (common roundworms)

The life cycle has already been described above and further details are given in Table 10.2. This very common infestation can cause clinical problems if heavy numbers in the larval stage affect the lungs, or large numbers of adult worms cause intestinal obstruction.

Table 10.2 Some major helminth infections.

Parasite	Disease	Site in host	Intermediate	Means of transmission	Location
Nematodes (roundworms)					
Ascaris lumbricoides	Ascariasis	Small intestine; via bloodstream to lungs and back to small intestine	—	Ingestion of faecally contaminated soil or food	World-wide
Toxocara canis	Toxocariasis	Larva can migrate to eye, brain, liver, lung (blindness possible)	Dogs	Ingestion of faecally contaminated soil	World-wide
Toxocara cati	Toxocariasis	As above	Cats	As above (rare)	World-wide
Enterobius vermicularis	Enterobiasis (pinworms/threadworms)	Large bowel	—	Faecal-oral via hands or clothing to food, (ingestion)	World-wide

Organism	Disease	Site in body	Development	Transmission	Distribution
Strongyloides stercoralis	Strongyloidiasis (threadworms)	Small intestine; larval forms excreted and reacquired through skin/lungs	Develop in soil	Through skin or autoreinfection	World-wide, especially the Tropics
Trichinella spiralis	Trichinosis	Striated muscle	Rats → pigs	Undercooked/raw pork	World-wide
Hookworms *Ancylostoma duodenale*	Hookworms	Small intestine; larvae to lungs & small intestine	Moist surroundings	Through skin or ingestion of contaminated water	Temperate areas
Necator americanus	Hookworms	As above	Moist surroundings	Through skin from contaminated soil	Tropics and North America
Filarial worms *Wuchereria bancrofti* and others	Filariasis (elephantiasis)	Lymphatic system; larval forms in blood	Mosquitoes	Inoculation by mosquito bite	Tropics (widely)
Onchocerca volvulus	Onchocerciasis (river blindness)	Subcut. nodules;	Black flies (*Simulium*)	Inoculation by fly bite	Sub-Saharan Africa, C. & S. America

Table 10.2 Continued.

Parasite	Disease	Site in host	Intermediate	Means of transmission	Location
Cestodes (tapeworms)					
Taenia saginata	Tapeworm	Small intestine	Cattle	Ingestion of raw/undercooked beef	World-wide
Taenia solium	Cysticercosis	Small intestine	Pigs	Ingestion of raw/undercooked pork	World-wide (rare in UK)
Echinococcus granulosus	Hydatid disease	Cysts: liver mainly, also lungs, spleen, long bones, etc.	Dogs via infected sheep	Ingestion of faecally contaminated material	Sheep-rearing areas, e.g. Australasia, Argentina

Hymenolepsis nana	Dwarf tapeworm	Small intestine	Man (insects)	Faecal–oral (direct), inoculation (indirect)	World-wide, especially India and southern USA
Diphyllobothrium latum	Broad fish tapeworm	Small intestine	Freshwater fish	Ingestion of uncooked fish	Scandinavia, Iceland, parts of North and South America, Japan, USSR
Trematodes (flukes) Blood					
Schistosoma haematobium	Schistosomiasis/ bilharzia	Bladder, liver, rectum in blood vessels	Freshwater snails	Through skin/mucous membranes in infected water (bathing)	Africa and Middle East
S. mansoni		Liver, colon, rectum in blood vessels	Freshwater snails	As above	Egypt and other parts Africa and tropics

Table 10.2 Continued.

Parasite	Disease	Site in host	Intermediate	Means of transmission	Location
S. japonicum		Liver and small intestine (blood vessels)	As above	As above	Far East
Lung					
Paragonimus westermani	Paragonimiasis	Lung, brain (intestines rarer)	Freshwater snails → crustacea	Ingestion of crustacea	Far East
Liver					
Clonorchis sinensis	Clonorchiasis	Liver in the bile ducts	Freshwater snails → crustacea	Ingestion of crustacea	Far East
Fasciola hepatica (sheep liver fluke)	Fascioliasis	As above	Freshwater snails → vegetation	Ingestion of contaminated vegetables/ vegetation	Sheep-rearing areas (occasionally UK)
Intestine					
Fasciolopsis buski (giant intestinal fluke)	Fasciolopsiasis	Small intestine, liver	As above	Ingestion of contaminated vegetables, e.g. water chestnut	Far East

N.B. There are many more helminths which occasionally cause illness, but the above are examples of those causing numerically important morbidity.

Toxocara canis (and *T. cati*)

Human infection occurs through ingestion of the eggs of *T. canis* or, more rarely, *T. catis*, from faecal contamination from playing with soil or, more rarely, contact with the fur or licking from an infected animal. (Cats cover their faeces so infection is less likely, although sandpits are an invitation to cats and should be kept covered when not in use). The worms do not mature in humans but the larval forms can cause major problems as they enter the bloodstream and can migrate to various organs causing allergic response and, rarely but more seriously, can lead to blindness due to retinal infection. There are about 300 new cases of toxocariasis recognised annually in the UK (Wright, 1990).

Enterobius vermicularis

This small pinworm or threadworm (1 cm long) whose life cycle has already been described, causes severe irritation and continuous reinfection and is a common problem (see Figure 10.3). This infestation can be diagnosed by placing cellophane tape on the patient's anal skin on waking, and the eggs may be seen when the slide with tape attached is examined under a microscope. It is probably the most common helminth infestation seen in the UK, and a cause of great anxiety and distress. The 5–12 years age group (and their parents) in particular are affected (Willis, 1990). Treatment with mebendazole or piperazine is effective if coupled with simple hygiene precautions and treatment of the whole family.

Cestodes (tapeworms)

Cestodes are flatworms which are in segments and can vary in length (at maturity) from the three-segmented

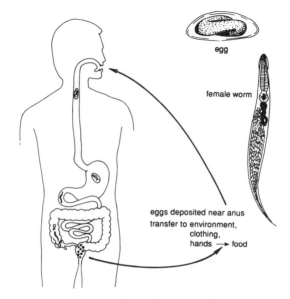

Figure 10.3 Life cycle of *Enterobius vermicularis*.

Echinococcus granulosus causing hydatid disease (only
3–6 mm long) and the dwarf tapeworm *Hymenolepsis
nana* (2–4 cm long) to the giant *Taenia saginata* and
Diphyllobothrium latum which can grow to several metres.
Each segment contains male and female reproductive
systems, so there is a vast capacity to reproduce. Unlike
nematodes, they have no digestive system.

Most tapeworms of man use an intermediate host, with
man as the definitive host, with two exceptions, *H. nana*
can be transmitted from one human to another by
the eggs without the development of larval stages in
intermediate hosts (*direct*), but also has an *indirect*
form using insects. The dog is the definitive host for

E. granulosus (causing hydatid disease), with man as the intermediate host.

Taenia saginatum (beef tapeworm)

Man acquires infection from raw or undercooked beef containing the larval form of the tapeworm. The cattle acquire the organism from eating grass contaminated with human faeces containing the eggs. *T. saginatum* rarely causes clinical illness beyond loss of appetite and vague abdominal discomfort, but the patient may well be horrified to see motile segments passed in the faeces and will be anxious to know that treatment (niclosamide) has been effective.

Taenia solium (pork tapeworm)

This tapeworm can lead to more serious infection than *T. saginata* since ingestion of the larvae from undercooked pork can lead to invasion and encysted forms of infection in muscle and brain causing *cysticercosis*. (This does not occur in man from the beef tapeworm.) The CNS may be affected including the brain and can lead to epilepsy, coma and eventual death. Only eight cases of cerebral cysticercosis have been recorded in the UK since 1981 (PHLS, 1990). Pigs may acquire the organism in uncooked swill.

Diphyllobothrium latum (fish tapeworm)

This worm needs two intermediate hosts to develop (see Table 10.2). It rarely causes clinical disease but may lead to pernicious anaemia as it has a tendency to consume vitamin B_{12}.

Echinococcus granulosus

Tapeworm eggs are acquired from dog faeces. Dogs are
the definitive host. They acquire the worm from eating
viscera of infected sheep (or cows) containing encysted
larvae. The dogs then pass eggs in their faeces and
humans can acquire them from ingestion of eggs (e.g.
after stroking contaminated fur). Large, fluid-filled cysts
can develop. Anaphylactic shock occurs if they rupture
and during surgery. Careful surgical excision may be
needed but some patients respond to antihelminthic
therapy.

Trematodes (flukes)

These are small hermaphrodite helminths which are flat,
unsegmented and have complicated reproductive systems.
They have an intermediate host, usually freshwater snails
(and a second intermediary in the form of crustacea, or
on vegetation in some cases) and man is the definitive
host.

Schistosoma haematobium, S. mansoni and S. japonicum

Schistosomes differ from the other flukes in that they
live in the circulatory system (other forms develop in
lungs, liver or intestines (see Table 10.2)), and do not
have an encysted stage or a second intermediate host.
They have been a major cause of disease in Africa and
the Far East in particular for centuries. The mature worm
lays eggs in the abdominal veins which spread to gut or
bladder, to be excreted to freshwater. The larvae from
the eggs enter freshwater snails and develop there for a
few weeks into cysts, emerging in a form known as
cercaria which then look for human hosts who drink from

or swim in the water. These re-enter the bloodstream and return to complete development in the abdominal veins (see Figure 10.4).

Symptoms and signs of infestation include abdominal pain, weakness, anaemia, diarrhoea, cirrhosis of the liver, enlarged spleen, and possible allergic skin rash from larvae dying in the skin. Antihelminthic drugs are quite effective. However, good sewerage systems, molluscicides and education are needed to reduce the impact of the disease. Unfortunately, most of the severely affected areas are quite unable to provide these, and so the cycle continues, causing a major strain on already poor economies.

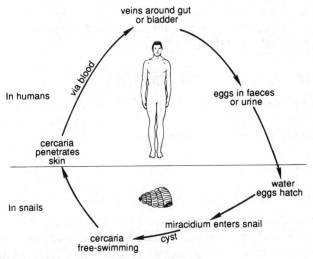

Figure 10.4 Life cycle of schistosomes.

Investigations

The presence of helminths is usually diagnosed by demonstration of the parasites themselves, or their ova, in faeces; by blood counts to demonstrate the eosinophilia which usually accompanies helminth infection; or by serology (enzyme-linked immunosorbent assay (ELISA) or immunofluorescence).

Prevention

Most infestations by helminths can be prevented by adequate systems of sewage disposal, coupled with good hygiene practice. Unfortunately, the regions with major problems are usually those where sewage disposal is not effective, and good hygiene is prevented by lack of basic facilities such as running water. Within the UK, emphasis is placed on the good management of pigswill, and the freezing and inspection of meat carcasses. Education in good hygiene is important to prevent helminth and protozoal infestation.

OTHER PESTS—ECTOPARASITES

Lice, bedbugs, fleas and scabies are infestations likely to be seen in the UK. Some brief details are given here as nurses may well encounter these.

Lice

Head louse (*Pediculus humanus capitis*)

This causes *pediculosis capitis* and is restricted to hair on the head. The female (1–4 mm long) has a life cycle of about 3 weeks, laying eggs which hatch in 8–10 days and leaving the shell attached close to the scalp on a shaft of hair (the *nit*).

Although more of a nuisance factor than a health risk in the UK, head lice may cause intense irritation after hypersensitivity develops to the saliva or faeces of the louse. It is estimated that 60% of children in some Third World countries are affected, and prolonged infestation can lead to general enervation, low-grade 'lousiness' or a feeling of illness, which is a burden to the population (Maunder, 1988).

Transmission: by close contact.

Treatment: usually with malathion or carbaryl based lotions, which are preferable to the shampoo preparations. To prevent resistance developing, it is usual to use one preparation in a region for, say, 3 years, and then change to the alternative (Maunder, 1988). The lotion is left in the hair for 12 h and then washed off. The following points should be noted.

1. The patient's hair should dry naturally, not dried with a hair drier, as many lotions contain alcohol (flammable) and heat inactivates the insecticide.
2. The itching may continue for some time after effective treatment, or may even increase. This is not an indication to treat again.
3. Gloves should be worn when handling these lotions.
4. Chlorine inactivates the insecticide. If the patient has recently been swimming, the hair should be washed before the lotion is applied.
5. Remember that nits are only *empty* egg sacs.

Body louse (*Pediculus humanus corporis*)

This causes *pediculosis corporis* and affects areas such as the collar line and shoulders, waistline and upper buttocks, as the eggs are laid in clothing seams. The lice are 2–4 mm long and, unlike head lice, they are related to living standards and tend to be found on people who do not wash their clothes, e.g. tramps. Sensitisation occurs, as with head lice.

Transmission: by close contact; possible transmission from clothing.

Treatment: drug treatment is not required. The patient should have a bath and a complete change of clothes. Clothes should be hot washed and tumble-dried to kill the lice, or dry cleaned.

Pubic lice (*Phthirus pubis*)

These cause *pediculosis pubis* or 'crab lice', where the eggs are laid near the pubic skin (they also may be found on eye lashes or eyebrows). They are broader and flatter than the other lice. They also have much wider claws and can only hang on to pubic hair or eyebrows. They hatch in 7–8 days and take another 2 weeks or more to mature, and may have been present for some weeks before sensitisation occurs.

Transmission: usually a sexually transmitted disease, but may be seen in children without any sexual origin to the infestation.

Treatment: all body hair is treated with an aqueous solution of one of the lotions already described. Shaving of the affected area is not necessary and bedding/clothing does not require treatment.

Scabies (*Sarcoptes scabei*)

This itch mite, the female of which is only 0.4 mm long and the male even smaller, burrows under the top layer of skin to lay eggs, leading to an allergic rash (not necessarily corresponding to the site of the burrows). The rash is often found on wrists, elbows, axillae, finger-webs, groins, and occasionally elsewhere, but *not* on the face. As with lice, sensitisation may take several weeks to occur.

Transmission: prolonged close contact, possibly sharing of linen/clothing. Sexual partners are often infected, as are patients within long-stay (elderly care or psychiatric) hospital areas where prolonged hand-holding may occur (a 'disease of affection').

Treatment: usually with lindane or malathion preparations, applied to all areas except the head and neck, and not washed off for 24 h.* Restrictions apply with regard to children and pregnant or lactating women for whom malathion is preferred. Clothing and bedding should be laundered. Gloves and a plastic apron should be worn during treatment by carers until treatment is completed.

Norwegian 'crusted' scabies

This is an extensive form of scabies seen in immunocompromised individuals (Robinson, 1986) whose bodies fail to restrict the mite and thus large numbers are found. These numbers of mites (up to 2 million mites in a severe infestation compared with an average infestation of 11 mites in ordinary scabies (Johnsen et al, 1991)) render the patient far more infectious. The organism may easily spread to health carers if basic hand hygiene is not strictly observed. Contacts of these patients should also be checked for evidence of infestation.

Fleas and bedbugs

Fleas

Most cases of bites by fleas in the UK are due to cat or dog fleas (*Ctenocephalides felis* or *C. canis*). These lay

---

* A third agent, permethrin cream has recently been introduced as there is now some resistance seen to lindane.

eggs in floors, carpets, furnishings and, especially, pets' bedding.

Acquisition: by bite from a flea, but they do not stay on humans, returning either to a pet or bedding.

Treatment: antipruritic treatment if needed, and preventative treatment with flea-powder sprays and regular cleaning of bedding area; treatment of animals with flea-powder or spray when needed.

Bedbugs

These insects (*Cimex lectularius* and others) lay eggs, and live, in walls, furniture and bedding.

Acquisition: usually from clothing, or bedding, from the infested premises; not usually seen on the affected individual, but on their clothing.

Treatment: the patient does not need treatment, but clothing, bedding or premises may need disinfestation with the help of the Environmental Health Department.

All these infestations may cause distress to patient, families and health carers, and every effort must be made to relieve these feelings. The physical effects of the accompanying pruritis can also be alleviated with antipruritics.

REFERENCES

Benenson AS (1990) *Control of Communicable Diseases in Man*. Washington, American Public Health Association.

Bodey GP (1988) The emergence of fungi as major hospital pathogens. *J. Hosp. Infect.* **11** (Suppl. A): 411–426.

BMA Guide (1989) *Infection Control*. Arnold (London).

Brooks RG and Remington JS (1986) Transplant-related infections. In *Hospital Infections* (eds Bennett JV and Brachman PS), 2nd edn. Boston, MA: Little, Brown and Co.

Burnie JP, Odds FC, Lee W, Webster C and Williams JD (1985)

Outbreak of systemic *Candida albicans* in intensive care unit caused by cross-infection. *Br. Med. J.* **290**: 746–748.

Burnie JP (1986) Leading article: *Candida* and hands. *J. Hosp. Infect.* **8**: 1–4.

Dewhurst AG, Cooper MJ, Khan SM, et al (1990) Investigation of aspergillosis in immunocompromised patients: potential hazards of infection. *Br. Med. J.* **301**: 802–804.

Hopkins CC, Weber DJ and Rubin RH (1989) Invasive aspergillosis infection: possible non-ward common source within the hospital environment. *J. Hosp. Infect.* **13**: 19–25.

Jawetz E, Brooks GF, Melnick JL, *et al* (1989) *Medical Microbiology*, 18th edn. London: Prentice-Hall.

Johnsen C, Bellin E, Nadal E and Simone V (1991) An outbreak of scabies in a New York City jail. *Am. J. Infect. Control* **19**(3): 162–163.

Maunder J (1988) Head lice: the beginning of the end. *Proceedings of 2nd Int. Conf. on Infection Control*. Cambridge: CMA Medical Data Ltd.

PHLS (Public Health Laboratory Service) (1989) Toxoplasmosis. *PHLS Microbiology Digest* **6**(3): 69–73.

PHLS (1990) *Summary of* Taenia *reports to CDSC*.

Robinson R (1986) Scratching the surface. *Nursing Times, J. Inf. Control Nursing* **34**: 71–72.

Shanson DC (1989) *Microbiology in Clinical Practice*, 2nd edn. London: Wright.

Thomas CGA (1988) *Medical Microbiology*, 6th edn. London: Baillière Tindall.

Tomkins AM (1977) Giardiasis. *Nursing Times* **9 Jun**.: 876–877.

Turnbull R (1989) Tom, a baby with toxoplasmosis. *Nursing Times* **85**(48): 44–45.

Willis J (1990) Common pests in *N. Times—Community Outlook* Sept. 1990.

Wright J (1990) Toxocariasis—the canine threat. *Prof. Nurse* **5**(10) 519–521.

11 Infection control—general

The information in the preceding chapters is intended to help the reader understand procedures designed to prevent the transmission of infection in both hospital and community. The scourges of plague, smallpox and typhus have all but disappeared. It would be easy to assume that modern technical knowledge, facilities and drugs would have overcome the problems of infection. We have come a long way from the doctrine of 'laudable pus': methods of asepsis and hygiene are well-established and a wide range of antimicrobial agents exists to treat infections.

However, there remains a continuing problem of community-acquired infection, despite immunisation and improved nutrition, and an increasing problem of hospital-acquired infection. Several factors contribute to this.

1. Increasing complexity of treatment for many diseases reduce a patient's ability to resist infection. These include new intense immunosuppressive therapies or invasive technologies.
2. The average age of the population is rising, and the elderly are more susceptible to infection.
3. The range of organisms found to be capable of causing human infection continues to expand. New pathogens are identified (e.g. *Legionella* and HIV) and long-established ones continue to 'wax and wane' in importance (Phillips, 1988). *Staphylococcus aureus* isolated from patients in one hospital may be of the epidemic, multiply antibiotic resistant variety, while

from those in another it may be antibiotic sensitive, but highly virulent. Both organisms may be responsible for costly outbreaks of surgical wound infections.

4. Human nature remains such that mistakes are still made. Simple steps to prevent transmission of infection are difficult to maintain constantly.

Infection continues to be a serious and costly problem affecting both hospitals and community. It indirectly affects the entire population by its drain on resources, depletion of labour force and the social and psychological stress inflicted upon individuals and their families. The prevention of infection transmission by immunisation or chemotherapeutic treatment has already been discussed. Effective sanitation and refuse disposal systems, and the safe treatment and maintenance of water and food supplies are necessary for the well-being of all people, and the avoidance of disease. The remaining chapters discuss these issues as part of *infection control*, but concentrate on:

- the prevention of transmission of infection between individuals in hospital and community,
- the methods used, and
- the nursing techniques used to care for those already infected or at high risk of infection.

HOSPITAL-ACQUIRED INFECTION

Hospital-acquired (nosocomial) infection (HAI) is that acquired by patients or staff in hospital whether it be from a patient, member of staff, the hospital environment or equipment (see also Chapter 3). How big a problem is this?

Two studies published in the 1980s, already mentioned in Chapter 3, have given us a wealth of data on the subject, and are borne out by a number of other investigations. It is important to distinguish between *prevalence* and *incidence* in understanding the statistics. *Prevalence rate* is the number of patients found with infection at any one time, as opposed to the *incidence rate* which is the number found over a specific time period of continuous recording. A prevalence rate for hospital infection is roughly twice the incidence rate because of the increased length of stay of an infected patient.

National Survey of Infection in Hospitals (1980)

This study of the *prevalence* of hospital infection was carried out in 1980. It involved 43 hospitals and 18 163 patients in England and Wales. The distribution of infection according to the body system affected is shown in Figure 11.1.

The findings show that 19.1% of patients were infected. Approximately half of these acquired the infection *before* entering hospital (Meers et al, 1981). This means that about 10% of patients at any one time will be suffering from a hospital-acquired infection (prevalence) and 5% of patients admitted to hospital without infection will acquire one (incidence).

Study on the Efficacy of Nosocomial Infection Control (SENIC)

This multi-phase study was carried out by the Centers for Disease Control in the USA from 1974 to 1983. It was intended to establish the extent to which surveillance and control of infection methods had been implemented, and assess their efficacy in reducing nosocomial (hospital-acquired) infection. It involved 338 randomly selected hospitals and identified a ratio of 5.7 nosocomial infections per 100 admissions. The authors of the reports (Haley et

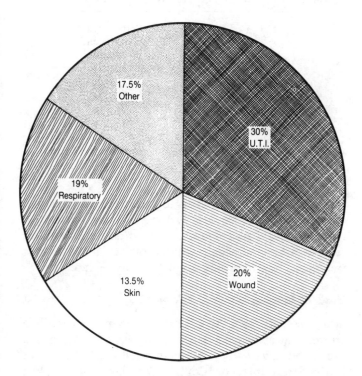

Figure 11.1 Distribution of hospital-acquired infection by affected system. (From Meers et al, 1981.)

al, 1985) estimated that there were over 2 million hospital-acquired infections in the USA in 1975–1976, which exceeded admissions for 'all cancers, accidents and myocardial infarctions combined'. Table 11.1 shows the distribution of infection by body system for the 1975–1976 survey.

These two studies give some idea of the magnitude of

Table 11.1 Frequency of major body systems involved in nosocomial infections: SENIC Project 1975–1976.*

	Percentage of all nosocomial infections
Urinary tract infection	42
Surgical wound infection	24
Lower respiratory infection	11
Bacteraemia	5
Other	18

* From Haley (1986).

the problem. It is important to relate this to costs and the consequences for health care, and also to bear in mind the *ethical duty of health-care professionals to reduce risks to patients* of acquiring infection as a result of their treatment, and to ensure a good quality of care.

Costs of hospital-acquired infection

Using the data from the UK prevalence survey described above, which assumes a 5% incidence of HAI, and a prolonged stay of 4 days for an infected patient, the joint DHSS/PHLS Infection Control Working Group (1988) estimated that HAI cost the NHS £111 million in 1986.

In addition to these actual costs, 950 000 hospital-bed-days were lost, causing further extension of waiting lists and stress to patients. For example, as part of an 8-year study of surgical wound infections at a Buckinghamshire general hospital, Leigh (1981) estimated that an outbreak of *S. aureus* wound infection in five male surgical patients, between five and ten patients were denied treatment in addition to the £1000 extra costs incurred.

In the USA it is estimated that the economic effects

of HAI cost approximately US$4 billion each year (Miller et al, 1989). In the current climate of concern for cost-effectiveness in health care, every effort should be made to reduce these costs. The SENIC project showed that, with effective methods to control infection, overall infection rates could be reduced by about one-third. Hospitals which lacked organised systems of surveillance and control showed an increase of about 18% in rates of HAI (Haley et al, 1985). Currie and Maynard (1989) estimated that, if an effective infection-control programme could be implemented throughout the UK, potential cost savings in the region of £15.6 million would be obtainable. Daschner (1989) stresses that, although infection-control measures require financing, they can be both cost-effective and also reduce some pollution side-effects of hospital waste. Miller et al (1989) suggest that financial incentives for 'value received' in terms of preventive care should be part of hospital management. This must be the approach taken in recognition of the value of infection control procedures which UK hospitals should adopt (see Government White Paper 'Working for Patients' (DOH, 1989)).

COMMUNITY-ACQUIRED INFECTION

Infection problems are not confined to hospitals. There is constant interchange between hospital and community. Those who work in hospitals mostly live outside them, many people with chronic infections live and work in the community, and patients are discharged from hospital at the earliest opportunity. An increasing number of surgical wound infections are developing after the patient has returned home. The preference of many to be cared for at home rather than in hospital means that people are now at home with devices such as urinary catheters, semipermanent lines for drugs and parenteral nutrition, continuous ambulatory peritoneal dialysis catheters (CAPD) and other systems open to risk of infection. The recent development of AIDS-related infections means that an increasing number of seriously ill individuals will be cared for and die in their own homes.

Whilst the potential for transfer of infection is greater inside hospital than outside, CAI is, nevertheless, an important issue. Clinical-waste disposal must be safely managed and carers must be aware of the potential for transferring infection. Conditions within the home may mean that simple hygiene is not easy to maintain, and sterile equipment is not readily available. Communication between hospital and community health-care workers has often been less than satisfactory and should be improved. District nurses and other community staff require tact and skill to achieve effective infection control in their work (Timoney, 1987).

Having established that HAI and CAI are a cause for concern, and before outlining who is responsible for the management of control of infection and what methods are used, a brief discussion follows on some of the main factors associated with hospital infection.

MAIN FACTORS ASSOCIATED WITH HOSPITAL INFECTION

- Hospitals are, by definition, places to which the sick are taken for treatment. In addition to 'healthy' patients admitted for planned surgical procedures, many will be suffering from infections ranging from gastroenteritis or chest infection to diabetic ulcers and other conditions which involve pathogenic organisms. These are potential sources of cross-infection.

- All staff and patients carry organisms but some are also healthy carriers of pathogenic bacteria, whilst others are known to be infected. The numbers of people thrown together within a limited area favours the spread of organisms. A ward may contain only 20 patients but many individuals will pass through the area in a working day. Figure 11.2 shows the potential for spread of infection in a ward. The outer circle shows individuals present in a ward with their accompanying flora, the inner circle the inanimate objects and the patient is at the centre, at risk from inner and outer circle sources.

- Antibiotic usage, estimated at 20–30% of all patients, favours the emergence of organisms with unusual

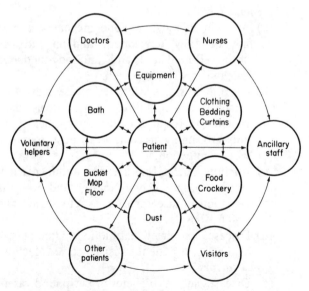

Figure 11.2 The cross-infection carousel.

or highly resistant characteristics which may 'show increased virulence or transmissibility' (DHSS/PHLS, 1988) and also restrict the choice of treatment.

- Special units may involve particular hazards. Intensive therapy units care for severely ill patients, a proportion of whom will be artificially ventilated, fed intravenously and catheterized—all procedures that bypass the natural defences of the body. Premature babies in special-care baby units are highly susceptible to infection for immunological reasons, but also need frequent handling and feeding, thus increasing opportunities for transfer of organisms.

- The susceptibility of patients to organisms varies widely according to their general and local powers of resistance (see Chapters 3 and 4). Some factors are listed below.

  1. *General factors*
     (a) Age—in infancy, immune mechanisms may not be fully developed, and in old age both cell-mediated and antibody-mediated mechanisms are impaired.
     (b) Nutritional states affect resistance: starvation increases susceptibility to tuberculosis, diarrhoeal and respiratory diseases. Obese patients are highly susceptible to post-operative wound infection.
     (c) Immune mechanisms are inhibited by corticosteroid drugs, chemotherapy and ionizing radiation in diseases such as leukaemia, and organ transplants.
     (d) Diseases requiring antibiotic treatment will also affect a patient's resistance to infection.

  2. *Local factors*
     (a) Diseases such as diabetes or peripheral vascular disease; these cause poor blood supply

and oxygenation of the tissues and eventually lead to the development of necrotic tissue. This establishes good conditions for bacterial multiplication.

(b) Investigations which bypass the normal defences increase the risk of introducing infection, e.g. catheterisation, biopsy and radiography.

We must accept that infection will always be present somewhere in a hospital, and our aim is to prevent its transmission. The nurse should keep in mind the three elements vital to allowing the spread of infection:

1. source of infection,
2. susceptible host, and
3. means of transmission (see Chapter 3).

Control and prevention will be aimed at all three but chiefly at prevention of transmission by the following.

1. *Removing the source* of infection either by treatment and/or sterilization of relevant contaminated articles.
2. *Protecting the susceptible host* by immunization when necessary or applicable; screening of hospital personnel where relevant; and, in surgery, by sterilization of all objects coming in contact with the patient's tissues and with minimal handling of the latter.
3. *Blocking the lines of communication* which would permit transmission: by isolation of infected or highly susceptible patients; by use of hand washing and strict aseptic techniques; control of carriers; and scrupulous hygiene in all hospital areas (including food preparation, waste disposal, laundry services and housekeeping programmes).

MEASURES TO PREVENT TRANSMISSION OF INFECTION

These can be discussed under the following headings.

1. Infection-control teams, committees, policies and programmes.
2. Education.
3. Architectural design and facilities.
4. Environmental hygiene, including services such as catering, domestic, CSSD (central sterile supply department), laundry, and waste disposal.
5. Aseptic practice and basic hygiene, e.g. hand washing.
6. Isolation/segregation of infected patients.

Discussion of the first two items follows. (3) and (4) are discussed as part of the patient's environment in Chapter 12. (5) and (6) are discussed in the final chapters which look at the care of infected and at-risk patients.

Control-of-infection management and teams

The National Survey of Infection in Hospitals report (1980) states that, despite the fact that endemic infection is ever-present in the wards, hospital staff frequently deny its existence, except in circumstances such as outbreaks when they may 'tend to overact, and from ignoring infection, become hypersensitive to it' (Meers et al, 1981). Staff need to know what is expected of them. They must be made aware of infection-control policies which attempt to minimise the incidence of nosocomial infections. An infection-control programme should form part of the overall audit of clinical practice so that the effect of policies can be surveyed, reported back, amended as necessary and resurveyed.

Following the outbreaks at Stanley Royd (*Salmonella* diarrhoea) and Stafford (legionellosis) hospitals, a joint

DHSS/PHLS Hospital Infection Working Group was set up to review departmental guidance on the subject of control of hospital infection, the first since 1959. Their publication (DHSS/PHLS, 1988) sets out management arrangements for infection control and also for outbreak control. The main points are summarised below.

1. Each Health Authority is responsible through the District General Manager (DGM) for establishing an Infection Control Committee (ICC).
2. The ICC delegates day to day work to an *IC team*: IC nurse (ICN) who works with an IC doctor (ICD), usually the microbiologist, and the DGM or unit general manager (UGM). In practice, the ICD and ICN form the team for day-to-day activities.
3. An expanded team (action group) is formed (by the ICT) to deal with any outbreak of infection.
4. Outlying hospitals should have a specific person, probably the nurse manager, to link with the ICN.
5. Arrangements should be in place for notifying the Medical Officer for Environmental Health, now usually *Consultant in Communicable Disease Control* (CCDC) of notifiable diseases (see Table 11.2), of a hospital outbreak of infection and of community outbreaks. Speed is of the essence.

Infection control committee (ICC)

The IC committee is to meet at least twice yearly (some meet as often as monthly) to advise the Health Authority, to determine policies, an annual programme, and monitor progress in its work. In addition to the main IC team members, membership will vary between hospitals, partly depending on their size and function.

Responsibilities of the IC team include:

Table 11.2 Statutory notifiable diseases 1988.

Anthrax	Plague
Cholera	Poliomyelitis (acute)
Diphtheria	Rabies
Dysentery	Relapsing fever
Encephalitis (acute)	Rubella
Food poisoning	Scarlet fever
Leprosy	Smallpox
Leptospirosis	Tetanus
Malaria	Tuberculosis
Measles	Typhoid fever
Meningitis (acute)	Typhus fever
Meningococcal septicaemia	Viral haemorrhagic
Mumps	fever
Ophthalmia neonatorum	Viral hepatitis
Paratyphoid fever	Whooping cough
	Yellow fever

1. day-to-day planning, implementing and evaluating IC activities;
2. developing and reviewing IC policies and procedures;
3. collection and analysis of IC data;
4. an education programme on infection risk assessment, prevention and control, and consultation on these items; and
5. investigation on suspicion of outbreaks of infection (Griffiths, 1991).

Infection control officer/doctor (ICD)

According to the DHSS/PHLS (1988) guidance, the ICD will be a consultant with experience, training and commitment to infection control. The medical microbiologist usually fills this role. Other qualities and expertise are also needed. This is summed up by Daschner (1988), for both ICD and ICN, as a combination of Sherlock

Holmes (determining sources of infection), Frances of Assissi (patience), Mary Poppins (pleasing everyone and managing the impossible) and Margaret Thatcher (financial toughness). (See also Figure 11.3.) The ICT should be empowered to act without having to convene the committee, and is a source of advice on all aspects of infection control including matters relating to antibiotic and disinfectant usage, sterilisation procedures, planning developments and patient care.

Figure 11.3 The qualities of an ICD/ICN.

Infection control nurse (ICN)

The ICN is a registered general nurse with further specialist training and experience to enable him/her to act as a source of information and advice on all infection control matters. The ICN aims to help staff achieve and maintain the highest possible standards of practice, with particular regard to the safety of patients, staff and members of the community against hazards of infection. He/she needs to be able to communicate freely with all levels and groups of staff, being an important link between laboratory, medical and nursing staff. The appointment is, therefore, at a senior level. The *duties* of the ICN are those of the IC team (except for those which are unique to the ICD) and can be divided into the following broad categories.

1. *Surveillance*—the ICN needs to be aware of the state of background infection in the hospital in order to identify any change rapidly. It should then be possible to prevent any escalation or development of an outbreak. Surveillance also involves conducting microbiological and epidemiological surveys with specific objectives. These may include:
   (a) evaluating prevention and control activities;
   (b) identifying groups of people who are at risk of disease;
   (c) providing information for service planning and resource allocation (Glenister et al, 1992),
   in addition to the pattern of disease alteration and outbreak identification already mentioned.
   Surveillance also includes 'analysis of data and dissemination of results so that appropriate actions can be taken' (Hughes, 1987).
2. *Education*—most of the ICN's time is spent in formal and informal education on all matters of infection

control. This includes lectures to all disciplines of hospital and community staff. Also discussions and advice at ward and departmental level with a wide variety of personnel, including visitors when appropriate.

3. *Monitoring*—this involves cooperation with all departments to ensure that IC policies are usable and working and that any new practices or equipment entering the patient's environment are assessed for infection risk.

4. *Research*—this involves acting as a nursing research resource for health-care workers on all aspects of infection control. It includes developing methods of improved practice in conjunction with other staff and keeping abreast of new information.

The ICN will sit on a variety of committees including 'nursing procedures', 'AIDS action/advisory' groups, 'health and safety' and 'control of infection'. The role is wide ranging (see Figure 11.4) and requires the attributes referred to by Daschner (1988), with tact, persistence, tolerance, intuition and a sense of humour. Kingston (1987) has described the required physical attributes of an ICN as: a large nose for 'poking into other people's affairs' and scenting trouble; good vocal cords to stop people in their tracks when failing to carry out procedures properly; big ears to pick up useful information; efficient muscles for carrying equipment, and small feet to lessen the damage caused when they are placed in his/her large mouth (Figure 11.5).

INFECTION CONTROL AND OCCUPATIONAL HEALTH

There should be a close working relationship between IC and occupational health (OH) staff. The roles are

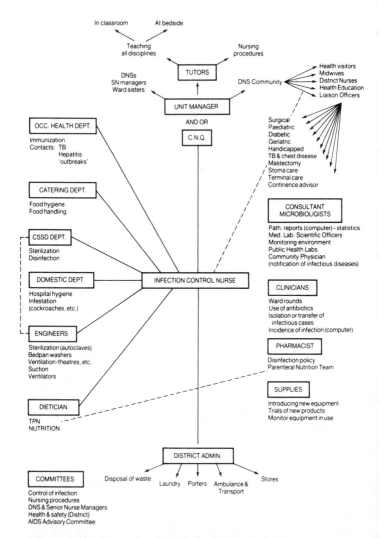

Figure 11.4 The role of the infection control nurse.

ALL THE BETTER TO TREAT YOU WITH . . .

BIRCH

Figure 11.5 The physical attributes of an infection control nurse!

interwoven and should be mutually beneficial. ICNs may become aware of staff sickness as they visit wards, and will alert the OH nurse (OHN) to any outbreak of infection among patients, e.g. sickness and diarrhoea, which could also affect staff. The discovery of a patient with previously unsuspected pulmonary tuberculosis or scabies infestation will involve both ICN and OHN in patient and staff contact tracing.

The OHN has an important role to play in educating staff in safety and personal hygiene as part of hospital IC programmes. They should ideally be responsible for the health and safety of all personnel employed by the health authority. Immunization status will be checked with regard to

1. tuberculosis,
2. poliomyelitis,
3. diphtheria,
4. tetanus,
5. rubella, and
6. hepatitis B (usually part of Health Authority programme)

and immunization offered if necessary. It is also useful to have a record of previous known infection with varicella–zoster virus.

Uptake of hepatitis B vaccine for health-care workers with 'hands-on' responsibility (including porters, domestics, laundry, engineering and works staff) should be encouraged. OH staff should be involved in inoculation injury protocols and appropriate counselling.

In addition to these localized control of infection teams, a number of national and international bodies are concerned with promotion of health and prevention of infection.

EPIDEMIOLOGY

The study of the distribution of disease in human populations is called *epidemiology*. Epidemiologists are involved in local, national and international organisations and combine their information with that of other specialists (e.g. microbiologists, sociologists, and geneticists) to promote better standards of health care. In order to prevent transmission of infectious diseases, the epidemiologist needs to know the 'when', 'where', 'how' and 'to whom' of any disease.

World Health Organization (WHO)

The WHO amasses a vast amount of information on the incidence of disease, makes regulations to minimise international spread of disease, acts as educators, trainers and investigators of particular diseases on a global basis. It was a WHO campaign which led to the eradication of the dreaded disease of *smallpox* by 1980. However, WHO has been defeated in its aim to eradicate malaria by a combination of adverse economic, political and biological factors (see Chapter 10). The ability of the mosquito to adapt to insecticides has been a crucial factor.

Problems will inevitably occur in trying to amass information from countries with widely differing organisational capabilities. However, the epidemiological information collected and produced by the WHO has played, and will continue to play, a vital role in understanding disease transmission. This will enable strategies to be formed to minimise the spread of disease and help achieve improved health for all.

The Public Health Laboratory Service (PHLS)

The PHLS is a network of 52 microbiological laboratories throughout England and Wales, which work closely with National Health Service (NHS) laboratories and link to central specialist facilities. They are concerned with diagnosis, prevention and control of human infections and communicable diseases. They provide resources to assist authorities in investigations of outbreaks such as food poisoning by botulism in 1990 (see p. 204). They offer training to medical and infection-control nursing personnel.

The Communicable Disease Surveillance Centre (CDSC)

This establishment is attached to the PHLS and is based at PHLS headquarters in London (Colindale). Laboratories throughout England and Wales voluntarily report data on infections and organisms to the CDSC, who analyse this information weekly and publish it in the *Communicable Disease Report* (CDR). Staff also offer guidance to local public health and hospital authorities in outbreak investigations and provide educational courses. An example of current ongoing surveillance information regularly monitored and produced in the CDR is the increasing incidence of AIDS (a confidential reporting system is in operation).

Scotland has its own Communicable Disease organisation (CD(S)U) and produces an equivalent of the CDR.

Centers for Disease Control (CDC)

This establishment in the USA at Atlanta, Georgia, is run by the US Federal Government and fulfils a similar role as, although established many years before, the CDSC. Its publication of information is in the *Morbidity and Mortality Weekly Report* (MMWR). Both the CDR and MMWR can usually be found in hospital laboratories or libraries.

EDUCATION

The buildings may be architecturally and practically ideal, policies and procedures may be up to date and appropriate, all supporting services may be adequately provided and wards well staffed, but if people do not understand how infection is spread and how they can prevent it, then spread of infection will inevitably occur.

Education is a key element in prevention and control of infection. To work it must be:

- aimed at the right level for the group being educated,
- clear, consistent and concise,
- interesting, and
- appropriate and up to date.

Studies have shown that personnel are more likely to comply with procedures if they understand the reasons for them (e.g. Gignac and Oermann, 1991). Any education programme must match the needs of those receiving the education. Although much of an ICNs time is spent educating nursing staff, it is important to remember that other groups need education too, and that they have fears and misunderstandings. The ward nurses who understand how infection is spread can play their part in educating other health-care workers who enter their ward. The advent of AIDS and all the concern that HIV infection has aroused, highlights the need for good education in order to prevent distressing and unnecessary measures being taken supposedly to prevent transmission of infection. It is not only the staff who need to understand procedures, but also patients, relatives and other visitors. The IC team has a role to play in ensuring educational programmes take this into account.

The *Strategy for Nursing* (1989) highlights a number of important educational targets including:

- Target 25—that all staff delivering health care are appropriately prepared for practice;
- Target 32—individual responsibility for keeping up-to-date; and
- Target 7—that clinical practice is founded on current information and research.

ICN education

In order to achieve his/her role as educator, the ICN must also receive appropriate training and education. There are centres which run a course for the Certificate in Infection Control Nursing, a foundation course for ICNs to be attended within the first 2 years of appointment. This takes the form of several study blocks and study within the nurse's own Health Authority, spread over a 12-month period. These may be established under the auspices of the Royal College of Nursing or Universities for Diploma or Advanced Diploma or degree accreditation, and replace the ENB 329 course. There is a national orientation programme for newly appointed nurses which is organised by the Infection Control Nurses Association (ICNA).

The ICNA has an Annual Conference, and many regional groups organise study days to up-date knowledge and skills. Teaching qualifications are also encouraged.

REFERENCES

A Strategy for Nursing (1989) London, Dept. of Health Nursing Division.

Currie E and Maynard A (1989) Economic aspects of hospital acquired infection. *Discussion Paper 56*. York: Centre for Health Economics, University of York.

Daschner FD (1988) The role of the infection control doctor. *J. Hosp. Infect.* **11** (Suppl. A): 396–399.

Daschner FD (1989) Cost effectiveness in hospital infection control—lessons for the 1990s. *J. Hosp. Infect.* **13**(4): 325–336.

DOH (1989) *Working for Patients. The Health Service: Caring for the 1990s*. London: HMSO.

DHSS/PHLS Hospital Infection Working Group (1988) *Hospital Infection Control* **HC(88)33**. London: HMSO.

Gignac D and Oermann MH (1991) Willingness of nursing students and faculty to care for patients with AIDS. *Am. J. Infect. Control* **19**: 191–197.

Glenister HM, Taylor LJ, Cooke EM and Bartlett CLR (1992) *A Study of Surveillance Methods for Detecting Hospital Infection*. London: Public Health Laboratory Service.

Griffiths G (1991) The role of the infection control nurse. *Infection Control Yearbook*, pp. 35–38. Cambridge: CMA Medical Data Ltd.

Haley RW (1986) Incidence and nature of endemic and epidemic nosocomial infections. In *Hospital Infections* (eds Bennett JV and Brachman PS), 2nd edn. Boston, MA: Little, Brown & Co.

Haley RW, Culver DH, White JW, *et al*. (1985) The efficacy of infection surveillance and control programs in preventing nosocomial infections in U.S. hospitals. *Am. J. Epidemiol.* **121**: 182–205.

Hughes JM (1987) Nosocomial infection surveillance in the United States: historical perspective. *Infect. Control* **8**: 450–453.

Kingston J (1987) All the better to treat you with . . . *Nursing Times, J. Infect. Control Nursing* **83**(37): 83–86.

Leigh DA (1981) An eight year study of postoperative wound infection in two district general hospitals. *J. Hosp. Infect.* **2**(3): 207–217.

Meers PD, Ayliffe GAJ, Emmerson AM, *et al* (1981) Report on the national survey on infection in hospitals. *J. Hosp. Infect.* **2** (Suppl.).

Miller PJ, Farr BM and Gwaltney Jr JM (1989) Economic benefits of an effective infection control program: case study and proposal. *Rev. Infect. Dis.* **11**(2): 284–288.

Phillips I (1988) Hospital infection into the 1990s. *J. Hosp. Infect.* **11** (Suppl. A): 3–6.

Timoney R (1987) Aspects of infection control in a community unit of management. *Proc. of ICNA Conf. 1986* (*ICNA Yearbook 1987*). St Ives: CMA Medical Data Ltd.

FURTHER READING

Antrobus M (1984) Infection control in hospital and the community. *Nursing* **2**(23) (Suppl.): 4–7.

Central Health Services Council (1959) *Staphylococcal Infections in Hospital: Report of a Sub-committee*. London: HMSO.

Gardner AMN and Oxon, BM (1962) The infection control sister: a new member of the infection control team in general hospitals. *Lancet* **ii**: 710–711.

Gillman M and Andrews S (1984) Practical problems in the community. *Nursing* **2**(23) (Suppl.): 1–4.

Jenner EA and O'Neill P (1984) Infection control and the community *Nursing* **2**(27) (Suppl.): 1–7.

Medical Research Council (1944) The control of cross-infection in hospitals. *MRC War Memorandum No. 11*. London: HMSO.

Ministry of Health (1959) Control of staphylococcal infections in hospitals. *HM(59)6*. London: Ministry of Health.

Pfaff RN and Terry BA (1980) Discharge planning—infection prevention and control in the hole. *Nursing Clinics N. America* **15**: 893.

12 The patient's environment

ORGANISMS IN THE ENVIRONMENT

The hospital environment is affected by staff, patients and visitors, and includes 'all structures, fixtures, fittings, furnishings, supplies, services' (Ayliffe et al, 1990) and waste products. Initially we will concentrate on the inanimate environment (see Chapter 3) and return to the other groups later.

Semmelweiss highlighted hands as a route of nosocomial infection transmission, but other studies have tried to identify additional routes and sources (McGowan, 1982). Collins (1988) points out that a microbe-free environment is neither practicable nor desirable. The aim of good environmental control should be to 'minimise the number of organisms present' and make the surroundings more favourable to those organisms least likely to cause problems. Surfaces should be kept in good order, be smooth, intact and dry, and spillages of any secretions and excretions should be cleared up promptly. Inanimate structures are unlikely to come into close contact with the *susceptible sites* of any individual. Virulent bacteria are also unlikely to survive long on clean, dry surfaces (Ayliffe et al, 1990). Those found will consist mostly of Gram-positive coagulase-negative staphylococci (e.g. *Staphylococcus epidermidis*) and a few diphtheroid species and aerobic spore-bearing bacilli (Collins and Josse, 1990) unlikely to cause infection except during implant surgery. Bacteria found on moist surfaces and equipment or in fluids are mostly Gram-negative bacilli (GNB) (e.g.

Pseudomonas spp.) and are best controlled by thorough cleaning and drying, and to a lesser extent disinfection and sterilisation methods. Other specific pathogens causing human infections such as *Salmonella* spp. will only be found environmentally:

1. *As part of a food source*—contamination of inanimate surfaces in the kitchen by uncooked food is common; good catering hygiene will prevent infection; or
2. *following contamination by patient secretions or excretions*—in order to prevent transmission, correct control policies for care of infected patients and disposal of waste materials should prevent spread.

Frequency of cleaning and its effect on the environment were discussed in Chapter 6. A study on the practices in UK health service hospitals found that cleaning frequency, methods and surface condition were unlikely to influence patient infection figures (Bibby, 1982). An excellent study done in the USA confirms this finding (Maki *et al.*, 1982).

A 500-bed hospital was moving from an old to a new building of 548 beds, with twice the area, modern ventilation, excellent isolation facilities, with all patients cared for in single rooms as opposed to the two- to eight-bed units in the old hospital. Matching areas of old and new hospitals were sampled during the last two months of 'old' hospital occupancy, the new building prior to occupancy, and for the first 6–12 months occupancy. Initially the new hospital yielded far fewer pathogens in environmental cultures, but after 6–12 months occupancy there was a considerable rise in numbers. However, the incidence of nosocomial infection was the same before and immediately after the move, and had not changed significantly after 10–12 months. Maki concluded that organisms found in a hospital environment 'contribute negligibly to endemic nosocomial infections'.

Environmental sampling

Surprisingly, sampling of the environment has a very limited value in hospitals, and is reserved for:

1. tracing sources of infection during outbreaks;
2. research (e.g. finding effective decontamination methods for new equipment);
3. specific situations such as ultra-clean theatre air;
4. education (to reinforce the need for basic hygienic cleaning or to show that certain equipment may harbour pathogens); and
5. as a check that basic hygiene and disinfection policies are being adhered to.

Three elements of the patient's environment are discussed next: architectural design and function, including air conditioning and fixtures and fittings; equipment (clinical and non-clinical); and services (catering, laundry, waste disposal, domestic).

ARCHITECTURAL DESIGN AND FUNCTION

A series of DHSS/DOH Health Building Notes (HBNs) exist, or are currently being drawn up, to provide guidance on design and function of health-care facilities. They cover wards and departmental areas and supporting services such as laundry and catering departments. HBN4 covers adult acute wards and gives advice on accommodation and service provision for acutely ill adult patients. Specialised units for renal dialysis, intensive-care and burns units are excluded, as are isolation facilities other than the recommendation for two single bedrooms with *en suite* shower and toilet per ward for 'isolation' use. Specialized units have, or will have, their own HBNs.

Main areas of concern related to infection control include the following.

- Separation of clean and dirty activities.
- Provision of an adequate percentage of single room facilities with separate toilet and storage provision.
- Good surface selection for safe maintenance and cleaning.
- Ventilation systems and control of air flow.
- Provision of sinks, toilets and other hygiene facilities.
- Facilities which allow for safe delivery of clean/sterile goods to the wards (CSSD, food, etc.).
- Safe disposal of waste.
- Adequate bed spacing.
- Design which excludes pest infiltration, e.g. rat-proof stores and fly screens.

Some of the above are dealt with in more detail below.

Ventilation systems and control of air flow

This can be separated into requirements for wards, and all general hospital departmental areas, and theatre suites.

General hospital areas including wards

The major factor creating a hazard will always be the number and activities of *people* using the available area, plus the number of air changes available (Ayliffe and Lowbury, 1982). Design should allow the environment to remain as free from contamination as possible. In general areas, simple ventilation by opening windows will dilute airborne organisms such as tuberculosis and virulent viruses.

Ayliffe and Lowbury (1982) have reported a study done in a burns unit in which a plenum-ventilated dressing station with 20 air changes per hour was introduced. Counts using a device known as a 'slit-sampler' showed 'enormous numbers of bacteria in the air during removal of dressings' from the burns, yet within 5 min of the patients leaving the room the air was 'as clean as at the beginning of the day'. Without adequate ventilation, airborne bacteria accumulated freely. This information was used to make a policy that patients wounds should be redressed in dressing rooms, using plenum ventilation to reduce the risk of acquiring organisms from the previous patient.

Operating theatres and special patient protection units

In the operating theatre where tissues normally protected by the skin and other natural barriers are exposed for a considerable time, it is important for the air to be as organism free as possible. Air is therefore filtered, humidified, warmed or cooled, then delivered and extracted at a measured rate by the air-conditioning plant. The circulation and direction in which air flows is also important; theatre suites are described in 'zones': sterile, clean and dirty—the pressure being highest in the sterile preparation area and operating theatre and lowest in the changing and sluice areas so that the air flows from sterile to clean to dirty areas and never in the reverse direction.

Several studies have shown that the greatest risk of infection acquisition in theatres is from people and their activities, and concentrations of bacteria seem directly related to the numbers of people present and their movements (Nagai et al, 1984; Suzuki et al, 1984). Hambraeus et al (1978) showed that post-operative theatre-floor contamination was the same after 'clean' and 'dirty' cases.

Twenty air changes per hour is recommended for ordinary operating suites. Ultra-clean-air systems such as those used for orthopaedic implants or sterile fluid preparation involve a laminar (non-turbulent) clean-air flow system. Evidence for the benefit of such a system in joint replacement surgery is given by Lidwell et al (1982). In a laminar air flow room, air moving at high speed is introduced through a filter bank which takes the place of one whole wall (horizontal flow), or the entire ceiling (vertical flow). It is extracted through the opposite wall in the first case and at floor level in the other. The advantage of this ventilation is the rate at which organisms are removed from the vicinity of the wound, lessening the possibility of contamination. Staff putting themselves in the way of the laminar flow will produce turbulence and will shed bacteria. This can be overcome by wearing a ventilated air-proof suit. However, some surgeons find these uncomfortable and their movements hindered.

Fixtures, fittings, furnishings

These should all be selected with ease of cleaning and maintenance in mind and be of suitable materials, easy to move (if needed) and have acceptable qualities both for those who will be required to maintain them and those who use them. Carpets have been the subject of some controversy but as with all materials and equipment, safe and prompt cleaning of any spillage (e.g. urine or blood) and regular efficient cleaning schedules are the vital factors. Carpets need more cleaning than plastic and are therefore more expensive to maintain.

Wash-basin and bath overflows and plugs should be omitted in *clinical* areas (as opposed to those for patient use), as they are difficult to keep clean and are often colonised with Gram-negative bacteria. Sinks should be fixed in such a way that they either stand clear of the wall or are flush and sealed. In this way moisture which may harbour Gram-negative organisms does not accumulate. Pests prefer the environment of plumbing ductwork. It is critical to make sure these areas can be thoroughly cleaned yet are sealed from the ward environment.

Walls

It was the practice for many years to 'fog' or fumigate rooms after occupancy by a patient with an infectious disease. This was followed by the actions of a team of 'wall washers' who extended the time that the room lay empty. It is no longer considered necessary to fumigate rooms. Wall washing is rarely needed as a smooth, impervious surface will not attract particles carrying virulent microorganisms. If splashes are dealt with promptly, there should not be a problem. A policy should be agreed between the Control of Infection Committee and Domestic Management for the appropriate decontamination of rooms occupied by infectious patients. (Wiping hard surfaces with a phenolic disinfectant after occupancy by a patient with MRSA may be appropriate.)

EQUIPMENT

Clinical equipment

The importance of adequate cleaning, disinfection and sterilisation of all equipment coming into patient contact was discussed in Chapter 6. 'High-risk' invasive equipment which penetrates or comes into direct contact with breaks in skin or mucous membranes (e.g. surgical instruments and intravenous or urinary catheters) requires sterilisation. More problems are often found with 'intermediate risk' equipment which comes into contact with skin or mucous membranes either directly or indirectly. Outbreaks of infection have been recorded: from an inadequately disinfected Ambu bag (Stone and Das,

1985), inadequately dismantled and cleaned breast milk pumps (Gransden et al, 1986), and several items of intensive-care-unit equipment, including suction apparatus and handwash dispenser nozzles (Standring, 1982).

It is important to have an approved regime for dealing with all clinical equipment and some method of monitoring that the agreed process of cleaning and disinfection has taken place (see Chapter 6). Many hospitals have a disinfection unit where items such as ventilators may be taken for decontamination and servicing. In cost-conscious times, the cost of disposable items must be balanced against the cost of reprocessing. Recent legislation suggests that in reprocessing a 'single-use' item, the operator then takes product liability (see HN(88) 3 (DHSS, 1988)) for the device (see Chapter 6). Product liability claims are subject to unlimited compensation.

Other equipment

Equipment used for cleaning was discussed in Chapter 6. Other items in patient contact include bedding, mattresses, duvets, wash bowls, baths and showers. Claesson and Claesson (1985) have described an outbreak of puerperal infection with β-haemolytic streptococci (group A) attributed to a hand-held shower head in communal use for perineal toilet. Mattresses have been implicated in an outbreak of *Pseudomonas aeruginosa* infection in burns patients (Lilly et al, 1982). The mattresses were found to be cracked, stained and colonised with the organisms. Loomes (1988) has reported on a study on mattresses from a burns unit and an intensive care unit. This revealed many stained covers and also staining of the foam interior in many cases. Sampling revealed bacterial growth in 15 of 29 mattresses sampled, including multi-resistant *Acinetobacter* spp. (see Chapter 8) in nine instances. This organism had been causing problems in both these units. All mattresses in the units are now regularly examined, and removed from use if they show staining.

A recent Safety Action Bulletin (SAB) from the combined Health Departments (DOH) gives advice on care and cleaning of mattresses, following recognition of their contribution to the spread of infections (DOH, 1991c). This stresses:

1. that cleaning with a solution of hot water and detergent is usually all that is required;
2. phenols and alcohols may damage the waterproof covering and should not be used;
3. a solution of hypochlorite (1000 ppm/0.1%) may be used on the advice of Control of Infection staff; and
4. mattresses should be allowed to dry to reduce the chance of mould growth occurring.

Regular turning also helps to increase the life of a foam mattress.

The use of duvets is still controversial (Ayton, 1983; Croton, 1990). Before introduction of any new equipment, the use, risks and costs must be assessed. In relation to duvets, adequate cleaning or laundering are critical.

Regular checks on *maintenance* are as important as the decontamination procedures; no equipment can be expected to stay permanently in good working order. A certificate stating that effective decontamination has taken place (see Chapter 6) must accompany equipment going for maintenance or repair. SAB (90)61 (DOH, 1990b) highlights the failure of some hospitals to follow the relevant systems and procedures outlined for this in 1987—staff should familiarise themselves and comply with the requirements.

Hospital therapy pools and recreational water facilities such as jacuzzis involve both hospital and community, and can be a source of infection (Brett and du Vivier, 1985; Friend and Newsom, 1986; Ringham, 1989). Effective checks are required for pool-side hygiene, pool maintenance, and water pH, temperature and chlorination (PHLS, 1990).

SERVICES

Catering

'Every piece of poultry, raw meat and vegetables that come into a kitchen is contaminated and has to be treated as such' (Wadey, 1988). The incidence of food poisoning in the UK is steadily rising, with the main organisms involved being

- *Salmonella* spp.
- *Campylobacter*
- *Staphylococcus aureus*
- *Bacillus cereus*
- *Clostridium perfringens*

Hospital patients are probably more susceptible to food poisoning than healthy individuals. The number of people 'at risk' is also greater in a hospital than in the average restaurant or cafe. The patients are also 'captive' and obliged to eat hospital food. (Food brought in by relatives is frowned upon because there is no control on its preparation.) It is essential that high standards of catering hygiene are constantly applied (see Figure 12.1). Mistakes can lead to the sort of disaster which occurred at Stanley Royd hospital in 1984 (see p. 214) in which about 450 individuals were infected with *Salmonella* sp. and 19 patients died. Partly as a result of this incident, Crown Immunity was finally removed from health service catering facilities in 1987.

Figure 12.1 Sources of food poisoning bacteria.

All hospitals must have comprehensive policies on the buying, handling, processing and delivery of food to the consumer, whether staff or patient. The present requirements are for inspection of all food preparation and consumption areas at least twice a year, both by hospital personnel (usually the Clinical Microbiologist) and by Environmental Health Officers.

All staff who have any contact with food delivered to staff or patients require regular education in personal and catering hygiene. It is standard policy in ward kitchens to display a 10-point catering code of hygiene to remind staff of their responsibilities (see Table 12.1). The Food Hygiene (General) Regulations (1970), Food Act (1984) (now replaced by the Food Safety Act 1990), Food Hygiene and Pest Control in the Health Service (DHSS, 1986a), Health Service Catering Hygiene (DHSS, 1986b), Food Safety Act (1990) and Food Hygiene (Amendment) Regulations (DOH, 1990a) are sources of detailed guidance.

Cook–chill systems of catering involve large-scale preparation of food well in advance of the time when it

Table 12.1 10-point catering code of hygiene.

1. ALWAYS wash your hands before touching food, and always after using the WC
2. Tell your supervisor at once of any skin, nose, throat or bowel trouble
3. Cover cuts and sores with waterproof dressings
4. Wear clean clothing and maintain personal hygiene
5. Smoking in a food room is illegal and dangerous. Never cough or sneeze over food
6. Clean as you go in food rooms and keep equipment and utensils clean
7. Keep food clean, covered and either cold or piping hot
8. Keep your hands off food as far as possible
9. Keep the lid on the dustbin
10. Remember the law requires clean, fully equipped, well lit and airy conditions for food preparation

Based on *Health Service Catering: Clean Food* (DHSS 1970).

is needed. It requires factory-style operation with large amounts of storage and adequate stock rotation. Guidelines are now available for these systems which have been introduced in a number of hospitals (DHSS, 1989).

Common abuses or misunderstandings of catering hygiene rules for nursing staff

The DHSS Health Service Catering Hygiene publication (1986b) states that the 'senior nurse is responsible for maintaining day-to-day standards of hygiene' in ward kitchens. In food hygiene training manuals it is specifically stated that nurses should not wear the same outer clothes to serve food as for other nursing duties. This does not necessarily mean having two sets of uniform or aprons, but a simple change of plastic apron would suffice.

One area particularly prone to breakdown in good catering hygiene practice is the management of meals saved for patients who are attending other departments at meal times. It is not satisfactory to reheat such meals in a ward microwave oven or in an ineffectively controlled conventional oven. Inadequate temperatures achieved in reheating food is one of the commonest causes of food poisoning (see Table 12.2). Clear rules about the use of microwave ovens should be available and understood in all areas where they are used. It is best not to allow any cooking at ward level, but the central kitchens must then be able to offer a flexible service for patients who have missed meals. Ward policies should be made concerning the storage of any food at ward level.

A further problem area is ward kitchen equipment, the cleaning and maintenance of which are often neglected. An outbreak of serious infections was recorded on one hospital ward which was traced to a food blender used

Table 12.2 The 10 commonest causes of food poisoning.

1. Food prepared too far in advance
2. Food stored at room temperature, i.e. not under refrigeration*
3. Cooling food too slowly prior to refrigeration
4. Not reheating food to high enough temperature to destroy food poisoning bacteria
5. The use of cooked food contaminated with food poisoning bacteria
6. Undercooking meat and meat products (including poultry)
7. Not thawing frozen meat and poultry for sufficient time
8. Cross-contamination from raw to cooked foods
9. Storing hot food below 63°C (145°F)
10. Infected food handlers

Source: *Health Service Catering; Hygiene*, Appendix 2 (DHSS, 1986b).
* See *Food Hygiene (Amendment) Regulations* (DOH, 1990a). From April 1993 cold food is to be stored at or below 5°C, currently the requirement is at or below 8°C.

to prepare milk-based drinks (Kiddy et al, 1987). A proper schedule of cleaning and clearly designated responsibility is essential.

Enteral feeding

The number of hospital patients receiving nutrition by enteral feeding has risen. These feeds are usually delivered by nasogastric tube, and other supplementary 'sip feeds' must also be made up and administered using the same hygienic precautions as enteral feeds. Nosocomial infections have been associated with enteral feeds (Casewell, 1982; Gibbs, 1983; Hobbs, 1989) and guidelines were brought out by the British Dietetic Association in 1986. It is recommended that unused (opened) feed should not be left at the bedside for longer than 4 h, after which it is to be thrown away (Anderton et al, 1986). Sterile feeds can have the 'hanging' time extended to 24 h maximum, as long as all handling is aseptically managed. Many hospitals now opt to use commercial preparations rather than having to provide a sterile environment for preparation. However, safe management of commercially prepared enteral feeds must still be controlled at ward level.

Laundry

The laundry department provides a vital service for the comfort and safety of patients and staff, but is often misunderstood and undervalued by nursing and other groups of staff. Most Occupational Health Departments could provide a list of injuries occurring in laundry staff due to careless bagging of linen at ward level. A wide variety of dangerous objects are received in the laundry (see Figure 12.2). Nurses must understand the workings of a laundry department (and the often unpleasant

Figure 12.2 Dangerous objects received in the laundry.

conditions under which the personnel work) in order to minimise the dangers to these staff.

Categories of linen

Since 1987 the following categorisation of linen has been recommended (DHSS, 1987):

1. used linen (both soiled and fouled)
2. infected, and
3. heat-labile.

Prior to these recommendations, both foul (linen soiled with urine, faeces or other secretions/excretions) and infected linen was to be bagged in alginate-stitched or water-soluble bags, to enable it to be put into a washing-machine without handling. The damage to machinery was considerable because so many linen bags contain extraneous items (see Figure 12.3). It is no longer considered necessary to treat *foul* linen in this way. However, many laundry workers prefer to continue to

Figure 12.3 Examples of miscellaneous objects received in the laundry.

receive such laundry separately bagged and not requiring handling. If it is convenient to the department, soiled and fouled linen may still be separated (see later in this chapter for blood-stained linen).

Temperature control

Heat disinfection is the aim of the linen washing cycle, but this may eventually be deemed unnecessary. There are no studies proving transmission of organisms such as hepatitis or HIV from infected linen (Daschner, 1989), but other organisms have occasionally been associated with cross-infection. However, this is usually associated with handling at ward level rather than involving laundry personnel. To remove any blood, faecal matter and other material, a pre-wash below 37.8°C (Collins and Josse, 1990) is followed by a minimum temperature of 65°C for at least 10 min or 71°C for at least 3 min. This must include the temperature at the coolest central part of the load so 'mixing' time must be added.

Colour coding

The DHSS recommendations include a colour-code for linen:

1. *white* for soiled or foul linen,
2. *red* for infected linen, and
3. *white with a prominent orange stripe* for heat-sensitive linen (usually personal clothing).

Infected linen

Linen classed as 'infected' includes that from patients suffering from enteric fever, other salmonella infections, dysentery, tuberculosis, hepatitis viruses, human immuno-deficiency virus, notifiable diseases and other infections designated by the Infection Control Officer. Any linen which is blood stained is now included in this category (DOH, 1991b). To avoid handling in the laundry, the linen is first placed in a water-soluble or alginate-stitched bag followed by a red laundry bag. Sodium hypochlorite can be added to the last rinse for infected heat-labile materials. Domestic washing machines are used in some hospitals and these are acceptable providing they have a cycle for disinfection temperatures (see p. 351).

Risks to laundry workers

Protective clothing (rubber gloves, overalls, plastic aprons, and boots where needed) should be used by laundry workers to avoid contamination with the normal and faecal flora which may be present on used and foul linen (Ayliffe et al, 1990). Combined with good personal hygiene, especially handwashing, this should be an adequate safeguard from these organisms. The danger from contaminated sharp objects inadvertently sent to the laundry in uniforms, white coats and bed linen, constitutes the main hazard to laundry workers. Laundry personnel should be encouraged to take part in the immunisation programme against hepatitis B virus. Linen is often bagged incorrectly, despite specific guidelines to avoid danger from contamination (see Figure 12.4).

Problem areas

1. Labelling of linen as 'biohazard' or 'infected' often causes anxiety to laundry workers and 'biohazard' labels should *only* be used if linen is thought to be contaminated with 'biohazard' organisms. These are pathogenic organisms from Hazard Group 3 or 4 (ACDP, 1990a) including hepatitis B virus, HIV, *Salmonella typhi*, *S. paratyphi*, and *Mycobacterium tuberculosis*. The internationally recognised colour to signify danger is yellow and it is now recommended that labels to warn of the possible presence of 'biohazard' organisms should state 'Danger of Infec-

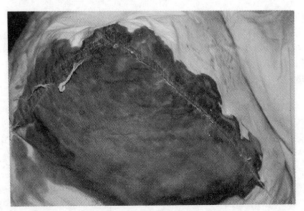

Figure 12.4 Incorrectly bagged blood-stained linen.

tion' in black print on a yellow background (ACDP, 1990b).
2. Labelling of linen with the *name* of an infection can also cause identification of the patient suffering from that disease, resulting in a breach of confidentiality. Linen which is bagged correctly enables the laundry worker to deal with it safely.
3. However, labelling with the name of the *ward* is the only way to identify the source of wrongly bagged linen and extraneous objects received in the laundry.
4. Sharp objects such as needles and scalpel blades, heavy items including monkey poles, contaminated items including bedpans, bottles and their contents, and an amazing variety of articles from slippers to fertiliser have been found in used linen bags. Routine visits to the laundry *by all grades of nursing staff* may help them understand the problems laundry workers have to contend with. Improved understanding here will also improve the service to the patient.

Nursing guidelines

The actual handling of linen by ward staff constitutes the major risk in terms of infection transmission. To prevent this:

*   linen should be handled without shaking (see Overton, 1988)
*   should be bagged according to local and DOH guidelines;
*   should be securely fastened;
*   plastic aprons should protect staff clothes during bed making; and
*   hands should be washed after this activity.

Waste disposal

The number of disposable products used in health care
has increased dramatically in recent years. There are also
misunderstandings among the general population about
the risks from waste products from hospital and community services. These have been heightened by public
fears about risks from body fluids in the light of HIV
infection (Pownall, 1989). Most of the organisms likely
to be found in hospital waste are common contaminants
such as Gram-negative enteric organisms (e.g. *Pseudomonas* spp. and *E. coli*), which are also found in homes
(Scott et al, 1982). However, it is reasonable to attempt
to prevent distress caused to the public by careless
disposal of waste which would enable blood or body-fluid
stained materials, or human tissue to be identified. The
aim is to remove the risk, however small, of transmission
of infection from clinical waste to other patients or
individuals (Griffiths, 1989).

Categories of waste and colour-coding system

Waste can be divided into the following categories.

1. *Household waste*—normal domestic rubbish including
   everything not mentioned below. Put in *black* bags
   and disposed of by landfill.
2. *Clinical waste*—first described in the Health and
   Safety Executive (1982) document and recently
   defined clearly by the London Waste Regulation
   Authority (LWRA, 1989) (see Table 12.3). Divided
   into:
   (a) that destined for incineration (*yellow* bags); and
   (b) that which may be sent for landfilling if inciner-
       ation is a problem (*yellow* bags with a *black*
       band).

Table 12.3 The LWRA definition of clinical waste.

1. Soiled surgical dressings, swabs and instruments
2. Material other than linen from infectious disease cases
3. All human and animal tissue and excretions, including blood
4. Discarded syringes, needles, cartridges, broken glass and other sharp surgical instruments in contact with 1, 2 and 3.
5. Pharmaceutical and chemical products utilized for treatment purposes
6. Used disposable bed-pan liners, urine containers, incontinence pads, sanitary towels, tampons and any other items contaminated as in 3

3. *Laboratory waste* including specimens, culture plates and media which require *autoclaving* before incineration. Put in *light blue* bags or transparent with light blue lettering.

HN(82)22 also describes other waste categories requiring special treatment such as cytotoxic waste and radioactive materials.

Management of waste collections

There should be simple, safe policies for operating and controlling waste collection (Townend, 1988). Containers should be:

- safely secured,
- easily identified, and
- collected at regular intervals.

Daily collections are the minimal requirement for clinical areas, twice daily being preferable. All staff should understand categories of waste and safe bagging, including medical, paramedical and nursing staff. The portering staff and incinerator attendant should be provided with protective clothing and advice on safe handling.

Clinical waste collections from the community are often a source of dispute. The person initiating home collections is often the district nurse, and the service is either provided by the council or can be contracted privately. Either may charge the health authority for this service (Gibbs, 1991). It is vital for confidentiality that these collections are carefully managed and do not lead to identification of a patient's diagnosis.

Storage

The area for storage of waste before removal or incineration needs to be easily cleaned and secure from animals and inquisitive children. Children are at particular danger from hospital waste, frequently having accidents with needles and syringes.

Problem areas

1. Within hospitals one of the commonest problems is incorrect bagging of waste (Taylor, 1988). Education of staff is almost impossible. Much rubbish which is not 'clinical' is often bagged as such, causing unnecessary costs or overloading on hospital incinerators. Conversely, when clinical waste is found in household waste, alarm is caused. Some hospitals have introduced a system where porters refuse to collect waste which is not labelled by the ward at point of origin. This can result in tracing the originator of the incorrect procedure, and has added benefits such as the retrieval of lost articles (Gibbs, 1990).
2. New rules are proposed for control of clinical waste incineration (Goss, 1991). The Environmental

Protection Act (1990) applies to health-service premises and plant. Many hospital incinerators will be unable to comply with the proposed standards concerning plant, storage, reception, incinerator design, chimneys, emissions, operation and monitoring (DOH, 1991a). Authorities will need to examine arrangements for clinical waste disposal and may need to seek alternative methods if they cannot meet new plant standards within the next five years.

The removal of Crown immunity from NHS premises in respect of clinical waste came into force on 1 April 1991 and from 1 April 1992 they are bound by a 'Duty of Care' for ensuring that wastes are properly disposed of (DOH, 1992).

'Sharps'

Any contaminated sharp instrument constitutes the most dangerous form of clinical waste (defined in Table 12.3). There is a definite risk of transmission of hepatitis B virus in particular (but also a number of other pathogens (Collins and Kennedy, 1987)) from an injury involving a sharp instrument contaminated with blood from a carrier or infected person.

Containers for 'sharps' should be robust, resist penetration and leakage, have a secure closure, a flap aperture to inhibit removal of sharps, be incinerable and be basically coloured yellow (DHSS, 1982). A new British Standard has been issued (BSI, 1990). There should always be a container *at the point of use* to encourage prompt disposal of all 'sharps'.

Common problems with 'sharps' disposal

1. The majority of 'needlestick' or 'sharps' injuries occur during preparation for *disposal* of the item (Jagger

et al, 1988). Education is needed to persuade people to:

(a) always dispose of the item *immediately* at the point of use (by the user!),

(b) avoid overfilling disposal containers, and

(c) to have sufficient containers regardless of cost arguments. (Compensation for occupationally acquired infection could obviate any saving made.)

2. Many needlestick injuries occur from resheathing of needles (e.g. Becker et al, 1990; Gerberding, 1990). This practice is specifically contraindicated in recent DOH documents (ACDP, 1990a; DOH, 1991a), and the BMA code of practice (BMA, 1990). This area is one in which nurses and doctors remain obstinately averse to change; Gerberding (1990) found that, despite good facilities and education on the matter, 50% of needles were still being recapped in a San Francisco hospital. The specification for containers also requests that needle and syringe should be disposed of as one unit.

3. Many nurses working in the community experience problems in disposing of waste and sharps. The range of disposal boxes include some specifically designed for community use. Some ignorance of correct practice is also recorded by Archer (1988), where nurses gave advice to their patients on disposal of needles in a variety of ways. The district nurse has a good opportunity to explain to people about safe disposal, and one method of ensuring this might be to allow those requiring injections (e.g. patients with diabetes) to take a container with them on discharge from hospital (Gibbs, 1991).

Education

This is a vital component of infection control and in relation to sharps disposal the ICNA in conjunction with Becton-Dickinson have recently brought out a pack containing a standard on use of sharps for managers and health care workers. There are accompanying posters and a five-point code (reproduced below). Gwyther (1990) points out that the perfect disposal container may never be found and that education for all 'sharps' users is paramount (see Figure 14.4).

Five points to remember

1. Always dispose of used sharps directly into an approved sharps disposal container.
2. Do not re-sheath used needles by hand.
3. Do not overfill sharps boxes—change when 3/4 full.
4. Whenever possible take a sharps disposal box to the point you use them.
5. Report all sharps injuries immediately, according to the Health Authority policy.

All District Health Authorities should have a clear policy on immediate and follow-up treatment for needlestick injuries (DOH, 1990), and ensure that all staff are fully conversant with this.

Disposal of excreta

With very few exceptions (e.g. patients suffering from Lassa fever and other viral haemorrhagic fevers in special isolation), urine, faeces and waste water from hospitals can be released into the sewage system without any special treatment. People suffering from typhoid and other infectious diseases in the community are not required to take any special precautions when disposing of their excreta, and it is illogical to ask hospitals to act differently.

Many nurses still feel that they should use disinfectant to cover excreta from patients with *Salmonella* infection before disposal. *This is ineffective and potentially dangerous as there is more chance of spillage occurring while the contents of the bed-pan are left in the sluice.* The safe and effective method of dealing with *all* excreta is the use of either a bed-pan washer/disinfector with a steam disinfection cycle of 80°C for 1 min (CSC, 1986), or a macerator which disposes of the *papier maché* bed-pan or urinal and contents together. In this case the nurse must ensure that the plastic bedpan holder is thoroughly washed in hot water and soap and dried to prevent any risk of residual contamination.

Domestic services

The principles of cleaning, disinfection and sterilization and the potential of spread of infection by inadequately maintained cleaning equipment have already been discussed in Chapter 6. Nurses need to understand the importance of domestic cleaning and make every attempt to cooperate with domestic staff as a team. Major misunderstandings arise when this cooperation is lacking, especially regarding cleaning of isolation rooms. Clear guidelines should be agreed between Control of Infection and Domestic staff, and ward staff should understand and help in their implementation.

REFERENCES

ACDP (Advisory Committee on Dangerous Pathogens) (1990a) *Categorisation of Pathogens according to Hazard and Categories of Containment*, 2nd edn. London: HMSO.
ACDP (Advisory Committee on Dangerous Pathogens) (1990b) *HIV—*

The Causative Agent of AIDS and Related Conditions, 2nd revision of guidelines. London: HMSO.

Anderton A, Howard JP and Scott DW (1986) *Microbiological Control in Enteral Feeding*. British Dietetic Association.

Archer HG (1988) Waste in the home. *Nursing Standard* 21(2): 26–27.

Ayliffe GAJ and Lowbury EJL (1982) Airborne infection in hospital *J. Hosp. Infect.* 3:217–240.

Ayliffe GAJ, Collins B and Taylor LJ (1990) *Hospital-acquired Infection: Principles and Prevention*, 2nd edn. London: Wright.

Ayton M (1983) Continental quilts—their use in hospitals. *Nursing Times* 79(30): 64–65.

Becker MH, Janz NK, Band J *et al* (1990) Noncompliance with Universal Precautions Policy: Why do physicians and nurses recap needles? *Am. J. Infect. Control* 18: 232–239.

Bibby BA (1982) Mathematic modelling of patient risk. Ph.D. thesis, Aston University.

Brett J and du Vivier A (1985) *Pseudomonas aeruginosa* and whirlpools. *Br. Med. J.* 290: 1024–1025.

BMA (British Medical Association) (1990) *A Code of Practice for the Safe Use and Disposal of Sharps*. London: BMA.

BSI (British Standards Institution) (1990) *BS 7320 British Standard Specification for Sharps Containers*. Milton Keynes: BSI.

Casewell M (1982) Bacteriological hazards of contaminated enteral feeds. *J. Hosp. Infect.* 3: 329–331.

CSC (1986) *Central Sterilising Club Report No. 1. Washer/disinfectors*.

Claesson BEB and Claesson UL-E (1985) An outbreak of endometritis in a maternity unit caused by spread of Group A streptococci from a showerhead. *J. Hosp. Infect.* 6: 304–311.

Collins B (1988) The hospital environment, how clean should a hospital be? *J. Hosp. Infect.* 11 (Suppl. A): 53–56.

Collins BJ and Josse ED (1990) The patient's environment. In (Worsley MA *et al* (eds)) *Infection Control. Guidelines for Nursing Care*, pp. 7–14. ICNA/Surgikos.

Collins CH and Kennedy DA (1987) Microbiological hazards of occupational needlestick and 'sharps' injuries. *J. Appl. Bacteriol.* 62: 385–402.

Croton CM (1990) Duvets on trial. *Nursing Times, J. Infect. Control Nursing* 86(26): 63–67.

Daschner F (1989) Cost-effectiveness in hospital infection control—lessons for the 1990s. *J. Hosp. Infect.* 13(4): 325–336.

DHSS (1982) *Specification for Containers for the Disposal of Used Needles and Sharp Instruments* TSS/S/330.015. London: HMSO.

DHSS (1986a) *Food Hygiene and Pest Control in the Health Service* HC(86) 14. London: HMSO.

DHSS (1986b) *Health Service Catering: Hygiene*. London: HMSO.

DHSS (1987) *Hospital Laundry Arrangements for Used and Infected Linen* HC(87)30. London: DHSS.

DHSS (1988) *Procurement—Product Liability* **HN(88) 3**. London: HMSO.

DHSS (1989) *Health Service Guidelines on Pre-cooked Chilled Foods* **HC(89) 19**. London: HMSO.

DOH (1990a) *Guidelines on Food Hygiene (Amendment) Regulations* **SI 1990 No. 1431**. London: HMSO.

DOH (1990b) *Decontamination of Medical Equipment and Devices prior to Investigation, Inspection, Service or Repair* **SAB (90) 61** London: UK Health Departments.

DOH (1991a) *Strategic Guide to Waste Management* **Circular EL(90)M/I**. London: Departments of Health.

DOH (1991b) *Decontamination of Equipment, Linen or other Surfaces Contaminated with Hepatitis B and/or Human Immunodeficiency Viruses* **HC(91) 33**. London: UK Health Departments.

DOH (1991c) (Safety Action Bulletin) *Hospital Mattress Assemblies: Care and Cleaning* **SAB(91) 65**. London: UK Health Departments.

DOH (1992) *Waste Management, the Duty of Care: A Code of Practice*. London: HMSO.

Environmental Protection Act (1990). London: HMSO.

Food Act (1984) London: HMSO.

Food Safety Act (1990) London: HMSO.

Friend PA and Newsom SWB (1986) Hygiene for hydrotherapy pools. *J. Hosp. Infect.* **8**(3): 213–216.

Gerberding J (1990) Post HIV exposure management: the San Francisco General Hospital experience. *AIDS Pat. Care* **4**(5): 22–24.

Gibbs J (1983) Bacterial contamination of nasogastric feeds. *Nursing Times, J. Infect. Control Nursing* **79**(7): 41–47.

Gibbs J (1991) Clinical waste disposal in the community. *Nursing Times* **87**(2): 40–41.

Gibbs J (1990) Waste line. *Nursing Times* **86**(13): 71–73.

Goss JP (1991) Technical aspects of Clinical Waste Incineration. *Infection Control Yearbook—ICNA*. St Ives: CMA Medical Data Ltd.

Gransden WR, Webster M, French GL and Phillips I (1986) An outbreak of *Serratia marcescens* transmitted by contaminated breast pumps in a special care baby unit. *J. Hosp. Infect.* **7**(2): 149–154.

Griffiths G (1989) Safety in disposal. *Nursing Standard* **4**(8): 52–56.

Gwyther J (1990) Sharps disposal containers and their use. *J. Hosp. Inf.* **15**(3): 287–294.

Hambraeus A, Bengtsson S and Laurell G (1978) Bacterial contamination in a modern operating suite. Effect of a zoning system on contamination of floors and other surfaces. *J. Hyg.* **80**: 57–67.

Health and Safety Executive (1982) *The Safe Disposal of Clinical Waste* **HN(82) 22**. London: HMSO.

Hobbs P (1989) Enteral feeds. *Nursing Times, J. Infect. Control Nursing* **85**(9): 71–73.

ICNA/Becton Dickinson (1990) *The Safe Use and Disposal of Sharps*. ICNA/Becton Dickinson Working Group, Sept. 1990.

Jagger J, Hunt EH, Brand-Elnaggar J and Pearson RD (1988) Rates of needlestick injury caused by various devices in a University hospital. *N. Engl. J. Med.* **318**: 284–288.

Kiddy K, Josse E and Griffin N (1987) An outbreak of serious klebsiella infections related to food blenders. *J. Hosp. Infect.* **9**: 191–193.

Lidwell OM, Lowbury EJL, Whyte W, Blowers R, Stanley SJ and Lowe D (1982) Effect of ultra-clean air in operation rooms on deep sepsis in the joint after total hip or knee replacement: a randomised study. *Br. Med. J.* **285**: 10–14.

Lilly HA, Kidson A and Fujita K (1981) Investigation of hospital infection from a damaged mattress and the demonstration of its mechanism. *Burns* **8**(6): 408–413.

Loomes S (1988) Is it safe to lie down in hospital? *Nursing Times, J. Infect. Control Nursing* **84**(49): 63–65.

LWRA (London Waste Regulation Authority) (1989) *Clinical Waste—An Appraisal and Guidelines for the Segregation, Handling and Transport of Clinical Waste.* London: LWRA.

Maki DG, Alvarado CJ, Hassemer CA and Zilz MA (1982) Relation of the inanimate hospital environment to endemic nosocomial infection. *N. Engl. J. Med.* **307**: 1562–1566.

McGowan JE (1982) Whence come nosocomial infections? *N. Engl. J. Med.* **307**: 1576–1577.

Nagai I, Kadota M, Takechi M, *et al* (1984) Studies on the mode of bacterial contamination of an operating theatre corridor floor. *J. Hosp. Infect.* **5**(1): 50–55.

Overton E (1988) Bed-making and bacteria. *Nursing Times* **84**(9): 69–71.

Pownall M (1989) Tipping the balance. *Nursing Times* **85**(11): 20.

PHLS (Public Health Laboratory Service) (1990) *Hygiene for Hydrotherapy Pools.* London: PHLS.

Ringham S (1989) A whirlpool of bacteria. *Nursing Times, J. Infect. Control Nursing* **85**(23): 77–80.

Scott E, Bloomfield SF and Barlow CC (1982) An investigation of microbial contamination in the home. *J. Hyg.* **89**(2): 279–293.

Standring JA (1982) A gentamicin-resistant *Pseudomonas aeruginosa* surveillance by the Control of Infection team. *Proceedings of 13th Conference of the ICNA*, London.

Statutory Instruments England and Wales (1970) *Food Hygiene (General) Regulations.* London: HMSO.

Stone JW and Das BC (1985) Investigation of an outbreak of infection with *Acinetobacter calcoaceticus* in a special care baby unit. *J. Hosp. Inf.* **7**(1): 42–48.

Suzuki A, Namba Y, Matsuura M and Horisawa A (1984) Airborne contamination in an operating suite: a 5 year survey. *J. Hyg.* **93**(3): 567–573.

Taylor LJ (1988) Segregation, collection and disposal of hospital laundry and waste. *J. Hosp. Infect.* **11** (Suppl. A): 57–63.

Townend WK (1988) The management of clinical waste. *Proc. 2nd*

International Conf. on Infection Control—ICNA. St Ives: CMA Medical Data Ltd.

UK Health Departments (1990) *Guidance for Clinical Health Care Workers*. London: HMSO.

Wadey C (1988) Removal of Crown Immunity and its implications. *Infection Control Yearbook*. St Ives: CMA Medical Data.

FURTHER READING

Centers for Disease Control (1989) Guidelines for prevention of transmission of HIV and HBV to health care and public safety workers. *MMWR* **38**: S-6.

Centers for Disease Control (1990) Public Health Service Statement on management of occupational exposure to HIV, including considerations regarding zidovudine postexposure use. *MMWR* **39**: RR-1.

Department of the Environment (1983) *Waste Management Paper No. 25: Clinical wastes*. London: HMSO.

Fuell WG (1980) The contribution of the laundry to infection control. *Proceedings of 11th Annual Symposium ICNA*.

Gibbs J (1990) Disposing of waste. *Nursing Times* **86**(51): 34–35.

Lacey R (1989) *Safe Shopping, Safe Cooking, Safe Eating*. London: Penguin.

Morgan DR (1988) Needlestick injuries: how can we teach people better about risk assessment? *J. Hosp. Infect.* **12**: 301–309.

Smith F (1991) Looking into the refrigerator. *Nursing Times* **87**(38): 61–62.

Statutory Instrument (1988) *No. 819: The Collection and Disposal of Waste Regulations*. London: HMSO.

Weinstein SA, Gantz NM, Pelletier C and Hibert D (1989) Bacterial surface contamination of patients' linen. *Am. J. Infect. Control* **17**(5): 264–267.

World Health Organisation (1985) *Management of Waste from Hospitals*. Regional Office for Europe. Copenhagen: WHO.

13 Care of the infected/at-risk patient—aseptic techniques and basic infection control measures

In Chapter 11 the groups of patients who make up most of those acquiring hospital-acquired infection were discussed briefly. This chapter describes the care of these patients—both those at risk of and those already having acquired infection—and how to minimize spread of these infections.

ASEPTIC TECHNIQUES

The principle of *asepsis* is to prevent the introduction of microorganisms into sites that are normally free of them, or in normally non-sterile areas to avoid the introduction of microorganisms from outside sources. This covers a wide range of activities from the operating department, where all materials coming into contact with tissues must be sterile, to ward and departmental procedures, including renewal of wound dressings, catheterisation, tracheal suction and suture removal. The principles of disinfection and sterilisation have been dealt with earlier in the text. This chapter highlights the care of patients receiving urinary and intravenous catheterisation, or undergoing surgery or parenteral nutrition. These patients are at increased risk of infection because these interventions all breach the body's natural defence mechanisms. Care is aimed at applying the principles of asepsis to prevent or minimise infection risks.

HANDS

Handwashing is stated to be the single (or one of the) most important elements in control of infection, particularly regarding transfer of organisms by contact (see e.g. Ackerman and Dunk-Richards, 1991; Ayliffe et al, 1990; Caddow, 1989; Garner and Favero, 1986; Steere and Mallison, 1975). However, a variety of studies have shown that hands are either inadequately, inappropriately or too infrequently washed (Albert and Condie, 1981; Gidley, 1987; Taylor, 1978; Williams and Buckles, 1988) and this applies to patients as well as staff (Pritchard and Hathaway, 1988). Outbreaks of infection associated with contaminated staff hands are well documented (e.g. Knittle et al, 1975; Casewell and Phillips, 1977).

Nurses and other health-care workers need to believe that hands can and do transmit infection, and realise that this can be prevented by good and appropriate hand-washing techniques. A final ingredient seems to be needed, some magical extra which combines to motivate personnel (see Figure 13.1) to actually do it!

What is on our hands?

This can be divided into two categories.

1. *Resident organisms*—mostly *Staphylococcus aureus* and diphtheroids; these cannot be permanently removed and are the reason a no-touch technique is needed for aseptic procedures.
2. *Transient organisms*—these are the organisms picked up in contact, e.g. with patients, equipment and the environment. They are mostly Gram-negative bacilli,

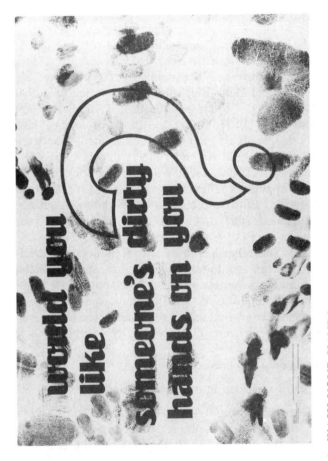

Figure 13.1 WASH YOUR HANDS . . . .

but may include a variety of others. It is these
organisms which have been implicated in hospital-
acquired outbreaks of infection, yet these are remov-
able by simple, efficient handwashing.

It is unpleasant to note that Jackson (1984) estimated
that 20% of patients with enteric infections get faeces on
their hands before a meal. Pritchard and Hathaway (1988)
observed that nurses failed to offer non-ambulant patients
a chance to clean their hands after using bed-pan,
commode or urinal. These two studies highlight that there
is both a *need* for care and a *cause for concern* at nurses'
lack of risk perception.

WHY do we need to wash our hands?

Patient-care activities which involve close contact with
patients' secretions or excreta will mean the carer has
probably been contaminated with the patient's normal
flora, even if they have no actual infection. As explained
in Chapter 3, the normal flora of one area, e.g. bowel,
will be the pathogen of another, e.g. urinary or respiratory
tract. Several nursing studies reveal a lack of understanding of this point (Pritchard and Hathaway, 1988; Sneddon,
1990).

WHEN should we wash them?

CDC (Centers for Disease Control) and other guidelines
suggest that hands should be washed (Simmons, 1982)

- before and after any aseptic technique/invasive procedure;
- before contact with any susceptible site (e.g. intravenous infusion site) or patient (e.g. immunosuppressed person);
- after contact with body fluids, excreta;

- after handling contaminated equipment, waste, laundry;
- before and after contact with any patient on isolation precautions;
- before serving meals or drinks;
- after using the toilet; and
- at the start and end of a spell of duty.

HOW should we wash them?

Studies have shown a wide range of hand-washing techniques, with times ranging from a few seconds to several minutes. However, what is important is to wash the hands under running water, as warm as tolerable, using either soap or a skin disinfectant according to the circumstances. A vigorous action rubbing the hands together is needed, and all areas of the hand should be covered. Taylor (1978) has demonstrated how certain areas of the hands and fingers are frequently omitted (see Figure 13.2). Rings should either be removed, or moved to ensure washing underneath them. (Nails should be kept short, unvarnished and the routine use of nail brushes should be avoided as the bristles can cause minor abrasions.)

After rinsing, the hands should be thoroughly dried. Efficient drying is of major importance—moisture left on hands can act as a culture media for bacteria and as a transfer mechanism. The taps should be turned off with elbows, or using a clean paper towel *after* drying (if elbow taps are not provided). Foot-operated pedal bins should be available for disposing of paper hand towels.

WHAT should we use?

The efficiency of the hand wash is the most important element. However, hand washing preparations can be divided into two groups.

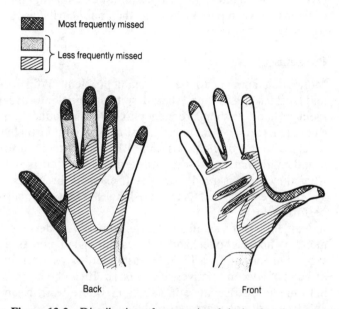

Figure 13.2 Distribution of areas missed during hand washing.

1. Soap and water for routine decontamination of hands. (Liquid soap in disposable containers avoids the problem of reservoirs which could become contaminated.) This is used after activities such as handling contaminated equipment, laundry, bed pans, or before serving food and drinks.
2. A skin disinfectant such as chlorhexidine gluconate (e.g. Hibiscrub). This has a residual, antibacterial effect on the skin and helps remove resident as well as transient organisms. It is advisable before aseptic procedures, in high-risk areas such as intensive care and special care baby units, and for pre-operative use by theatre teams.

(An alcoholic hand rub is also useful for decontamination of hands between patient contact when not heavily/visibly soiled.)

Problems

Motivation appears to be the main problem. Williams and Buckles (1988) found that, despite an initial improvement in hand washing frequency following an education campaign, after 6 months the situation had virtually reverted to the original position. They, and others, also found that what health-care workers say they do is not what they are observed to do. Staff claimed three times as many episodes of hand washing as they actually performed!

Availability of facilities is also essential. The development of an alcoholic hand rub was designed not as a substitute for hand washing, but as an aid to disinfection of hands between relatively clean tasks. It can be a great help to the district nurse in situations where wash basin and soap are not readily available.

Good products for washing and drying hands are needed if staff are even to come close to complying with hand washing recommendations. Sore, chapped hands will dissuade staff from washing and are also a potential source of infection. Hand cream to maintain smooth hands should always be a personal, not a communal, item.

Perhaps the use of shock tactics (see Figure 13.3) are needed periodically to remind staff about the need for hand washing.

CARE OF THE CATHETERIZED PATIENT

The high percentage of hospital-acquired infection (HAI) which is due to urinary tract infection has already been

Figure 13.3 Hands.

mentioned. In addition to that of Meers et al (1981), a variety of studies have attributed 35–45% of HAI to urinary tract infections (UTIs). Most UTIs occur in catheterised patients, either those with in-dwelling catheters (about 80%) or after some form of instrumentation such as cystoscopy (about 20%) (Stamm, 1986). As many patients are also managed at home with long-term indwelling catheters, this is a source of concern within the community (UTI was responsible for 14.5% of community-acquired infection (CAI) in the UK prevalence study).

It has been estimated (Kunin, 1979) that 1 in 10 of all patients in hospital are catheterised. The potential discomfort, cost and prolongation of bed occupancy due to UTI is considerable. The most serious complication of UTI is septicaemia, and UTI accounts for 30–40% of all Gram-negative hospital-acquired bacteraemias (Stamm, 1986) with a mortality rate of about 30%.

The organisms most commonly involved are Gram-negative rods, notably *Escherichia coli*. Table 13.1 shows a list of the organisms causing most UTIs in two infection surveys. Many infections originate from the patient's own flora, especially those occurring early in

Table 13.1 Pathogens commonly causing UTI.

Pathogen	Meers et al (1981)	NNIS*
E. coli	43.7	31.9
Proteus spp.	12.9	6.7
Klebsiella spp.	8.3	8.8
Gp. D streptococci	7.2	14.4
P. aeruginosa	5.2	11.5

* National Nosocomial Infections Study (Haley et al, 1985).

catheterisation. There is an increasing problem with antibiotic-resistant or virulent strains of bacteria. Outbreaks of infection have been caused by transference via staff hands or improperly cleaned equipment such as urinals or jugs (Casewell et al, 1977; Speller, 1980).

Risk factors

Certain host factors are known to increase the risk of UTI after instrumentation or catheterisation. The following are unalterable: age (older people are far more susceptible); sex (women are more at risk); underlying severe illness increases risk; and colonisation of the meatal area. However, certain other factors which also increase the risk of infection *can* be altered:

* catheterisation when alternatives exist;
* number of times catheterisation takes place;
* length of time catheter in place (risk rises daily);
* catheter-care techniques (see below); and
* drainage system in use.

Care of the catheterised patient

As the nurse is the person giving most care to patients with in-dwelling catheters, he/she must understand the potential for infection and apply appropriate care.

Entry of infection

1. Entry along the lumen of the catheter may occur due to failure in aseptic technique on insertion of the catheter, or possibly by retrograde spread from the drainage bag, perhaps in air bubbles. Various nursing studies have documented failure by nursing staff to

either understand the principles of a *closed system of drainage* or to apply that understanding in its care (e.g. Seal and Ward, 1983; Crummy, 1985; Crow et al, 1986; Glenister, 1987; Mulhall et al, 1988). Breaking the system when emptying or changing drainage bags, or taking specimens incorrectly can introduce bacteria from the nurse's hands into the drainage system.

2. Entry may occur between the catheter and the wall of the urethra. Securing the catheter to the patient's leg correctly will prevent the piston-like effect of the catheter dragging up and down (Jenner, 1977). Contamination at the catheter–meatal junction may occur from staff hands or contaminated equipment. Figure 13.4 shows the entry points where bacteria may gain access to a urinary drainage system.

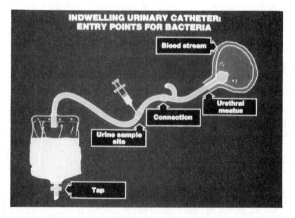

Figure 13.4 Entry points for bacteria in a urinary drainage system.

Urethral care

Much research has been done on the effectiveness or otherwise of cleansing the catheter–meatal junction with antiseptics to prevent infection transmission via the periurethral space. No conclusive evidence has been found to support this procedure (Britt et al, 1976; Burke et al, 1981; Gibbs, 1986). However Glenister (1990) points out that for patient comfort or a visibly dirty catheter, simple cleaning with soap and water is a reasonable measure. There is evidence to suggest that using antiseptics may predispose to selection of resistant organisms (Baillie, 1987) and is, therefore, to be avoided.

Measures to prevent infection

1. Never use a catheter when it is possible to find an alternative. If catheterisation is imperative, use for as short a time as possible. If long-term catheterisation is needed, use the appropriate material.
2. Use appropriate gauge and balloon sizes (to ensure minimal trauma), and correct length, e.g. female catheters which are much shorter than the male length. This is due to the difference in length of the male and female urethra, and allows ambulant female patients to hide the drainage bag under clothing. The 'use-by' date should be checked, and details of catheter batch number and amount of water used to fill the balloon should also be documented in nursing or medical notes.
3. Ensure that all staff involved in catheterisation are aware of the dangers of infection and perform the procedure using a full aseptic technique.
4. Maintain the closed system of drainage—do not disconnect the bag from the catheter (disconnection is associated with increased incidence of infection):

- use the sampling sleeve to take urine specimens, first cleaning the sleeve with an alcohol wipe and allow to dry;
- use bags with drainable taps, and a leg bag link system for ambulant patients;
- do not use spiggots; and
- avoid bladder irrigation if possible, and use a three-way Foley catheter if irrigation is necessary.

5. Wash and dry hands carefully whenever having any contact with the catheter-drainage system, even if using gloves.

6. Take care not to contaminate the system when emptying the drainage bag. Do not let the tap touch the floor, or the container, and ensure that containers used to drain the urine into are either disposable or heat disinfected.

7. When positioning the drainage bag always ensure that there is no traction on the catheter caused by tubing becoming twisted or flattened. Do not allow the drainage bag to be held above bladder level or retrograde infection may occur.

8. Assist the patient to understand and manage the system themselves when possible, and help them maintain their comfort and dignity.

9. Spatial separation of catheterised patients is advisable, especially if infection has occurred.

   Hand hygiene is probably the most important infection control measure in this as in most areas.

Education

Most hospitals and community services have guidelines for catheterisation and catheter-care procedures. However, there is abundant evidence that nurses either do not apply, or fail to understand the rationale for these procedures. Several surveys (noted earlier) have demonstrated instances of:

- nurses allowing bags to touch the floor;
- failure to wash hands after emptying bags;
- failure to decontaminate emptying devices before reuse, or using inappropriate antiseptics to try and achieve this; and
- changing drainage bags as frequently as several times a day.

All this despite knowledge of proper procedures. Two recent surveys describe improvement in techniques after introduction of policies (Wyatt and Timoney, 1987; Wilson, 1990). This must be backed up by an educational programme so that nurses can appreciate their role in patients acquiring or avoiding a UTI (Barnett, 1991). Information must also be given to patients who need long-term indwelling catheters if these are to be successfully managed (Roe, 1989).

PATIENTS WITH SURGICAL WOUNDS

Surgical wound infections (SWIs) are the second or third (according to survey) largest cause of nosocomial infections in most studies, comprising 12–24% of all such infections (Brown et al, 1987). They are more costly than UTIs and may be associated with significant morbidity.

The *aim* of all wound management should be to treat the whole individual and not only the wound.

There are several major *risk factors* influencing surgical wounds:

1. *host susceptibility*, including age, nutritional state, the presence of underlying or additional disease and/or infection, and drug treatment;

2. *surgical technique* (careful and minimal tissue handling, good haemostasis, good approximation of wound
   edges, no failure of asepsis); and
3. *the amount of bacterial contamination at surgery*
   (Bibby et al, 1986; Garner, 1986; O'Brien, 1986).

Infection can occur either in the operating theatre
(most often) or in the ward. Many detailed assessments
of pre- and peri-operative procedures (*in addition to the
type of operation*) have shown the following to be relevant
to the incidence of SWI:

- length of pre-operative stay in hospital,
- skin preparation (skin cleansing and hair removal),
- skin preparation of surgeon's hands,
- theatre ventilation,
- theatre clothing and drapes,
- theatre team activities,
- length of operation time, and
- foreign bodies, i.e. suture material, wound drains
  (see Figure 13.5).

Although it may appear that the nurse can do little to
influence many of the factors listed above, there are
others over which the nurse has some control, and these
are discussed briefly.

Skin cleansing and hair removal

Pre-operative bathing has long been part of the 'routine',
but evidence for the effectiveness of showering or bathing
with use of an antiseptic is still confusing (Cruse and
Foord, 1980; Hayek et al, 1987; Rotter et al, 1988).
Ayliffe et al (1990) suggest that a single antiseptic bath
will have little effect, but two or more may be of
value. Certain operations commonly have a pre-operative
multiple-bath or local application of antiseptic routine,
e.g. before hip replacement surgery.

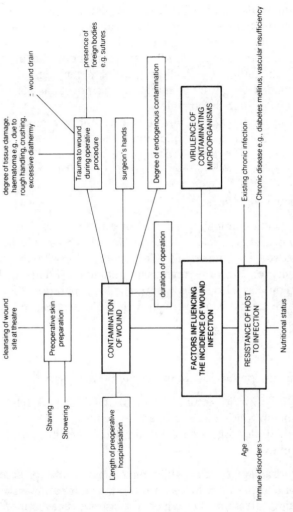

Figure 13.5 Factors influencing the incidence of wound infection.

382 MICROBIOLOGY FOR NURSES

Shaving of the operation site has been shown to cause local skin damage which will increase infection risk (Hamilton et al, 1977). There is also a higher rate of infection than in patients undergoing hair removal by depilatory cream (Seropian and Reynolds, 1971). Many surgeons and nurses are reluctant to abandon shaving the site altogether but, where possible, they should be persuaded to permit minimal hair removal (as close to operation time as possible).

Skin preparation in theatre is a well-proven method of avoiding endogenous infection from the patient's own skin flora. Povidone–iodine or alcoholic chlorhexidine preparations are routinely used (Cruse, 1986).

Theatre conditions

Air conditioning and design of theatre suites so that flow of work is from clean to dirty areas have already been discussed in Chapter 12. The effect of movement and activity on airborne organisms potentially entering the incision has also been mentioned. (Preparation of the theatre teams' hands is dealt with in the section on hand washing.)

Drainage

Drainage of surgical wounds may be necessary:

- to prevent accumulation of fluid in cavities, if haemostasis has been hard to achieve;
- or if an abscess has to drain before healing can take place.

Any drainage system (which maintains a route for access of organisms via a break in the skin) adds to the risk of wound infection. Strategies for aseptic care must be carefully planned. Closed systems of drainage should be used whenever possible. Penrose-type drains increase infection risks as they allow bacteria entry to the tip of the drain, take much longer than suction drains to attend to, and are uncomfortable for the patient (Cruse, 1986).

Direct nursing involvement

The nurse on the ward needs to know what procedures to follow and what signs or symptoms of impending infection to look out for. Garner (1986) cites three essentials in post-operative wound care.

1. Strict hand-washing before and after attention to a wound.
2. No touching of an open or fresh wound directly without the use of sterile gloves, or a 'no-touch' technique.
3. Removal of a dressing if leakage has occurred or the patient complains of pain, has fever or other sign of infection.

The nurse should aim to prevent the wound being contaminated from the outside, and observe for changes indicating problems within (David, 1986). Apart from leakage, a dressing should be observed for bulging or bruising around it. Any pyrexia, or reporting by patient or nurse of pain, smell or irritation requires investigation.

The following section highlights a few areas of concern and misunderstanding.

Dressings

The following applies to wounds healing by primary **or** secondary intention.

1. A common accusation made between surgeon and nurse is that wound infection has followed failure of

aseptic technique while handling wound dressings. This can be minimised if rules are understood and strictly adhered to by both parties. Most surgical areas have a policy to leave a wound dressing alone for 24–48 h post-operatively, unless any of the symptoms listed above have occurred. As clean and undrained incisions will seal within 24 h, there is no need to reapply a dressing when the original one is removed, assuming that no leakage is occurring (Chrintz et al, 1989). Nursing time and dressing material costs are reduced, and ease of observing the wound is enhanced. The patient is also in a better position to manage personal hygiene. Chrintz' study (which involved 1202 patients) also suggests that these patients should be encouraged to bathe or shower normally.

2. The time-honoured practice of ceasing activities such as bed making and ward cleaning for a set time before performing dressings is rarely practicable. Dressing 'rounds' are not compatible with individual-ised patient care, and airborne transfer of organisms at ward level is less likely than transfer by hands (Ayliffe et al, 1990).

3. *Materials* used for dressings (particularly those used for chronic wounds, e.g. leg ulcers) have undergone tremendous advances in recent years. Several series have appeared in the nursing press, and books by Westaby (1985) and David (1986) go into considerable detail. The 'ideal' dressing has been much discussed (see Table 13.2). It is helpful to have a wound-care policy agreed by interested parties, and a single example of each type of dressing (e.g. hydrocolloids, hydrogels, alginates, foam and deodourising dressings) made available on an agreed formulary,

Table 13.2 Characteristics of an 'ideal dressing'.

1. Provides the best environment for wound healing
2. Maintains a moist environment at wound–dressing interface
3. Provides thermal insulation
4. Provides an intact barrier to microorganisms
5. Allows gaseous exchange of oxygen, carbon dioxide and water vapour
6. Free from particulate contaminants
7. Has good absorption properties
8. Non-adherent
9. Easy to use and acceptable to the patient
10. Non-toxic, non-allergenic, non-sensitising and non-inflammable, i.e. *safe* to use
11. Allows monitoring of the wound
12. Protects the wound from further trauma
13. Requires infrequent changing and removes without pain/trauma to the patient
14. Sterilisable
15. Flexible and conformable
16. Capable of standardisation and evaluation
17. Properties remain constant
18. Carrier for medicaments
19. Available to both hospital and community
20. Cost effective

Based on Morgan (1990).

so that staff can have a limited, but appropriate, selection to use.

4. Routine cleaning of wounds is no longer considered necessary and may in fact be positively harmful (Thomlinson, 1987). Shedding of fibres into the wound may occur and application of antiseptics may cause tissue damage (e.g. Murray, 1988; Cameron and Leaper, 1988). Organisms may be redistributed,

not removed (Ayliffe et al, 1990). Understanding of the process of wound healing is essential.

The nursing process and wound management

At the start of this section, it was stated that wound management should be part of a holistic approach to the patient. The central elements of assessment, planning, implementation and evaluation of care seem ideally suited to wound care and allow the patient to be involved in setting appropriate goals (Griffiths-Jones, 1991). Jaber (1986) and Morrison (1987) describe assessment and treatment strategies according to classification of the state of the wound. Faugier (1988) compares the stages of healing to psychological growth stages, addressing the problems of guilt and disgust which both patient and nurse may feel concerning infected wounds (and chronic ones such as leg ulcers and pressure sores).

Summary

The nurse has an important role to play in the prevention of wound infection and in treatment of the patient who is suffering from such an infection. It is a field in which knowledge is constantly expanding, and frequent updating is required.

RESPIRATORY TRACT INFECTIONS AND PATIENT CARE

This category of nosocomial infection is the third most numerous HAI, although many infections are acquired in the community (Meers et al, 1981). This section concentrates on hospitalised patients, where infection is both costly and may be life-threatening. There is little likelihood of respiratory infection spread within the community except in cases of viral infection, e.g. common cold or influenza. In those instances it is important that the nurse, wherever she works, does not attend susceptible patients if she is ill. It is rarely possible to isolate patients with influenza during outbreaks, but in single instances every effort should be made to keep infected persons separated.

Diagnosis

This is the hardest category of infection to define precisely as it is often difficult in the laboratory to distinguish colonisation from infection, since most respiratory pathogens can also be found naturally in the upper respiratory tract.

Risk factors

These can be divided into:

1. *host factors*—age, obesity, smoking history, underlying disease (especially respiratory disease) and diabetes;
2. *general factors*—anaesthesia, intoxication or convulsions, coma, local or generalised pulmonary oedema, shock; and
3. *external factors*—instrumentation which bypasses natural defences, use of respiratory equipment if inadequately cleaned, presence of infected or colonised patients nearby.

Measures to prevent infection

1. Prevention of cross-infection from colonised or infected patients by *effective hand washing between*

patient contact. Gram-negative bacilli in particular can be transferred on hands directly or via equipment to other patients.

2. Adequate cleaning and disinfection of all equipment including nebulisers, humidifiers, ventilators and other personal patient equipment.

3. Maintenance of good oral hygiene (see Figure 13.6) to prevent build up of bacteria which could be spread to the lungs by suction equipment, or other instrumentation bypassing defences (Sanford, 1986).

4. Isolation of patients with chest infections if they have a resistant strain of an organism.

5. Avoidance of abuse of antibiotics which could otherwise lead to selection of resistant bacteria. Cross-infection with highly antibiotic-resistant strains is a special hazard (Ayliffe et al, 1990).

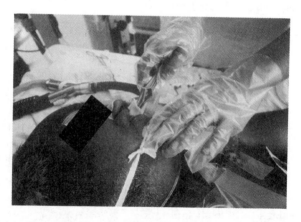

Figure 13.6 Oral hygiene (n.b. if gloves are worn for patient care procedures, latex would now be advised).

Post-operative pneumonia

Organisms commonly involved are *Haemophilus influenzae* and *Streptococcus pneumoniae*. The Centers for Disease Control (CDC) published guidelines in 1983 for prevention of nosocomial pneumonia (Simmons and Wong, 1983). In addition to the measures noted above concerning hand and equipment hygiene, these stress:

- the need for pre- and post-operative education of the patient in breathing and coughing techniques,
- early ambulation,
- control of pain which would otherwise inhibit these movements and activities, and
- avoidance of routine use of systemic antibiotics.

The surgical ward nurse can do much to motivate, help and encourage the patient in these infection prevention activities.

Care of respiratory equipment

Ventilators/anaesthetic machines

The machines themselves, if properly used, should rarely need decontamination, providing machines with disposable or autoclavable circuits are used. This is essential for infected patients (e.g. someone with pulmonary tuberculosis), and there are filters available to protect machines from contamination (Gallagher et al, 1987) which can be placed to protect both inspiratory and expiratory circuits. The tubing should be changed between patients, or daily on long-term patients if filters are not in use (although there is evidence that 48–72 h changes are acceptable (Ayliffe et al, 1990; Craven et al, 1982). Tubing should be washed and heat disinfected, or autoclaved.

Humidifiers and nebulisers

These items have been implicated in several outbreaks of infection already described. Gram-negative organisms such as *Pseudomonas* spp. will thrive in the moist conditions provided by this equipment, if allowed to contaminate it. Daily washing and drying is essential, with heat disinfection in a washer being ideal especially for use on intensive care unit patients. Fluids should never be used to top up the containers, but fully replaced, to avoid risk of contamination.

Wall suction

Suction bottles should be stored dry, and emptied and washed with detergent and hot water daily and between patients. Dry thoroughly. Tubing from patient to reservoir should be changed daily (and between patients) and that from wall to reservoir should be wiped daily and changed at an agreed interval, e.g. monthly. This again is because of the potential for Gram-negative organisms to thrive in moist situations. Disinfectants should not be used on a routine basis.

Endotracheal suction is potentially dangerous in that it bypasses the natural defence mechanisms. Sterile suction catheters should be used once only, with good hand hygiene and use of gloves, and prompt disposal of catheter and gloves after the procedure. The tube itself must be kept clean, and all handling should be performed aseptically.

Airways should be single use or autoclavable.

Oxygen masks should be of the single-use, disposable type.

INTRAVENOUS CATHETERISATION

The number of hospitalised patients receiving intravenous (IV) therapy has increased as more advanced treatments become available. In a large European study reported in 1983 (Nystrom et al, 1983), it was found that 63% of surgical patients surveyed 'had an IV device inserted at some time during their hospital stay'. Maki (1986) reported that over half of the 40 million patients hospitalised in the USA received an IV administration. Infection problems from intravenous devices may be in the form of:

- phlebitis (two or more signs and symptoms, e.g. erythema, tenderness, swelling, or a palpable cord),
- septic phlebitis/thrombophlebitis (pus), and
- bacteraemia or septicaemia (Speechley, 1986).

Although much cannula-related phlebitis is due to chemical or mechanical causes, 20% of infusion-related phlebitis has been attributed to cannula wound infection (Maki, 1986). Incidence ranged from 7.8% to 28.4% between different countries in Nystrom's study (1983). This study revealed 3.7 hospital-acquired bacteraemias per 1000 patients with intravenous devices and quotes Pinner et al (1982) as finding bacteraemia the second most expensive HAI. (Catheter-related septicaemia can only be confirmed when the same organism has been isolated from the catheter tip or from purulence at the insertion site, and from blood cultures.) Shanson (1989) states that septicaemia develops in 0.2–8% of patients receiving intravenous fluids. Any infection caused by this procedure is potentially serious and should be minimised by reduction of major *risk factors*, i.e.

- only using an intravenous line when strictly necessary;

- maintaining strict asepsis during insertion and care of the device; and
- ceasing use of the device at the earliest opportunity.

An intravenous device causes a break in the body's natural defence system, the skin. This may allow entry of organisms directly into the circulation. Contamination may come from the equipment itself, e.g. cannula, giving set, or contaminated fluids (Ayliffe et al, 1990). It may be:

1. *intrinsic*—present before use, probably due to asepsis failure during manufacture or storage (Goodinson, 1990a); or
2. *extrinsic*—introduced during use and often associated with lack of knowledge and/or failure of aseptic technique during device insertion or subsequent manipulations to the system. Figure 13.7 shows the possible areas through which microorganisms may gain entry.

Organisms responsible for catheter-related infections include:

> *Staphylococcus aureus*
> *Staphylococcus epidermidis*
> *Escherichia coli*
> *Klebsiella, Serratia* and *Enterobacter* spp.
> *Pseudomonas aeruginosa* and *P. cepacia*
> *Candida* spp.

For further information see Goodinson (1990a, b), Greene (1990), Keenlyside (1992), Maki (1986) and Speechley (1986). These authors give extensive reviews of most aspects of infection associated with the use of intravenous devices. For the purpose of this chapter, care of the patient during and after device insertion will be

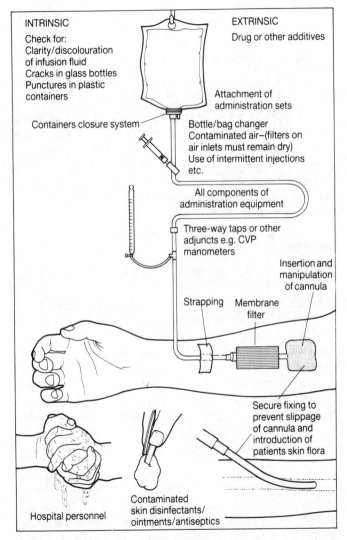

Figure 13.7 Intrinsic and extrinsic contamination of an intravenous infusion.

the main area of concern. However, selection of the correct site, equipment and site preparation, although mostly carried out by medical staff, are also highly relevant. The nurse who understands the equipment and the risks of intravenous therapy can give valuable care.

Site

This should be away from bony prominences and joints, preferably in the upper limb as this has less association with complications (Speechley, 1986). Other factors are venous accessibility, the age and state of the patient such as mobility, mental state (e.g. confusion), the length of time the device is expected to remain in situ, and patient preference (including dominant hand).

Equipment

Cannula material and design

Devices made from Teflon are considered more inert, less thrombogenic and despite early studies suggesting higher infection rates, are currently preferred to steel cannulae (Speechley, 1986). The flexibility of silicone elastomer and polyurethane catheters in addition to the properties above, make these advisable for central venous lines (Greene, 1990). A parallel-sided cannula with a defined hub is advised rather than one with a tapering design which may encourage movement, causing mechanical phlebitis and also pumping bacteria into the circulation.

Administration sets

These should be as simple as possible. The minimum of connections are advisable to reduce risks from contamination, and stopcocks and three-way taps should be avoided for the same reason. When stopcocks must be used they should be disinfected with 70% isopropyl alcohol before use (Greene, 1990). If not in continuous use, a sterile covering should be in place and be renewed (not reused) after any use of the device (Jakobsen et al, 1986). They should also be changed when the administration set is changed (Goodinson, 1990) (see also p. 398).

Filters

These are designed to prevent unwanted matter gaining access to an infusion, e.g. particulate matter, microbial contamination, and air, or to extend the life of a giving set. A variety of designs are in existence and the user must ensure that the filter in use (if it is needed at all) is appropriate for that patient and particular infusion. Filters are still a source of controversy regarding prevention of infection (Spencer, 1990). Some solutions, including blood, fat emulsions and some drugs (e.g. insulin and antibiotics), cannot be given through an end-line $0.22~\mu m$ filter which retains bacteria and fungi (Keenlyside, 1992). The danger of endotoxin release from bacteria trapped in filter material used to be one reason for 24-hourly change of filters. A filter capable of retaining endotoxins for 96 h has been developed (Baumgarthner, 1986; Maki, 1987) and may be used in certain circumstances. Most filter use probably occurs in units where patients have lines requiring frequent access, e.g. intensive care units. Several authors have concluded that they may be justifiable for patients at increased risk of complications from therapy (Falchuk et al, 1985; Friedland et al, 1985; Francombe, 1988), but they should never be used as a substitute for aseptic technique. Always consult manufacturers and pharmacists as necessary (Allcutt et al, 1983; DHSS, 1973).

Preparation of the site

Insertion of an intravenous device is a minor surgical procedure (Goodinson, 1990b) and requires an aseptic technique. This involves using sterile apparatus and fluids, with *good hand washing* and skin disinfection, and a 'no-touch' technique for inserting and maintaining the infusion. Skin flora have been associated with intravenous-related sepsis (Elliott, 1988) and hand washing should be accorded a major role in all aseptic techniques. In a small study of hand washing, Krakowska (1986) found that only 2 (11%) of 18 medical staff always washed their hands before inserting a peripheral device. Hands should first be washed either with a soap-and-water wash followed by an alcohol hand rub, or by use of a product such as chlorhexidine and detergent, which has a residual antibacterial effect. For insertion of a central venous line, sterile gloves *must* be worn. Use of gloves for insertion of peripheral lines is usually a matter of personal choice, but should be worn if contact with blood is anticipated (DOH, 1990).

The patient's skin should be physically clean at the insertion site. It is cleaned prior to cannula insertion with alcoholic chlorhexidine, povidone–iodine or 70% alcohol solutions (e.g. Simmons, 1982; Ayliffe et al, 1990). Excessive hair should be clipped rather than shaved if needed, as shaving can predispose to infection (Maki et al, 1973). A quick dab with an alcohol impregnated wipe is not sufficient to disinfect the skin, although a not uncommonly observed practice! The CDC recommendation states that the antiseptic 'be applied liberally and allowed to remain in contact for at least 30 seconds' prior to venepuncture. Hospitals should have clearly written policies and procedures for both insertion and maintenance of intravenous devices. Every effort should be made to see that they are used, and not afforded lip service only (Krakowska, 1986).

Care of the patient undergoing intravenous catheterisation

The nurse is usually present when an intravenous device is sited, collects the fluid to be administered, and frequently primes the administration set. Those nurses who have undertaken training for the extended role of the nurse (UKCC, 1984) may also be responsible for administration of intravenous substances. The nurse is also responsible for hour-by-hour care of the patient with an infusion. Insertion of intravenous devices and the accompanying fluids/drugs should always be documented in both medical and nursing records.

Fluids

These must always be checked for any defects (e.g. cracks in bottles), macroscopic contamination, for clarity, labelling of contents, and expiry date. Major changes in production and quality assurance by manufacturers followed outbreaks of infusion-associated septicaemia in both the UK and the USA in the 1970s. DHSS advice (1972, 1975) details procedures to be followed in administering infusions and reporting any suspected contamination. Once opened, fluids should be used within 24 h, or in some cases within 12 h (especially if additives present) (Speechley, 1986).

Administration sets

The packs should be checked to ensure intactness for sterility, and DHSS (1973) recommendations require changing of these sets every 24 h. There is a growing body of evidence to suggest that sets can be used for 48–72 h without ill effect (Jakobson et al, 1986; Maki et al, 1987) and current CDC recommendations are for 48-h changing. At present the UK DHSS ruling is still in force (although under review, in connection with possible use of filters), so hospitals which opt to use the sets for a longer time do so at their own discretion.

Central venous catheters require daily changing of administration sets (see p. 400). The sets should be changed immediately after administration of blood, blood products and lipids (CDC, 1982; Speechley, 1986).

Dressings

Once inserted the cannula or needle must be carefully secured to maintain stability and should be covered with a *sterile* dressing. The dressing, and not tape, should cover the wound unless the tape is sterile (and *never* the roll of tape carried in the nurse or houseman's pocket!). A variety of dressing are used and there still appears to be a need for further evaluation, but a transparent, water-vapour-permeable dressings has advantages over gauze dressings. The insertion site can be inspected without manipulation and is impermeable to bacteria (see also Ayliffe et al, 1990; Greene, 1990). Whichever dressing is used, the integrity of that dressing is paramount and it must be changed if this has been impaired. Maki and Ringer (1987) recommend that the dressing should be changed at 48–72 h intervals. As CDC recommendations are for cannula renewal at that interval whenever possible, this can be performed at one time.

Site care

The site should be inspected at least every 24 h, and it would seem good nursing practice to ensure the comfort and safety of the patient by checking during each nursing shift. Any redness, pain, swelling or other indication of local infection or phlebitis should be promptly reported to medical staff. A swab should be taken from the site if there is discharge, followed by disinfection of the site with 70% isopropyl alcohol and cannula removal.

Other aspects of patient care

In addition to care of the device and associated equipment, nurses must also consider the other restrictions this places on the patient and cater for those needs. Planning should include maintenance of the patient's ability to carry out their own personal hygiene, or to help with this as needed. Care must be taken to keep the patient as mobile and comfortable as possible, e.g. positioning the locker by the non-catheterised arm.

Removal of the device

This is frequently a nursing intervention, and again requires an aseptic technique. When the device is removed, a sterile dressing should be firmly fixed over the site.

Summary

1. Handwashing remains a critical element in sound management of the patient with an intravenous device.
2. All manipulations of the system should be aseptically performed, and kept to a minimum to maintain the 'closed system'.

3. The line should be securely anchored and dressed with either a sterile gauze swab or a transparent intravenous dressing.
4. The site should be checked at least once every 24 h, and patient comfort checked at least every shift.
5. Any problems should be reported to medical staff immediately.
6. All details of attention to and maintenance of the site and infusion should be recorded.

CENTRAL VENOUS CATHETERS AND PARENTERAL NUTRITION

Several references have already been made to central venous catheters. These have increased hazards of infection associated with their positioning. Whereas contamination of a peripheral intravenous infusion site is most likely to lead to phlebitis, sepsis associated with a central venous catheter is highly likely to lead to *septicaemia*. Nystrom et al (1983) found that 44.8 per 1000 patients had bacteraemia associated with a central venous catheter. Patients requiring this procedure are also likely to be extremely ill or already compromised and particularly susceptible to infection. Central venous lines used for parenteral nutrition have the added hazard that the solutions used, e.g. fats and proteins make ideal growth media for any bacterial contamination.

Catheters should be inserted with rigorous aseptic technique (see guidelines on p. 396), and the procedure should take place in an operating theatre except under exceptional circumstances. The right subclavian vein is the one most frequently used for central venous catheterisation, or the right internal jugular. If the line is likely to be required long-term it may be 'tunnelled'.

This distances the skin insertion point from the point of entry into the vein, to try and reduce any access of microorganisms. Although the rate of cannula-related infections may not be affected by this measure, it may simplify nursing care of patients receiving parenteral nutrition (Williams, 1985). Dacron cuffs also allow granulation to occur around catheter and cuff to provide a barrier to skin organisms (Wilkinson, 1991). Correct positioning of the catheter is checked by X-ray. Intravenous lines are increasingly used for patients undergoing treatment involving home care (Wood, 1991). This includes those requiring antibiotics or chemotherapy, e.g. for cystic fibrosis or leukaemia, those receiving parenteral nutrition at home, and those requiring intravenous fluids and electrolytes to replace intestinal fluid losses. Developments like these which allow the patient to spend less time in hospital and enjoy a better quality of life are to be welcomed. It is up to medical and nursing staff to ensure the families are well advised over care of these lines (Cluroe, 1989), that they may be safely self-caring whenever possible. According to Holden (1991) rates of catheter sepsis are lower in patients receiving parenteral nutrition at home than for those in hospital.

The British Intravenous Therapy Association have produced *Guidelines for the Nursing Care of Patients Receiving Parenteral Nutrition* to help all areas develop safe local policies for this procedure. These give clear guidance on all aspects of care for patients receiving parenteral infusions. Briefly, they stress:

1. Thorough handwashing.
2. Adequate disinfection of the new container, and of the connection between the old set and catheter or extension tubing when changing administration sets. When changing containers, the port of the new

container and the old container–administration set
junction must be disinfected.

3. Use of sterile field for equipment preparation and
use of sterile gloves.

4. Regular observance of the site for signs of phlebitis.

5. Replacement of the dressing 2–3 times a week*,
using full aseptic technique and using alcoholic
chlorhexidine to clean around the entry site.

6. All interventions to be recorded in the nursing notes
for the patient.

Additives

Although there are now many commercially available
preparations for parenteral nutrition, there are still
occasions when solutions must be prepared within the
hospital, and additional items compounded. This should
'ideally be carried out in appropriate environmental
conditions under the direct control of a pharmacist'
(DHSS, 1976). This service is being further developed in
some authorities to comprise a central intravenous
additive service (CIVA). This includes reconstitution and
preparation of a large number of intravenous injections
in the pharmacy before distribution to the wards (Neary,
1989). All additions at ward level involve breaking the
'closed circuit', even if additions are correctly made, so
any reduction in these occurrences should be beneficial.

Summary

*Whenever the intravenous route is used, this should be
with care by all concerned, and for the minimum of time.*

* New guidelines on this and a variety of issues relating to care of
central and peripheral lines are awaited.

REFERENCES

Ackerman V and Dunk-Richards G (1991) *Microbiology: An Introduction for the Health Sciences*. London: Harcourt Brace Jovanovich.

Albert RK and Condie F (1981) Handwashing patterns in medical intensive care units. *N. Engl. Med.* **304**: 1465–1466.

Allcutt DA, Lort D and McCollum CN (1983) Final in-line filtration for intravenous infusions: a prospective hospital study. *Br. J. Surg.* **70**: 111–113.

Ayliffe GAJ, Collins BJ and Taylor LJ (1990) *Hospital-acquired Infection*, 2nd edn. London: Wright.

Baillie L (1987) Chlorhexidine resistance among bacteria isolated from urine of catheterised patients. *J. Hosp. Infect*, **10**: 83–86.

Barnett J (1991) Preventive procedures. *Nursing Times* **87**(10): 66–68.

Baumgarthner TG, *et al* (1986) Bacterial endotoxin retention by in-line intravenous filters. *Am. J. Hosp. Pharmacol.* **43**: 681–684.

Bibby BA, Collins BJ and Ayliffe GAJ (1986) A mathematical model for assessing risk of post-operative wound infection. *J. Hosp. Infect.* **8**: 31–39.

British Intravenous Therapy Association (BITA) *Guidelines for Nursing Care of Patients Receiving Parenteral Nutrition*.

Britt M, Burke JB, Miller WA, Steinmuller W and Garibaldi RA (1976) The non-effectiveness of daily meatal care in the prevention of catheter-associated bacteriuria. *Proc. 16th Interscience Conf. on Antimicrobial Agents and Chemotherapy*, Chicago, p. 141.

Brown RB, Bradley S, Opitz E, Ciprian D, Pieczarka R and Sands M (1987) Surgical wound infections documented after hospital discharge. *Am. J. Infect. Control* **15**(2): 54–58.

Burke JP, Garibaldi RA, Britt MR, Jacobson JA and Conti M (1981) Prevention of catheter-associated urinary tract infections—efficacy of daily meatal care regimens. *Am. J. Med.* **70**: 655–658.

Caddow P (ed.) (1989) *Applied Microbiology*. London: Scutari Press.

Cameron S and Leaper D (1987) Antiseptic toxicity in open wounds. *Care—Science and Practice* **5**(2): 19–20.

Casewell MW, Dalton NT, Webster M and Phillips I (1977) Gentamicin-resistant *Klebsiella aerogenes* in a urological ward. *Lancet* ii: 444–446.

Casewell M and Phillips I (1977) Hands as route of transmission for *Klebsiella* species. *Br. Med. J.* **2**: 1315–1317.

CDC (Centers for Disease Control) (1988) Update: universal precautions for prevention of transmission of human immunodeficiency virus, hepatitis B virus and other bloodborne pathogens in health care settings. *MMWR* **37**: 377–388.

Chrintz H, Vibits H, Cordtz TO, *et al* (1989) Need for surgical wound dressing. *Br. J. Surg.* **76**: 204–205.

Cluroe S (1989) Parental involvement in intravenous therapy. *Nursing Times* **85**(9): 42–43.

Craven DE, Connolly MG, Lightenberg DA, *et al* (1982) Contamination of mechanical ventilators with tubing changes every 24 and 48 hours. *New Engl. J. Med.* **306**: 1505.

Crow R, Chapman R, Roe B and Wilson J (1986) *A Study of Patients with an Indwelling Urinary Catheter and Related Nursing Practice.* Guildford: Nursing Practice Research Unit, University of Surrey.

Crummy V (1985) Hospital-acquired urinary tract infection. *Nursing Times, J. Infect. Control Nursing* **5 Jun.** (Suppl.): 7–12.

Cruse PJE (1986) Surgical infection: incisional wounds. In *Hospital Infections* (eds Bennett JV and Brachman PS) 2nd edn., pp. 423–436. Boston, MA: Brown and Co.

Cruse PJE and Foord R (1980) The epidemiology of wound infection— a 10-year prospective study of 62,939 wounds. *Surg. Clin. N. Am.* **60**(1): 27–40.

David JA (1986) *Wound Management—A Comprehensive Guide to Dressing and Healing.* London: M. Dunitz.

DHSS (1972) *Guidelines on Administration of Parenteral Infusion Fluids* **DS 216/72.** London: HMSO.

DHSS (1973) *Medicines Commission: Report on the Prevention of Microbial Contamination of Medicinal Products.* London: HMSO.

DHSS (1975) *Reporting on Transfusion Incidents involving Suspected Contamination* **HSC (IS) 41 & 118.** London: HMSO.

DHSS (1976) *Health Service Development. Addition of Drugs to Intravenous Infusion Fluids* **HC (76) 9.** London: HMSO.

Elliott, TSJ (1988) Plastic devices: new fields for old microbes. *Lancet* **i**: 30–31.

Faugier J (1988) On being wounded. *Senior Nurse* **8**(1): 18–19.

Falchuk KH, Peterson L and McNeil BJ (1985) Microparticulate-induced phlebitis—its prevention by in-line filtration. *N. Engl. J. Med.* **312**: 78–82.

Francombe P (1988) Intravenous filters and phlebitis. *Nursing Times* **84**(26): 34–35.

Friedland G (1985) Infusion-related phlebitis—is the in-line filter the solution? *N. Engl. J. Med.* **312**: 78.

Gallagher J, Strangeways JEM and Allt-Graham J (1987) Contamination control in long-term ventilation. *Anaesthesia* **42**: 476.

Garner JS (1986) CDC Guidelines for prevention of surgical wound infections 1985. *Infect. Control* **7**(3): 193–200.

Garner JS and Favero MS (1986) CDC Guidelines for Handwashing and Hospital Environmental Control. *Infect. Contr.* **7**(4): 233–235.

Gibbs H (1986) Catheter toilet and urinary tract infections. *Nursing Times* **82**(23): 75–76.

Gidley C (1987) Now, wash your hands! *Nursing Times* **83**(29): 40–42.

Glenister H (1987) The passage of infection. *Nursing Times, J. Infect Control Nursing* **83**(22) (Suppl.): 68–73.

Glenister H (1990) The catheterised patient. In *Infection Control: Guidelines for Nursing Care* (ed. Worsley MA *et al*). ICNA.

Goodinson SM (1990a) Good practice ensures minimum risk factors. *Prof. Nurse* **6**(3): 175–177.

Goodinson SM (1990b) Keeping the flora out: reducing risk of infection in IV therapy. *Prof. Nurse* **5**(11): 572–575.

Greene C (1990) In *Infection Control: Guidelines for Nursing Care* (eds Worsley MA *et al*), pp. 57–64. ICNA.

Griffiths-Jones A (1991) Wound care: can the nursing process help? *Prof. Nurse* **6**(4): 208–212.

Haley RW, Culver DH, White JW, *et al* (1985) The efficacy of infection surveillance and control programs in preventing nosocomial infections in US hospitals. *Am. J. Epidemiol.* **121**: 182–205.

Hamilton HW, Hamilton KR and Lone FJ (1977) Preoperative hair removal. *Can. J. Surg.* **20**: 269.

Hayek LJ, Emmerson JM and Gardner AMN (1987) A placebo-controlled trial on the effect of two pre-operative baths or showers with chlorhexidine detergent on postoperative wound infection rates. *J. Hosp. Infect.* **10**: 165–172.

Holden C (1991) Home parenteral nutrition. *Paediatr. Nursing* **3**(3): 13–16.

Jaber F (1986) Charting wound healing. *Nursing Times* **10 Sep.**: 24–27.

Jackson MM (1984) From ritual to reason—with a rational approach for the future. *Am. J. Infect. Control* **12**(4): 213–220.

Jakobsen CJ, Grabe N, Neilsen E, *et al* (1986) Contamination of intravenous infusion systems—the effect of changing administration sets. *J. Hosp. Infect.* **8**: 217–223.

Jenner EA (1977) A closed system of urinary drainage. *Nursing Mirror* **145**(18) (Suppl.): 1–5.

Keenlyside D (1992) Every little detail counts: infection control in IV therapy. *Prof. Nurse* **7**(4): 226–232.

Knittle MA, Eitzman DV and Baer H (1975) Role of hand contamination of personnel in the epidemiology of Gram-negative nosocomial infections. *J. Paediatr.* **86**(3): 433–437.

Krakowska G (1986) Practice versus procedure. *Nursing Times, J. Infect. Control Nursing* **34**: 64–69.

Kunin C (1979) *Detection, Prevention and Management of Urinary Tract Infection*, 3rd edn. Philadelphia: Lea and Fabiger.

Maki D (1986) Infections due to infusion therapy. In *Hospital Infections* (eds Bennett JV and Brachman PS), 2nd edn, pp. 561–580. Boston, MA: Little, Brown and Co.

Maki D, *et al* (1973) Infection control in intravenous therapy. *Ann. Intern. Med.* **79**(6): 876–887.

Maki DG and Ringer M (1987) Evaluation of dressing regimens for prevention of infection with peripheral intravenous catheters. *J. Am. Med. Assoc.* **258**: 239–243.

Maki DG, Botticelli JT, LeRoy ML and Thielke TS (1987) Prospective study of replacing administration sets for intravenous therapy at 48 vs 72-hour intervals. 72 hours is safe and cost effective. *J. Am. Med. Assoc.* **258**: 1777–1781.

Meers PD, Ayliffe GAJ, Emmerson AM, *et al* (1981) Report on the national survey of infection in hospitals. *J. Hosp. Infect.* **2** (Suppl.): 1–53.

Morgan DA (ed) (1990) *Formulary of Wound Management Products*, 4th edn. Bridgend, Welsh Centre for Quality Control of Surgical Dressings.

Morrison M (1987) Wound assessment. *Prof. Nurse* **1**(10): 315–317.

Mulhall A, Chapman R and Crow R (1988) The acquisition of bacteriuria. Emptying urinary drainage bags. *Nursing Times* **84**(4): 61–66.

Murray Y (1988) Tradition rather than cure? *Nursing Times* **84**(38): 75, 79–80.

Neary C (1989) Centralising the intravenous service. *Nursing Standard* **40**(3): 20–23.

Nystrom B, Oleson Larsen S, Dankert J, Daschner F, Greco D, Gronroos P, Jepsen OB, Lystad A, Meers PD and Rotter M (1983) Bacteraemia in surgical patients with intravenous devices: A European multicentre incidence study. *J. Hosp. Infect.* **4**: 338–349.

O'Brien DK (1986) Post-operative wound infections. *Nursing* **3**(5): 178–182.

Pinner RW, Haley RW, Blumenstein BA, Schaberg DR, von Allmen SD and McGowan Jr JE (1982) High cost nosocomial infections. *Infect. Control* 143–149.

Pritchard V and Hathaway C (1988) Patient handwashing practice. *Nursing Times, J. Infect. Control Nursing* **84**(36): 68–72.

Roe B (1989) Study of information given by nurses for catheter care to patients and their carers. *J. Adv. Nursing* **14**: 203–210.

Rotter ML, Larsen SO, Cooke EM, *et al* (1988) A comparison of the effects of pre-operative whole body bathing with detergent alone and with detergent containing chlorhexidine gluconate in the frequency of wound infections after clean surgery. The European Working Party on Control of Hospital Infections. *J. Hosp. Infect.* **11**: 310–320.

Sanford JP (1986) Lower respiratory tract infections. In *Hospital Infections* (eds Bennett JV and Brachman PS), 2nd edn, pp. 385–422. Boston, MA: Little, Brown and Co.

Seal D and Ward K (1983) Basic techniques for aseptic catheterisation of urinary tract. *Nursing* **2**(13): 5–6.

Seropian R and Reynolds BM (1971) Wound infections after preoperative depilatory versus razor preparation. *Am. J. Surg.* **121**: 251–254.

Shanson DC (1989) *Microbiology in Clinical Practice*, 2nd edn. London: Wright.

Simmons BP (1982) CDC Guidelines for prevention of intravascular infections. *Infect. Control* **3**: 61–72.

Simmons BP and Wong ES (1983) Guideline for prevention of nosocomial pneumonia. (CDC Guidelines for the prevention and control of nosocomial infections.) *Am. J. Infect. Control* **11**(6): 230–239.

Sneddon JG (1990) A preventable course of infection. *Prof. Nurse* **6**(2): 98–104.

Speechley V (1986) Intravenous therapy: peripheral/central lines. *Nursing* **3**(3): 95–100.

Spencer RC (1990) Use of in-line filters for intravenous infusions. *J. Hosp. Infect.* **16**: 281.

Stamm WE (1986) Nosocomial urinary tract infections. In *Hospital Infections* (eds Bennett JV and Brachman PS), 2nd edn, pp. 375–384. Boston, MA: Little, Brown and Co.

Steere AC and Mallison GF (1975) Handwashing practices for the prevention of nosocomial infections. *Ann. Intern. Med.* **83**: 683–690.

Taylor LJ (1978) An evaluation of handwashing techniques, 1 and 2. *Nursing Times* **74**(2): 54–55; **74**(3): 108–110.

Thomlinson D (1987) To clean or not to clean. *Nursing Times, J. Infect. Control* **35**: 71.

UKCC (1984) *Code of Professional Conduct for the Nurse, Midwife and Health Visitor*. London: UKCC.

UK Health Depts. (1990) Guidance for Clinical Health Care Workers: Protection Against Infection with HIV and Hepatitis viruses. London, HMSO.

Westaby S (ed.) (1985) *Wound Care*. London: Heinemann.

Williams WW (1985) Infection control during parenteral nutrition therapy. *J. Parenteral Enteral Nutr.* **9**(6): 735–746.

Williams E and Buckles A (1988) A lack of motivation. *Nursing Times, J. Infect. Cont. Nursing* **84**(22): 60–64.

Wilkinson R (1991) The challenge of intravenous therapy. *Nursing Standard* **5**(28): 24–27.

Wilson M (1990) Catheterisation under scrutiny. *Nursing Times, J. Infect. Control Nursing* **86**(49): 71–72.

Wood S (1991) Extending the principle of self-care: intravenous therapy in the community. *Prof. Nurse* **6**(9): 543–549.

Wyatt TD and Timoney R (1987) The effect of introducing a policy for catheter care on the catheter infection rate in a small hospital. *J. Hosp. Infect.* **9**: 230–234.

FURTHER READING

Barnett J (1991) Preventive procedures. *Nursing Times, J. Infect. Control Nursing* **87**(10): 66–68.

Catchpole A (1989) Cystic fibrosis: intravenous treatment at home. *Nursing Times* **85**(12): 40–42.

Clarke R (1990) A cost-effective system for TPN. *Nursing Times* **86**(31): 65–68.

Fay MF (1987) Drainage systems—their role in wound healing. *AORN J.* **46**(3): 443–455.

Harrild N (1988) A stitch in time . . . *Nursing Standard* **19 Mar.**: 36–38.

Jenner EA (1977) Intravenous infusion—a cause for concern? *Nursing Times* **3 Feb.**: 156–158.

Moir-Bussy B (1986) The surgical wound. *Nursing* **3**(3): 92–94.

Oldman P (1991) A sticky situation? Microbiological study of adhesive tape used to secure IV cannulae. *Prof. Nurse* **6**(5): 265–269.

Sedgwick JA (1990) We must assess the care we give. *Prof. Nurse* **5**(12): 624–630.

Sims R and Fitzgerald V (1986) Wound care in the community. *Nursing* **3**(6): 209–215.

Speller DC (1980) Clinical problems of urinary tract infection by multi-resistant bacteria. *Proc. of 11th ICNA Symposium.*

Walsh M and Ford P (1989) *Nursing Rituals: Research and Rational Actions.* Oxford: Butterworth-Heinemann.

14 Care of infected and at-risk/susceptible patients (isolation nursing)

The need to prevent transmission of infection from one individual to another is by now apparent. Isolation techniques (often referred to as 'barrier nursing') are *'steps to prevent the spread of an infectious agent from an infected or colonised person to another person'* (Garner and Simmons, 1986). *They should be designed to ensure maximum infection control with minimum patient distress* (Coleman, 1987).

Isolation is anathema for human beings (Denton, 1986). Defined as quarantine, it also means detachment, loneliness, disconnection and exile. The term 'barrier nursing' referred to the actual placing of a physical barrier between the person in isolation and all others. Although still found in many textbooks and nursing manuals, it has overtones of an obstacle or agency that keeps apart or prevents communication. It is increasingly replaced by phrases which imply *care* rather than separation of the infected patient. *It is, after all, the organism which we are trying to isolate, not the patient.*

HISTORY

Early forms of isolation have already been described in Chapter 1. These date back more than 2000 years, through fourteenth-century quarantine for sailors to the fever hospitals of the eighteenth century. Jackson and Lynch (1985), reviewing the history of isolation practices from 1860 onwards, note that Florence Nightingale, although concerned with a clean environment, put greater emphasis on contact transmission from body substances than environmental transmission. Attitudes altered in the early twentieth century, where anything in the room with an infected patient was considered to be contaminated. Relatively recently there has been a return to some of Florence Nightingale's ideas with the additional benefit of understanding organisms and their routes of transmission.

Along this road there have been many fears and prejudices which have caused unnecessary suffering to the truly 'isolated' person. It is sad to note that, despite modern knowledge, many isolation techniques are still based on ritual rather than reason. Even today people react with panic to some infections, and develop a cavalier attitude to others.

METHODS OF ISOLATION

Two main methods of isolation have been described for some time, namely:

1. *Source isolation*—caring for the infected patient and preventing infection transmission.
2. *Protective isolation*—or caring for the at-risk patient who needs extra protection from normally harmless organisms. This may be due to impaired resistance or increased susceptibility to pathogens or potential pathogens in the hospital environment.

Protective isolation

This may consist of relatively simple measures such as caring for the patient in a single room and the wearing of protective clothing by staff and visitors. In some hospitals more complex facilities have been used since the 1970s, notably for patients with leukaemia undergoing treatment leading to bone marrow suppression. These may have laminar-air-flow systems or 'life islands' which completely separate the patient from the carer. The idea was to try and render the patient germ free and protect him/her from staff or environmental sources of contamination.

However, studies have shown that most of these patients actually succumb to infections *from their own flora* and attempts to prevent this have never been wholly successful. Antibiotic protocols to eliminate gut flora may also lead to emergence of antibiotic-resistant organisms (Wood, 1989). These protected environments are also extremely costly and lack physical contact for the patient who may need considerable psychological support (Armstrong, 1984). The stress experienced may be offset in some by the feeling of being 'special' and they may resent leaving their protected room when they recover (Lesko et al, 1984).

Overall, there has been a failure to demonstrate prolongation of life in patients undergoing protective isolation (Nauseef and Maki, 1981). Many hospitals now put major emphasis on basic hand washing, rigorously encouraged, and avoidance of raw foods (the intestinal tract has often been the source of life-threatening infection).

Source isolation

There are Regional Infectious Disease Units (IDUs) for the care of patients suffering from certain infectious diseases. A few of these are designated centres to which a patient would be transferred if he/she was suspected to be suffering, for example, from a viral haemorrhagic fever, e.g. Lassa Fever. They can provide extensive containment facilities as detailed by the (then) DHSS (1986). However, most of source isolation in general hospitals takes place in single rooms on general wards. The actual system of giving care for patients in source isolation has been dealt with in one of two ways: category specific precautions and disease-specific precautions.

Category-specific precautions

Diseases are grouped according to their *route of spread* and appropriate techniques are applied to prevent this. This system was introduced in the USA as documented in *Isolation Techniques for Use in Hospital* (CDC, 1970). At about the same time Northwick Park Hospital (UK) was built with a specially designed isolation unit where patients were nursed using a similar category system. The categories chiefly used are: *strict* isolation for highly infectious disease, where patients would ideally be transferred to an IDU; *respiratory* (e.g. pulmonary tuberculosis and chickenpox); *wound and skin* (for those with wounds colonised or infected with organisms such as *Streptococcus pyogenes*); *enteric* (e.g. gastroenteritis and poliomyelitis); and, more recently, *blood* precautions (e.g. hepatitis B and HIV infection). The main problem associated with these systems was lack of individually planned care, which resulted in some patients being overisolated. However, Jenner (1990a) feels that the system can be used to enhance, rather than detract from, individualised patient care if carefully and appropriately planned.

Disease-specific precautions

This system allows for more individual care planning as the patient is nursed according to the problems associated with his specific disease/infection. It also calls for more knowledge and information on the part of the carer. In Britain, this was first suggested by Shooter et al (1963). In 1983, the CDC published their revised guidelines and suggested use of *either* the category-specific system *or* changing to a disease-specific system. Their reasons for introducing the alternative system were:

1. the realisation that patients were sometimes assigned to inappropriate categories;
2. increasing problems with antibiotic-resistant organisms in hospital patients causing outbreaks of HAI, especially in areas where invasive techniques are common, e.g. ICUs; and
3. newly identified syndromes.

Recent developments

The one drawback to both the above systems has been highlighted by the advent of HIV infection. The majority of isolation is initiated by *diagnosis*, and yet many patients infected with, for example, hepatitis B virus and HIV will not have clinical signs of infection to make this diagnosis apparent.

Jackson and Lynch (1984) describe the care given to two patients who were both admitted with cirrhosis of the liver, one secondary to alcohol abuse and the other to chronic hepatitis B infection. Care with blood is taken with the latter under blood/body fluid isolation category, but the first patient is considered non-infectious. A nurse who had a cut on her hands and got blood from the 'non-infectious' patient on her hands is horrified later to discover that he is HBsAg positive. Had he been receiving care as a patient on special precautions she would be far more likely to have covered this cut *and* been wearing gloves for procedures involving blood contact (see later).

Denton (1986) points out that of three patients with Lassa fever reaching the UK, two were undiagnosed until some time after hospital admission! Lynch and Jackson (1988) state that communicable diseases are all infectious *before* a diagnosis is established.

Much discussion has taken place over the last few years regarding systems which are *procedure driven*. This means that precautions are taken according to the likelihood of contact with blood and various body fluids. The following systems are implemented in various hospitals and may be used in conjunction with some already existing isolation systems (see below).

Body substance isolation (BSI)

This was first proposed by Jackson and Lynch (1984), partly to avoid the problems of the person with undiagnosed infection who therefore would not be isolated under category or diagnosis-driven systems. It was also intended to reduce transmission of pathogens from patients' own flora which could cause hospital-acquired infection (HAI). The authors point out that hospitals use two types of procedure to prevent nosocomial infections:

1. infection-control practices routinely used in all patient care such as handwashing and aseptic techniques, e.g. for tracheostomy care and urinary catheterisation; and
2. diagnosis-driven isolation procedures for patients known or suspected to be suffering from specific infections/diseases.

They advocate consistent barrier precautions (use of gloves, in particular) being applied when health-care workers are exposed to *all* patients' 'moist body substances, mucous membranes and non-intact skin'. This obviously has financial implications, and some people feel there is a danger that handwashing may be neglected due to the sense of security which some carers associate with glove use (Valenti, 1988).

Universal precautions (UP)

This procedure was first recommended by the CDC in 1985 as *Universal Blood and Body Fluid Precautions* (CDC, 1985). These have been amended in 1988 (*CDC*, 1988) to refer to blood and body fluids *excluding* faeces, urine, nasal secretions, sputum, tears, sweat or vomit *unless* they contain visible blood.

Gloves are advocated for contact with those fluids above, and protective glasses/goggles/visors for protection of mucous membranes during invasive procedures where blood splashing may occur (see Figure 14.1). The Expert Advisory Group on AIDS recommend similar precautions (see Table 14.1). Both this (UK Health Departments, 1990) and CDC's *advice is concerned primarily with prevention of transmission of HBV, HIV and other blood-borne infections* (see also Hart, 1991).

These precautions should be allied to *good skin care at all times and safe infection control practice*.

1. Cover any cut, graze, etc. with a waterproof dressing.
2. Good basic hygiene practices with regular hand washing.
3. Protection of mucous membranes of eyes, nose and mouth from blood splashes (e.g. goggles and visors).
4. Avoid contamination of clothing and person with blood.
5. Avoid sharps injuries.
6. Clear up blood spillages promptly, disinfecting the contaminated surface.

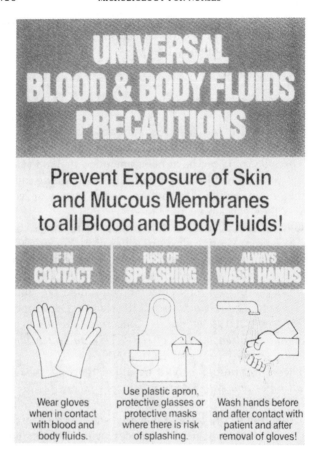

Figure 14.1   Universal precautions for blood and body fluids.

RATIONALE FOR ISOLATION PRECAUTIONS

Accepting that it is necessary to take care as described above with blood and blood-stained or deep body fluids of *all* patients, we must still have methods for observing

Table 14.1 Body fluids, etc., to be treated with the same precautions as blood.

1.	Cerebrospinal fluid
	Peritoneal fluid
	Pleural fluid
	Pericardial fluid
	Synovial fluid
	Amniotic fluid
	Semen
	Vaginal secretions
2.	Any body fluid containing visible blood
3.	Saliva in association with dentistry
4.	Unfixed organs or tissues

From UK Health Departments publication *Guidance for Clinical Health Care Workers* (1990).

these precautions and for dealing with those known or suspected to be infected with other organisms. As described in Chapter 3, three elements are needed for infection to be transmitted.

1. *Source*—the main sources in hospital will be patients, staff and visitors.
2. *Susceptible host*—neonates, elderly, immunosuppressed, those undergoing invasive procedures or having chronic illness (see Chapter 4).
3. *A means of transmission*—direct or indirect contact; air-borne; common vehicle; vectors; blood-borne (*ingestion*, *inhalation* or *inoculation*).

Preventive care is aimed at breaking this chain. The following questions should help the carer identify how to deal safely with a patient with infection.

1. What and where is the causative organism?

2. How can it spread from that patient?
3. Are other patients and staff vulnerable?
4. How can spread or contamination be prevented?

N.B. It is also necessary to assess any additional *risks* involved according to the particular circumstances of:

1. the patient (e.g. physical, psychological and emotional state, age, other underlying conditions, and social factors); and
2. the ward, unit or clinical area in which the patient is being cared for.

The answers to these questions can be used as part of a problem-solving approach incorporated in the nursing process and written into the care plan for the patient (see p. 428). Every patient should have their status assessed with regard to infection risk, on admission to hospital. This suggestion has been developed by Bowell (1992a, b) with assessment tools and planning guides for care of both infected and at-risk patients. A scoring system may be used to allocate points according to the degree of risk (see also Bowell, 1989).

MEASURES FOR CARE OF INFECTED/AT RISK PATIENTS

General principles

- The environment is kept clean and well ventilated to reduce the number of microorganisms. Equipment is kept to a minimum.
- Always wash and dry hands after patient care activities. Hands are the commonest agents in the transmission of infection (see Figure 14.2).
- Limit the number of people in direct contact with an

> PS: WASH YOUR HANDS
>   SHOW THE DOCTOR THE SINK

Figure 14.2 P.S. Wash your hands. Show the doctor the sink.

infected person, and check their immune status where relevant (e.g. chickenpox, rubella).

- Safely contain contaminated material at the point of use—including any secretion/excretion-soiled items. This should apply to all patients; clinical waste is all dealt with in the same fashion. Dispatch for incineration or disinfection/sterilisation in appropriate secure containers which are readily distinguished.
- Record the reason for single room or other means of isolation nursing in the nursing care plan, with the date commenced and the special precautions needed. Amend/delete as the patient's situation alters/resolves.

Staff responsibilities

It is the responsibility of the medical staff caring for a patient to take the decision to isolate a patient, *in consultation with the nursing staff and Control of Infection team*. In practice, it is usually the nursing staff or the Control of Infection Team who first become aware of the need to isolate a patient. Patients with certain conditions should be isolated immediately, for example if they are suffering from:

1. undiagnosed rashes or pyrexias;
2. diarrhoea and vomiting;
3. new or suspected 'open' pulmonary tuberculosis;
4. patients readmitted who are known MRSA carriers, until screened (see Care Plan 1).

(These conditions may only come to light during nursing or medical assessments.)

It is the responsibility of *all* staff to comply with infection-control procedures, including care of patients in isolation.

Nurse/midwife/health visitor responsibility

1. To care for patients in a manner which will comply with the UKCC code of conduct.
2. To assess each patient individually (as an ongoing process), using a relevant nursing model in conjunction with the nursing process, and document this care clearly.
3. To use appropriate protective clothing as indicated.
4. To follow hospital policies for disposal of used equipment, materials, discharges, excreta.
5. To inform patients, visitors and fellow workers of the reason for the precautions taken, while maintaining patient confidentiality.
6. To consult the Infection Control Nurse/Doctor in reviewing or changing care of infected/at risk patients.

HANDS

As already discussed in the previous chapter, hand washing is the most important element in control of infection. (Refer to Chapter 13 and see Figure 14.3.)

PROTECTIVE CLOTHING

Use of some form of protective clothing has long been accepted as part of isolation techniques. During the Plague doctors wore elaborate protective gowns, gloves and strange masks. Many health-care workers feel they

THE GREAT GERM FIGHTERS—
SOAP AND WATER

SOAP

WATER

USE
OFTEN

Figure 14.3 The great germ fighters—soap and water.

must be safer wearing protective clothing, but it is not always used logically. Much of the use has been unproven and ritualistic (Ayton et al, 1984). Even in recent years it has been inappropriately used, as patients with AIDS will testify, when ambulance workers appeared in outfits more suited to space travel. Ayliffe et al (1979) concluded that clothing is not an 'important mode of transfer' of microorganisms after investigating its use in a unit for source and protective isolation over 18 months.

Ayton et al (1984) produced a report on behalf of the Infection Control Nurses' Association (ICNA) which tries to rationalise the use of clothing and prevent expensive, dangerous and/or offensive misuse. Since then there have been further developments.

Aprons and gowns

Plastic aprons which are cheap, easy to put on, impermeable and disposable, offer an effective means of protecting nurses' uniforms at the area of most likely contamination (bed height). Some concern is expressed about lack of protection of arms and shoulders, and the slippery nature of aprons when nursing small babies. *If* protection here is vital then gowns which are water repellent and disposable are required. These are available but are relatively expensive and should be reserved for use in specific situations such as avoidance of blood splashing. Cotton gowns are potentially dangerous as they are not a true barrier, and once wet will easily allow passage of organisms (Babb et al, 1983). However, they can be used over a plastic apron in the nursery situation, and then laundered.

Gloves

Possibly more articles have appeared in medical and nursing press on the use of gloves than any other topic, and they are still a source of some controversy. Jenner (1990b) suggests that there should be an international standard for all types of glove. She also reminds us that *intact skin and hand-washing* are equally important. Gloves are now advised (UK Health Departments, 1990) for all procedures where blood contamination is probable; for handling disinfectants; dealing with spillages; cleaning equipment; and for venepuncture in certain instances (although the latter is left in some cases to the discretion of the practitioner).

There is a UK specification for latex gloves (UK Health Departments, 1991) which are recommended for all situations where sterile surgeons gloves are not needed, with the exception of heavy-duty (household rubber) gloves which are used in certain circumstances, e.g. when using glutaraldehyde. Hospitals should have a protocol to encourage appropriate use of gloves. Sterile gloves have frequently been used where unsterile would do, involving unnecessary cost. However, if gloves are worn for an aseptic procedure, they should be sterile.

Gloves are not a substitute for hand-washing and should

never be used as such. Their removal often leads to contamination of the hands and staff should remember that they are wearing them for protection of patients as well as themselves.

Guidelines
- Check gloves for obvious defects.
- Do not reuse gloves, or go from one patient to another with them on.
- Wash your hands after removal of gloves.

Masks

Masks can again be a hazard rather than a proven benefit, and are now generally advised only as part of protection in situations likely to involve blood or body fluid splashes as a protection for mucous membranes. When used they should be well-fitting, filter-type, should be discarded when wet, and should never be taken down and then re-used. Orr (1981) has suggested that even in theatre masks may be unnecessary, and theatre discipline (e.g. no talking over exposed wounds) may be more beneficial. Recent work by Mitchell and Hunt (1991) reached similar conclusions, with the 'exception of high risk surgery'.

There is a place also for a specifically designed filter mask in endoscopy units to prevent inhalation of glutaraldehyde fumes, in addition to the protection from splashes.

Visors/goggles

These are increasingly used in theatre and labour ward situations as mucous membrane protection. Current advice to dentists by the British Dental Association also recommends the use of eye and mouth protection for dealing with all patients when exposure to aerosolised blood and saliva may occur.

Any protective clothing should be used with understanding and care, and handwashing must accompany its removal.

CONTAINMENT OF USED MATERIALS

Linen, waste materials, used equipment and 'sharps' were all discussed in Chapter 12. Their safe containment applies to all patients, although the category used will in certain instances depend on what is the problem for that particular patient.

Linen

The Department of Health (DOH) has stated that all linen which is blood stained should be treated as infected. This is in line with the discussion above of universal precautions with blood/body fluids. The nurse is usually responsible for dealing with linen and must be familiar with the categories for linen-bagging (see p. 350).

Clinical waste

As described in Chapter 12, all disposable articles in contact with patients secretions or excretions are to be regarded as clinical waste for incineration and should be bagged in the appropriate colour (*yellow*) plastic bag. New proposals are under discussion in connection with the removal of Crown immunity regarding waste management in 1991, the Environmental Protection Act (1990) and to bring the UK in line with the European Community legislation.

Sharps

Used needles, syringes and other sharp implements should *all* be treated as if carrying blood-borne pathogens. As

Figure 14.4 Some containers for safe disposal of "sharps" and of broken glass/aerosols.

As stated in Chapter 12, the closer the 'sharps' container is to the point of use, the more likely it is to be promptly and safely disposed of (see Figure 14.4).

Crockery and cutlery

There has long been misunderstanding over the need for disposable feeding utensils for infected patients. This can be a source of acute distress to patients (King, 1990) and there is negligible evidence to support its use. Jackson (1984) has estimated the chance of salmonella infection being transmitted from an infected patient to kitchen staff at 1 in 5000. If the patient is able to wash his/her hands, the chances are zero. Most sources now do not advise the use of disposable crockery or cutlery, although some authorities recommend them if patients with blood-borne viruses are bleeding from the mouth. Dishwashers which have a final rinse cycle of 82°C will adequately disinfect items. (Hand washing of eating utensils may well not be performed at a sufficiently high temperature, and the two-sink method may still not ensure correct rinsing.)

OTHER PROCEDURES

Disinfection and sterilisation

Equipment which requires reprocessing should be safely bagged and despatched to CSSD according to local policy. If equipment is for repair this despatch should be in accordance with DOH guidelines (1987), being decontaminated first and accompanied by an appropriate decontamination certificate (see Chapter 12).

Spillages

Any spillages of blood or body fluids should be dealt with promptly, with the carer using appropriate protective clothing (gloves and plastic apron) and disposable cloth/paper towel. Paper is used to absorb the spill, disinfectant is added and left for a few minutes. The area is cleaned with detergent. Chlorine releasing granules may now be used to absorb blood/blood-stained spillages and make the clearing-up process simpler (see Figure 14.5). They are contraindicated for use with large volumes of urine and in enclosed spaces because of vapour release (SAB, 1990).

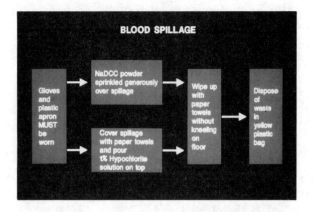

Figure 14.5 Dealing with spillage of blood/body fluids.

Domestic cleaning

The domestic staff need to understand the reasons for their methods of work, and this is one area where communication often breaks down and leads to misunderstanding. The patients' sense of isolation will be increased if cleaning of their room is omitted.

The areas where infected patients are cared for should be cleaned *last*, and the at-risk patient area *first*. Designated cleaning equipment should be kept, and must be cleaned, dried and stored in that area after use. Ideally mop heads should be laundered daily. Domestic staff should be shown how and when to use the appropriate protective clothing.

Terminal cleaning

After the patient no longer requires separate care, the room (including all horizontal surfaces) can be cleaned thoroughly with hot water and detergent. In certain circumstances, the infection control doctor may advise use of a disinfectant (e.g. after a patient has received care while colonised or infected with MRSA). Disinfection is not usually required if spillages have been dealt with correctly, and wall-washing or 'fogging' are not necessary. Curtains may need to be laundered if the patient has had an airborne infection such as chickenpox, MRSA or tuberculosis.

Transport

Part of good communication is ensuring that other departments are aware of any precautions they need to take for both infected and at-risk patients, while still observing strict confidentiality.

Specimen collection

The rules for safe collection and transport of specimens outlined in Chapter 7 should be followed for *all* patients. '*Biohazard*' or '*Danger of Infection*' labels should be reserved for specific named infections.

Occupational health

All health-care workers involved in direct patient care should have appropriate and up-to-date immunisation/vaccination (see Chapter 11). If unsure of their immune status (e.g. for rubella or chickenpox immunity) they should check with their Occupational Health Department.

PLANNING CARE OF INFECTED/AT-RISK PATIENTS

Planning care of patients who are infected or at risk from infection should consist of an individualised, systematic, problem-solving approach (the frequently misunderstood *nursing process*). The nursing process is a way of providing the nursing care patients require in their particular situation (Ashworth, 1984), and the care plan is the documented record of implementing care planning. The four stages of the process are *assessment*, *planning*, *implementation* and *evaluation*.

Nursing models and care planning

These stages should be implemented in conjunction with one or a combination of nursing models. Infection control elements should be incorporated into the care plan for every patient and can be used with any model. Two *partial* care plans are shown below, which use adaptation of two different nursing models. As these have been written to stress the infection control elements in particular, they are simply an example of how to incorporate these elements, and *not* written with specified time limitations.

Care Plan 1 (for an infected patient)

This shows use of Roper's well-known model (Roper et al, 1985) which uses the activities of daily living. The plan is for the care of a 56-year-old lady who has undergone a cholecystectomy for gall stones. Her recovery has been delayed by the development of a surgical wound infection caused by methicillin-resistant *Staphylococcus aureus*. The following *partial* care plan shows how elements of the activities of daily living have been used to assess problems/potential problems and develop plans to overcome or avoid these problems. An accompanying rationale is included where needed. *As with all care plans, they must be evaluated daily (or more frequently) and adjusted as necessary.*

Table 14.2 Elements of a care plan for a patient with MRSA wound infection

Activity (identifying problem/potential problem)	Goal/objective	Nursing action/intervention (and rationale)
1. Maintaining a safe environment Mrs King has an infection (MRSA) which can cause serious problems to others if cross-infection occurs	Further complications will be minimised	Nurse Mrs King in single room with door closed. *(The organism may be spread by contact (especially staff hands) or (less likely) by airborne route)*
		Equipment will be reduced to essential items. Mattress and pillow covers will be checked for intactness (to prevent contamination of underlying material)
		Carers will wash and dry hands efficiently, using approved agent, before *and* after attending patient. An alcoholic hand rub will also be used after leaving the room.* *Hands are the most likely route of transmission.* Carers will wear disposable aprons and latex gloves for significant patient contact, e.g. bed-making, helping patient to wash, etc.

All dressings and other waste will be treated as clinical waste, i.e. placed in yellow bags for incineration

Bed-linen should be bagged according to policy for 'infected' linen, e.g. alginate-stitched/soluble inner bag and outer red bag.
Bed-linen will be changed daily.* (Patient's own clothing can be safely dealt with by a relative using a domestic machine)

Any equipment leaving the room must be thoroughly cleaned with soap and water, and finally with a phenolic*, using appropriate protective clothing (aprons and gloves)

Staff will explain to the Mrs King about her infection. They will reassure her that there is no danger to visitors who may be encouraged to visit. Any extra interests Mrs King feels able to pursue should be encouraged

Mrs King will understand why she is being nursed separately and will be able to accept this

2. Communication
(a) Mrs King may experience loneliness, anxiety and rejection

Table 14.2 Continued.

Activity (identifying problem/potential problem)	Goal/objective	Nursing action/intervention (and rationale)
	Mrs King will have every normal opportunity to talk to carers and express needs	The need for single-room care will not prevent nurses from spending time with Mrs King, or restrict their care. They will explain the use of protective clothing and other 'special' measures taken
(b) Mrs King may experience pain from infected wound	Mrs King will be comfortable	Observe Mrs King closely and record evidence of pain (*people vary in responses to pain*). Give analgesia as prescribed and before pain becomes acute, timing this also for maximum comfort during dressing changes. Place bed cradle in position to avoid pressure on wound area
3. Controlling body temperature		
Mrs King may complain of feeling hot, sweaty and unwell due to pyrexia	Further complications will be minimised, and Mrs King's discomfort alleviated	Ensure Mrs King is receiving all prescribed medication
		Make sure Mrs King has adequate changes of night clothes and change bed linen after any episode of sweating (see (5) also)

432

4. Eating and drinking

(a) Mrs King may experience thirst or become dehydrated due to excessive fluid loss in sweating. This may lead to dehydration	Mrs King will not experience thirst or become dehydrated	Help Mrs King to understand the need for and to achieve a good fluid intake. Record fluid intake and output to ensure correct balance is maintained
(b) Mrs King may feel reluctant to eat	Mrs King feels both comfortable and confident enough to eat	Give analgesia if needed (see (2b)). Allow Mrs King to choose diet for herself, involve dietician if necessary. (*Wound healing is enhanced by proper nutrition*)

5. Personal cleansing and hygiene

(a) Mrs King may feel 'dirty' because of infected wound, and sweaty from pyrexia	Mrs King will understand treatment and process of wound healing, and will not feel uncomfortable. Conditions for Mrs Kings' wound healing will be optimised	Spend time explaining progress to Mrs King so that she is reassured. Redress wound daily if appropriate (*to assess progress of infected wound*), using an aseptic technique. If 'strikethrough' occurs, always redress wound. Use sterile normal saline to clean wound as needed. Record and report any change in wound appearance
(b) Mrs King will need help with personal hygiene		Help Mrs King to maintain personal hygiene

Table 14.2 Continued.

Activity (identifying problem/potential problem)	Goal/objective	Nursing action/intervention (and rationale)
(c) Mrs King may develop dry, sore mouth	Mrs King will maintain a moist mouth and not develop any soreness or infection	In addition to encouraging fluid intake (above), give or assist Mrs King with mouth care. This will help the mouth remain moist and make food and fluid intake easier
(d) Mrs King may have other sites colonised by MRSA*	Mrs King will not have any other body sites colonised by MRSA	Take swabs from nose, axillae, groins and any other lesions (see Figure 14.6). If MRSA found, carry out staphylococcal eradication programme according to hospital policy. Rescreen sites and wounds not less than 48 h after completion of eradication protocol. Repeat this screen twice at 3-day intervals†

* Certain steps are additional to most source isolation procedures, specifically designed to prevent spread of this problem organism.
† (May vary according to Health Authority/Unit policy)

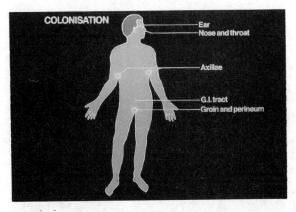

Figure 14.6 Colonisation with MRSA—sites for screening.

This organism (MRSA) has caused major problems in hospitals because of its multiple-resistance to antibiotics. Since the early 1980s, notably in the North-East Thames Region of London, a particular strain (EMRSA-1 or *epidemic* MRSA-1) has been specifically implicated. Although the term includes many different strains, and not all of them cause epidemics, most hospitals take the view that any MRSA must be treated as a potential problem. The patient is accordingly isolated until the strain can be further identified where possible. Guidance given by the Hospital Infection Society and British Society for Antimicrobial Chemotherapy combined working party in 1986 has been recently updated (1990). This contains appendices with detailed practical procedures for controlling epidemic strains of MRSA. For additional information on MRSA see the 'Further reading' list at the end of this chapter and Chapter 8.

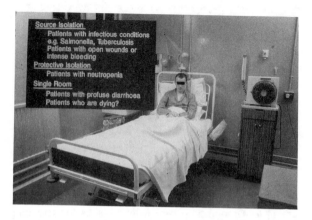

Figure 14.7 Source and protective isolation for patients with AIDS.

Partial Care Plan 2 (for a patient who is both infected and 'at risk' from infection—see Figure 14.7)

This care plan is presented differently and is based on *Orem's self-care nursing model* (1985). This has been selected to try and stress the approach of helping a patient to care for himself as and when his condition (physical and mental) allows. Orem's model, first described in 1971, uses the concept of three sets of self-care needs.

1. *Universal self-care needs*—air; food; water; elimination; avoidance of hazards; solitude and social interaction; a balance between activity and rest; and being 'normal'.
2. *Developmental self-care needs*—e.g. related to an individual's stage of development, and to changes in life style or experiences.

3. *Health deviation self-care needs*—brought about by illness, injury, or disablement.

The nursing aim is to help the patient restore himself/herself to a state of balance where self-care demands and abilities are not in conflict (Miller, 1989).

The following care plan is for a patient who is initially in need of a great deal of wholly compensatory nursing intervention, but is expected to make a reasonable recovery from his present pulmonary infection. The underlying problem of HIV positivity which has now progressed to AIDS means there are many self-care demands which will be constantly changing. As the patient's condition alters, the care plan must be continuously reassessed and altered to meet the changing self-care deficit situation.

Care plan 2 is for a 35-year-old HIV-positive man admitted to hospital with pulmonary tuberculosis. This is Robert's second opportunistic infection. Nursing interventions will be altered as the patient progresses, gradually restoring self-care to the patient as his condition improves.

Figure 14.8 All things must pass—even isolation!

Table 14.3 Elements of a care plan for a patient who is infected *and* 'at-risk' of infection.

Self-care demand	Self-care deficit (problem)	Goal—self-care	Action to be taken by carer/patient	Potential for self-care (evaluation)
Ability to breathe unaided	Robert is unable to maintain adequate air intake unaided because of his infection	Robert will be able to breathe easily, unaided	1. Help Robert assume most comfortable position to assist respiration 2. Ensure adequate ventilation, maintaining air flow from inside the room to outside the building (spread of pulmonary tuberculosis is in droplets) 3. Reassure Robert and try to alleviate his anxieties 4. Administer oxygen if helpful 5. Administer antitubercular therapy as prescribed	Long-term: self-care. Short-term: be able to find more comfort in assisted breathing

	Problem	Goal	Nursing action	Evaluation
	Robert is anxious because of breathing difficulties	Robert will be able to breathe without anxiety	1. Reassure him as in (3) above, outlining expected progress 2. Ensure Robert can reach and use 'nurse-call' system 3. Check that he understands how to use the oxygen	Long-term: self-care. Short-term: will state that he feels less anxious.
Ability to maintain adequate food intake	Robert is reluctant to eat due to general exhaustion (from effects of TB and AIDS)	Robert will manage to eat adequate food	1. Ask Robert for his food likes and dislikes 2. Give small, appetising portions until appetite improves 3. Supplements may be needed 4. Involve dietician if required 5. Encourage Robert to select own diet as his condition improves	Long-term: self-care. Short-term: he will receive food which he can eat

439

Table 14.3 Continued.

Self-care demand	Self-care deficit (problem)	Goal—self-care	Action to be taken by carer/patient	Potential for self-care (evaluation)
Ability to maintain sufficient intake of water	Robert is too exhausted to drink adequately, and is dehydrated.	Robert will not be dehydrated and will be able to drink adequately	1. Explain to Robert the need for rehydration, involving intravenous infusion 2. Encourage sips of acceptable fluids as desired (iced water may be appreciated)	Long-term: self-care. Short-term: he accepts infusion and tolerates increasing oral fluids
Avoidance of hazards—to self	Robert may be at risk of infection because of his immuno-suppressed state	Robert will not develop infection due to his stay in hospital	1. Robert will initially be cared for in a single room (because of his TB) and the reasons for this will be explained to him 2. Carers will wash hands carefully *before* caring for Robert as well as after	Long-term: Robert wil be fit to leave the single room. Short-term: he will understand the need for 'isolation'. He

440

Robert's IV infusion will not be a source of infection. Robert will feel clean and comfortable. He will not develop an oral infection. He will be free of pressure sores or skin infections

3. Disposable aprons will be worn for any direct patient care
4. No carer will attend Robert if they are suffering from conditions which pose an infection risk, e.g. cold sores
5. Carers will look at Robert's IVI for signs of inflammation. Strict asepsis will be used in caring for the site
6. Robert will be bed-bathed or assisted to wash himself and carry out mouth care. Dental floss may help to keep his mouth clean
7. Robert's skin will be closely observed for development of pressure sores or breaks in the skin

will not develop any hospital-acquired infection

Table 14.3 Continued.

Self-care demand	Self-care deficit (problem)	Goal—self-care	Action to be taken by carer/patient	Potential for self-care (evaluation)
Avoidance of hazards—to others*	Robert is a possible source of infection to others because of his TB and HIV-positive status	Robert will understand his capacity to be a source of contamination or infection to others	1. Carers will explain the potential routes of infection from Robert to others, and explain the use of protective clothing and other procedures 2. Robert's carers will wear latex gloves and disposable aprons when dealing with his blood, sputum, or any secretions or excreta which may be blood-stained; also when dealing with contaminated items, e.g. blood-stained bedding or equipment (i.e. IVI) 3. Extreme care must be taken with 'sharps'	Long-term: self-care, with safety. Short-term: no infection will be transmitted from him

442

disposal. A 'sharps' box will be available in his room

4. Carers will wash their hands after removing aprons and gloves, drying them thoroughly. They will wash them again or use an alcoholic chlorhexidine handrub on leaving his room

5. Linen will be removed from Robert's room in accordance with hospital policy, and labelled 'biohazard'

6. Clinical waste will be placed in yellow bags and sent for incineration

7. Robert will use normal crockery and cutlery sent for processing in ward or central wash-up facility according to local practice

Table 14.3 Continued.

Self-care demand	Self-care deficit (problem)	Goal—self-care	Action to be taken by carer/patient	Potential for self-care (evaluation)
Solitude/social interaction	Robert may feel distressed and 'isolated' because of single-room care and his diagnoses	He will understand the reasons for his care	1. Carers will discuss all care with Robert so that he understands the use of protective measures being taken both for his own and others' safety. They will ensure that no unnecessary measures are taken	Long-term: he will be self-caring, and able to mix.
		He will be able to communicate with others as he feels fit to, and will not feel rejected.	2. No action or discussion concerning Robert's diagnosis takes place without his express permission 3. The 'nurse-call' system is available at all times.	Short-term: he accepts restrictions until able to resume contact with others as he wishes

Radio, TV, etc. will be provided for Robert if desired.

4. Encourage visitors for Robert when he feels well enough for company

5. If Robert lacks support from friends or family, discuss possible 'support' systems with patient (e.g. Terence Higgins Trust or local HIV-positive support groups)

6. Reassure Robert that when his tuberculosis is responding to treatment he will be able to mix with other patients if he so wishes

---

* Although Orem's model concentrates on avoidance of hazards to 'self', the incorporation of infection control elements with a patient's potential for infecting others, and avoidance of same, is not out of place with the philosophy of the model.

445

N.B. This is only *part* of a care plan for Robert. Much of the care described highlights measures to prevent transmission of Robert's pulmonary tuberculosis. The care described for prevention of transmitting infection from blood/bloodstained body fluids should be part of the care for all individuals now, as described earlier in this chapter. Simple measures have also been described to safeguard Robert from acquiring nosocomial infection. These are logical and necessary measures to take for his safety, but this immunocompromised group of patients tend to succumb more to reactivation of latent infection than to hospital-acquired infection.

There are many aspects to the care of patients with AIDS, and a great deal of information available on this subject. Issues of staff attitudes in caring for patients who are HIV-positive have also received much attention. There are references in the 'Further reading' list at the end of this chapter for the reader to seek more detailed information.

REFERENCES

Armstrong D (1984) Protected environments are discomforting and expensive and do not offer meaningful protection. *Am. J. Med.* **76**: 685–689.

Ashworth P (1984) Infection control and the nursing process—making the best use of resources. *J. Hosp. Infect.* **5** (Suppl. A): 35–44.

Ayton M, Babb J, Mackintosh C and Maloney MH (1984) *Report of an ICNA Working Party on Ward Protective Clothing.* ICNA.

Ayliffe GAJ, Babb JR, Taylor L and Wise R (1979) A unit for source and protective isolation in a general hospital. *Br. Med. J.* **2**: 461–465.

Babb JR, Davies JG and Ayliffe GAJ (1983) Contamination of protective clothing and nurses' uniforms in an isolation ward. *J. Hosp. Infect.* **4**: 149–157.

Bowell B (1989) Nursing intervention in *Applied Microbiology* pp. 159–188. ed. Caddow. Scutari Press, London.

Bowell B (1992a) Protecting the patient at risk. *Nursing Times* **88**(3): 32–35.

Bowell B (1992b) A risk to others. *Nursing Times* **88**(4): 38–40.

CDC (1985) Recommendations for preventing transmission of infection with human T-lymphotropic virus type III/lymphadenopathy-associated virus in the workplace. *MMWR* **34**: 681–686, 691–695.

CDC (1988) Update: universal precautions for prevention of transmission of human immunodeficiency virus, hepatitis B virus, and other bloodborne pathogens in health-care settings. *MMWR* **37**: 377–382, 387–388.

Coleman D (1987) The when and how of isolation. *Registered Nurse*, **Oct.**: 50–57.

Denton PF (1986) Psychological and physiological effects of isolation. *Nursing* **3**: 88–91.

DHSS and the Welsh Office (1986) *Memorandum on The Control of Viral Haemorrhagic Fevers*. London: HMSO.

DHSS (1987) Decontamination of health care equipment prior to inspection, service or repair. HN (87)22.

Garner JS and Simmons BP (1986) Isolation precautions. In *Hospital Infection* (eds Bennett JV and Brachman PS), 2nd edn. Boston, MA: Little, Brown and Co.

Hart S (1991) Blood and body fluid precautions. *Nursing Standard* **5**(25): 25–27.

Jackson MM (1984) From ritual to reason—with a rational approach for the future: an epidemiologic perspective *Am. J. Infect. Control* **12**(4): 213–220.

Jackson MM and Lynch P (1984) Infection control. Too much or too little? *Am. J. Nursing* **Feb.**: 208–210.

Jackson MM and Lynch P (1985) Isolation practices: a historical perspective. *Am. J. Infect. Control* **13**: 21–31.

Jenner EA (1990a) Aspects of isolation care. *Nursing* **4**(20): 17–21.

Jenner EA (1990b) Seeking a rationale for glove use. *Nursing Times* **86**(37): 73–74.

King R (1990) Hepatitis B: more care less scare. *Nursing Times* **86**(5): 54–57.

Lesko LM, Kern J and Hawkins DR (1984) Psychological aspects of patients in germ-free isolation: a review of child, adult, and patient management literature. *Med. Paediatr. Oncol.* **12**: 43–49.

Lynch P and Jackson MM (1988) Isolation practices: How much is too much or not enough? *Asepsis* **10**(3): 12–15.

Miller J (1989) DIY Healthcare. *Nursing Standard* **43**(3): 35–37.

Mitchell NJ and Hunt S (1991) Surgical face masks in modern operating rooms—a costly and unnecessary ritual? *J. Hosp. Infect.* **18**(3): 239–242.

Orem DE (1985) *Nursing: Concepts of Practice*, 3rd edn. New York: McGraw Hill.

Orr NW (1981) Is a mask necessary in the operating theatre? *Ann. R. Coll. Surg. UK* **63**: 390–392.

Nauseef WM and Maki DG (1981) A study of the value of simple protective isolation in patients with granulocytopaenia. *N. Engl. J. Med.* **304**: 448–453.

Report of a Combined Working Party of the Hospital Infection Society and the British Society for Antimicrobial Chemotherapy (1990) Revised guidelines for the control of epidemic methicillin-resistant *Staphylococcus aureus. J. Hosp. Infect.* **16**: 351–377.

Roper N, Logan WW and Tierney AJ (1985) *The Elements of Nursing*, 2nd edn. Edinburgh: Churchill Livingstone.

SAB (1990) *Spills of Urine: Potential Risk of Misuse of Chlorine-Releasing Disinfecting Agents* **SAB(90) 41**. London: UK Health Departments.

Shooter RA, O'Grady FW and Williams REO (1963) Isolation of patients in hospital. *Br. Med. J.* **4**: 924.

UK Health Departments (1990) *Guidance for Clinical Health Care Workers: Protection against Infection with HIV and Hepatitis Viruses.* London: HMSO.

UK Health Departments (1991) *Specification for Non-sterile, Natural Rubber Latex Examination Gloves. NHS Procurement Directorate.* **TSS/D/300.010/1**. London: HMSO.

Wood K (1989) Protective isolation. *Nursing Standard* **36**(3): 54.

FURTHER READING

Aggleton P and Chalmers C (1985) Orem's self-care model. *Nursing Times* **2 Jan.**: 36–39.

Ayton M (1990) Infection control. *Practice Nurse* **Jul./Aug.**: 140, 142, 144, 146, 148.

Bateman W (1990) Imported organisms. *Nursing Times, J. Infect. Control Nursing* **86**(26): 73–75.

Bond S, Rhodes T, Philips P and Tierney AJ (1990) HIV infection and community nursing staff in Scotland 1. Experience, practice and education. *Nursing Times* **86**(44): 47–50.

Bond S, Rhodes T, Philips P and Tierney AJ (1990) HIV infection and community nursing staff in Scotland 2. Knowledge and attitudes. *Nursing Times* **86**(45): 49–51.

Brown-Peterside P, Sibbald B and Freeling P (1991) AIDS: knowledge, skills and attitudes among vocational trainees and their trainers. *Br. J. Gen. Pract.* **41**: 401–405.

Burnard P (1989) Exploring nurses' attitudes to AIDS. *Prof. Nurse* **5**(2): 84–90.

CDC (1989) Guidelines for prevention of transmission of human immunodeficiency virus and hepatitis B virus to health-care and public safety workers. *MMWR* **38** (Suppl. S6).

Claxton R (1989) Looking after the children. *Nursing Times* **85**(39): 41–43.

Editorial (1983) methicillin-resistant *Staphylococcus aureus. J. Hosp. Infect.* **4**(4): 327–329.

Edwards S (1989) Breast-feeding and HIV. *Nursing Times* **85**(43): 69–70.

European Collaborative Study (1991) Children born to women with HIV-1 infection: natural history and risk of transmission. *Lancet* **337**: 253–260.

Evans BG, Gill ON, Gleave SR, Mortimer PP and Parry JV (1991) HIV-2 in the United Kingdom—A Review. *CDR* **1**: Review No. 2.

Howe J (1989) AIDS—the right approach. *Prof. Nurse* **5**(3): 156–159.

Jevons MR (1961) 'Celbenin'-resistant staphylococci. *Br. Med. J.* **1**: 124.

Keane CT, Coleman DC and Cafferkey MT (1991) Methicillin-resistant *Staphylococcus aureus*—a reappraisal. *J. Hosp. Infect.* **19**(3): 147–152.

MacQueen S (1989) Positive practice. *Nursing Times* **85**(43): 67–68.

Mehtar S, Drabu YJ and Mayet F (1989) Expenses incurred during a five-week epidemic methicillin-resistant *Staphylococcus aureus* outbreak. *J. Hosp. Infect.* **13**: 199–203.

Miller D, Weber J and Green J (1986) *The Management of AIDS Patients*. London: Macmillan.

Murphy K and Atkinson J (1990) Nutritional support: a practical approach. *Nursing Standard* **5**(4): 54–56.

Pavillard R, Harvey K, Douglas D, *et al* (1982) Epidemic of hospital-acquired infection due to methicillin-resistant *Staphylococcus aureus* in major Victorian hospitals. *Med. J. Aust.* **1**: 451–454.

Pratt RJ (1991) *AIDS: A Strategy for Nursing Care*, 3rd edn. London: Edward Arnold.

Speller DCE, Shanson DC, Ayliffe GAJ and Cooke M (1990) Acquired immune deficiency syndrome: recommendations of a Working Party of the Hospital Infection Society. *J. Hosp. Infect.* **15**(1): 7–34.

Stanford J (1988) Professional care for people with HIV/AIDS. *Prof. Nurse* **4**(2): 76–80.

Taylor LJ (1990) Infection control at your fingertips. Procedures for preventing and controlling MRSA. *Prof. Nurse* **5**(10): 547–551.

UKCC (1992) *Anonymous Testing for the Prevalence of the Human Immunodeficiency Virus (HIV)* Annexe 2 to Registrar's Letter 24/1992. London: HMSO.

UKCC (1989) *UKCC Statement on AIDS and HIV Infection* Annexe 1 to Registrar's Letter 24/1992. London: HMSO.

UK Health Departments (1991) *AIDS—HIV Infected Health Care Workers. Occupational Guidance for Health Care Workers, their Physicians and Employers*. London: HMSO.

UK Health Departments/HEA (1990) *HIV & AIDS. An Assessment of Current and Future Spread in the UK*. Symposium proceedings. London: HMSO.

Webster M (1986) Control measures. *Nursing Times* **5 Feb.**: 26–28.

APPENDIX: GUIDE TO TRANSMISSION AND MANAGEMENT OF IMPORTANT INFECTIONS/ DISEASES

The table below is based on Bloomsbury Health Authority's Control of Infection Manual.

Table 14.4 Guide to Transmission and Management of Important Infections/Diseases

Disease and/or infective agent	Period of infectivity to others	Source	Route of transmission	Isolation required	Comments
AIDS: *see* Human immunodeficiency viruses					
Anthrax: *Bacillus anthracis*	Until lesions are free from bacilli	Contaminated animal tissue or hide, and soil	Cutaneous—inoculation, direct contact Respiratory—inhalation	Yes	Hands and equipment may be contaminated from vesicles. Strict isolation needed for pulmonary infection (IDU)
Bronchiolitis of infants	While symptomatic (5 days or longer)	Infected people	Airborne and by direct contact (hands)	Yes	Common organisms: RSV, parainfluenza, etc. Highly infectious
Brucellosis: *B. abortus*, *B. melitensis*, etc.	Nil	Infected animals; contaminated food	Contact with animal tissues, blood, especially placentae of infected animals. Ingestion of contaminated food, especially milk products	No	Trammision from man to man is not known

Table 14.4 Continued.

Disease and/or infective agent	Period of infectivity to others	Source	Route of transmission	Isolation required	Comments
Burns: Non-infected	Susceptible while healing	Nil		Protective	Degree of protective isolation decided by medical staff
Infected: MRSA, Group A streptococci, *Pseudomonas*, etc.	While colonised		Direct or indirect contact with colonised patients, staff or environment	Yes	Isolate until bacteriologically negative
Candidiasis: *C. albicans*, etc.	Susceptible while immuno-suppressed	Usually endogenous	Contact with excretions	No	Can be spread by hands or equipment contaminated with exudates

Cellulitis: e.g. Group A streptococci, *Pseudomonas aeruginosa*	While colonised		Direct contact	Yes	Until organism eradicated on culture
Chickenpox, varicella–zoster virus	1–2 days before rash, until all lesions have dried: (6 days in non-immunosuppressed)	Vesicles, respiratory tract of infected persons	Inhalation or direct contact with vesicle fluid	Yes. Ideally home or to IDU	Contamination of articles, hands or equipment with vesicle fluid may cause infection. Staff attending patient must be immune
Cholera *Vibrio cholerae*	During diarrhoeal phase	Usually infected drinking water	Ingestion after faecal contamination	Yes	Case-to-case transmission is rare, but diligence still required

Table 14.4 Continued.

Disease and/or infective agent	Period of infectivity to others	Source	Route of transmission	Isolation required	Comments
Conjunctivitis	While symptoms present	Infected people	Usually respiratory or direct contact	Preferable	Many agents involved. May suggest highly infectious diseases, e.g. measles, adenovirus
Cryptococcosis: *Cryptococcus neoformans*	Susceptible when immuno-suppressed	Environment (pigeon faeces)	Inhalation probably	No	Disease common in AIDS. Causes pneumonia, meningitis, etc.
Cytomegalovirus (CMV)	Chronic carriage and intermittent shedding for life. May reactivate in immunosuppressed	Blood and secretions of infected people	Blood transfusion, intimate contact e.g. during delivery	Not usually (possibly neonates)	Staff hands or equipment contaminated with infectious urine or saliva may transmit infection

Diarrhoea:

Salmonella spp., *Shigella* spp., *Campylobacter* spp. etc.	Treat as infection risk during diarrhoeal phase	Infected person or carrier; contaminated food. Infected animals	Faecal–oral ingestion	Usually, but assess individual risk factors	Always wear gloves and aprons when dealing with diarrhoeal stools. Case-to-case spread of *Campylobacter* unlikely
Enteropathogenic/toxic *E. coli*: (many serotypes can cause infantile gastroenteritis)	While shedding	Infected person (or cattle—serotype 0157)	Ingestion of contaminated food or infant feeds. (Direct contact less frequent)	Yes	Serotype 0157 can cause bloody diarrhoea, may lead to haemolytic uraemic syndrome
Clostridium difficile: see Pseudomembranous colitis					
Toxins—*S. aureus, C. perfringens*					Not infectious to others

Table 14.4 Continued.

Disease and/or infective agent	Period of infectivity to others	Source	Route of transmission	Isolation required	Comments
Food poisoning	There are also many non-microbial causes of food poisoning to consider				
Diphtheria: *Coryne-bacterium diphtheriae*	Infectious until throat swabs negative	Carriers or infected people	Respiratory or direct contact (local lesion)	Yes— transfer to IDU	Vaccinate in infancy but effective antibodies may not persist. Contact tracing and screening required
Dysentery: 1. Bacillary *Shigella* spp.	Infectious while shedding in stools	Infected person	Faecal–oral transmission (ingestion)	Yes	Highly infectious. Nursery outbreaks are caused by direct or indirect hand transmission
2. Amoebic: *Entamoeba histolytica*	During faecal carriage	Man contaminating food or water	Faecal–oral (ingestion)	No	No transmission in temperate climates

456

Ebola fever: *see* Viral haemorrhagic fever

Encephalitis (viral)	Varies according to cause	Varies according to cause	Faecal–oral or respiratory	Yes	Many enteroviruses and mumps are infectious. Isolate until cause known
Enteric fever: *Salmonella typhi* or *S. paratyphi*	While shedding in stools	Man, case or carrier	Faecal–oral (ingestion)	Preferable	A patient with acute typhoid fever will rarely infect another. Carriers may inadvertently infect food
Erysipelas: (Group A streptococci)	While lesions or carrier sites positive	Infected people or carriers	Direct contact	Yes	Usually isolate for 24–48 h after antibiotics given. Some cases may require negative screening swabs

Table 14.4 Continued.

Disease and/or infective agent	Period of infectivity to others	Source	Route of transmission	Isolation required	Comments
Food poisoning: *see* Diarrhoea					
Gas gangrene: *Clostridium perfringens (welchii)*	NA	Man—bowel	Own bowel flora or direct inoculation (surgery)	No	Trauma patients susceptible. Organisms are part of normal gut flora
Giardiasis: *Giardia intestinalis*	NA	Man	Ingestion of contaminated drinking water	If incontinent or has diarrhoea	Often acquired abroad
Glandular fever: (Epstein–Barr virus); infectious mononucleosis	Intermittently; excreted virus	Infected person	Intimate contact, probably saliva exchange	No	Contaminated staff hands may infect infants. Other viruses may lead to glandular fever-like illness (e.g. CMV, HIV) but are monospot negative

Gonorrhoea: *Neisseria gonorrhoeae*					
1. Genital infection	Until organism eradicated (especially women)	Infected person or carrier	Sexually transmitted (vaginal & urethral discharges)	No	Women commonly asymptomatic carriers
2. Neonatal infection: e.g. *Ophthalmia neonatorum*		Intrapartum infection from infected mother	Conjunctival discharges	Yes	Can be spread by staff hands/equipment to other neonates. Meticulous hand hygiene necessary
3. Secondary arthritis		Spread via bloodstream	N/A		
Hepatitis: *see* Chapter 9					
Hepatitis A virus	Before jaundiced (preicteric phase)	Usually sewage-contaminated food (e.g. shellfish), water	Faecal–oral (ingestion)	Only if known before jaundice detectable	Use gloves and aprons when handling excreta. Give γ-globulin to family contacts

459

Table 14.4 Continued.

Disease and/or infective agent	Period of infectivity to others	Source	Route of transmission	Isolation required	Comments
Hepatitis B virus	See Table 9.2 Chapter 9	Infected person or carrier	Sexually transmitted or blood inoculation. Neonates: transplacentally or intrapartum (mucous membrane)	If bleeding	Meticulous care with 'sharps' to avoid staff infection. Equipment in contact with blood *must* be correctly decontaminated. Biohazard labels required. Active and passive immunisation available ('sharps' injury protocol needed)
Hepatitis C, D and E (non-A, non-B viruses)	See Table 9.2 in Chapter 9				See Chapter 9

460

Herpes simplex: Type 1 (cold sores, herpetic whitlows)	Active lesions infectious; also intermittent shedding into oral secretions	Infected person	Direct and close contact with lesion exudate	No	Risk from staff with *active cold sores or whitlows* to immunosuppressed patients or neonates, or eczematous patients. Personal hygiene essential to prevent transmission
Type 2 (genital herpes)	Active lesions infectious	Infected person	Sexually transmitted	No	
Type 2 (neonatal herpes)	May be present at birth or soon after	Infected mother	Intrapartum transmission	Yes	Separate infant from other neonate (high virus load). Secretions from mother and baby to be handled with hygienic precautions

Table 14.4 Continued.

Disease and/or infective agent	Period of infectivity to others	Source	Route of transmission	Isolation required	Comments
Herpes–zoster: *see* Shingles					
HIV (human immuno-deficiency viruses)	After virus acquired, then for life	Infected person	Sexually transmitted, blood inoculation. Neonate: transplacental or intrapartum (mucous membrane)	If bleeding, confused, or has other infection which is a hazard (e.g. TB or salmonellosis) May need protective isolation (see Figure 14.7)	Extreme care required with handling of 'sharps'. Biohazard labels needed.

Disease/Organism		Source	Transmission	Infectious?	Notes
Impetigo: S. aureus, Group A streptococcus	While shedding	Infected person	Direct contact	Yes	Children often highly infectious to others
Lassa fever: see Viral haemorrhagic fevers					
Legionnaire's disease: Legionella pneumophila	NA	Aquatic environment	Inhalation of infected aerosols. N.B. No person-to-person spread occurs	No	History of travel and work place needed to trace source. Outbreaks in UK. See Chapter 8
Leptospirosis (Weil's disease) L. ictero-haemorrhagiae, etc.	NA	Water contaminated by infected animals, e.g. rat and dog urine	Inhalation or mucous membrane inoculation (occasionally ingested)	No	Occupational or recreational hazard. Blood and urine contain organism but person-to-person transmission most unlikely

Table 14.4 Continued.

Disease and/or infective agent	Period of infectivity to others	Source	Route of transmission	Isolation required	Comments
Listeriosis: *Listeria monocytogenes*	Products of conception highly infectious	Infected dairy products, contaminated food	Ingestion of contaminated food. Direct cross-infection	Neonates	Neonatal infections acquired *in utero*. May be very infectious to other neonates delivered at same time. Elderly and immunocompromised at risk
Lyme disease: *Borrelia burgdorferi*	NA	Tick borne (especially deer)	Inoculation from tick bite	No	Not spread from person to person
Malaria: *P. falciparum, P. vivax, P. ovale, P. malariae*	NA	Mosquitoes	Bite from mosquito. Contaminated blood transfusion.	No	No person-to-person spread except by transfusion

464

Marburg virus: *see* Viral haemorrhagic fevers

	Period of infectivity	Source	Mode of spread	Isolation	Comments
Measles	Before rash appears until rash + 5 days	Infected person	Aerosol spread from respiratory tract	Yes—IDU or home	Causes outbreaks in Paed. Unit and is dangerous to immuno-suppresed children. Gamma globulin available for susceptible patients

Meningitis: Isolate until diagnosis is known.

	Period of infectivity	Source	Mode of spread	Isolation	Comments
Neisseriae meningitidis (meningococcal meningitis)	Carriers are infectious to others	Man	Respiratory tract, close contact, direct inoculation of mucous membranes	First 24 h of antibiotic therapy	Secondary cases do not occur in hospital. Rifampicin prophylaxis to close *family* contacts
Streptococcus pneumoniae (1), *Haemophilus influenzae* (2)	Organisms present in carriers	Man	Respiratory, mucous membrane inoculation	Not usually	(1) If penicillin-resistant. (2) Rifampicin prophylaxis to all household contacts if children under 3 years

Table 14.4 Continued.

Disease and/or infective agent	Period of infectivity to others	Source	Route of transmission	Isolation required	Comments
Viral meningitis (enteroviruses, mumps, etc).	Before and during acute illness	Man	Faecal–oral or respiratory spread (depends on agent)	Until agent known	Some agents are infectious and can cause outbreaks (e.g. neonates). Basic hand hygiene essential
MRSA: *see* Staphylococcal infections					
Mumps	7 days before definite symptoms, then for about 9 days	Man	Respiratory spread, and direct contact with saliva	Yes—preferably IDU or home	Highly infectious. Non-immune staff should not nurse patient

Disease	Period	Source	Spread	Isolate	Comments
Ophthalmia neonatorum: *Neisseria gonorrhoeae*, *Chlamydia trachomatis*	While symptomatic until treated	Infected mother's genital tract (intrapartum)	Conjunctival discharges	Yes	Caution with other neonates. Examine and treat mother—contact tracing to be arranged
Paratyphoid fever: *see* Enteric fever					
Pemphigus neonatorum	While shedding from active lesions	Man	Direct contact	Yes	Usually caused by a particularly virulent *Staphylococcus aureus* acquired from nasal carrier or/hand lesion of carer
Pneumonia: *Streptococcus pneumoniae* (1) *Mycoplasma pneumoniae* (2) *Chlamydia pneumoniae* (3)	While symptomatic	Infected patients or carriers	Respiratory, direct contact	Not usually. Yes (2) & (3)	(1) Isolate if antibiotic-resistant. (2) & (3) Transmission from person to person possible.

467

Table 14.4 Continued.

Disease and/or infective agent	Period of infectivity to others	Source	Route of transmission	Isolation required	Comments
Poliomyelitis	While respiratory symptoms persist. Faecal carriage	Man	Direct contact, respiratory, faecal–oral	Yes—transfer to IDU	Faecal shedding prolonged in children. Care needed when handling recently vaccinated infants' nappies. Immunise staff routinely
Pseudomembranous colitis: *Clostridium difficile*	While excreting in stools	Man and environment	Faecal–oral (indirect contact)	Yes	Isolate if has diarrhoea. Often associated with antibiotic use. May cause infection in immunocompromised patients

Pseudomonal infections: *Pseudomonas* spp.	While shedding	Carriers and environment	Direct and indirect contact	No (unless resistant)	Common environmental organism which may cause infection in immunocompromised patients
Psittacosis: *Chlamydia psittaci*	While shedding. Cultures highly infectious to laboratory staff	Various birds	Respiratory	No	Person-to-person transmission unlikely
Puerperal fever/sepsis: *Streptococcus pyogenes*, *Clostridium perfringens*	While shedding	Carriers	Respiratory tract, direct inoculation to genital tract	Yes	Isolate until cultures negative—lochia are heavily contaminated
PUO: many causes					Should be isolated pending diagnosis

469

Table 14.4 Continued.

Disease and/or infective agent	Period of infectivity to others	Source	Route of transmission	Isolation required	Comments
Rotavirus	Up to 7 days	Infected cases	Faecal–oral and respiratory (?)	If practicable (always on paediatric wards)	Use gloves and aprons handling excreta. Outbreaks in elderly care and paediatric units not uncommon
Respiratory syncytial virus (RSV)	While symptomatic	Man	Respiratory tract and direct contact	Yes	Highly transmissible in paediatric ward. Strict hand hygiene essential as probably most often spread by direct contact

Rubella	4 days before rash until 7 days afterwards	Man	Respiratory tract and direct contact. (Urine of congenitally infected babies)	Yes—preferably IDU if admission necessary	Incubation period 14–21 days. Carers should be rubella immune. In congenital rubella, babies excrete virus for months
Salmonellosis: *see* Diarrhoea					
Scabies: *see* Chapter 10					
Scarlet fever: Group A streptococcus	While throat colonized	Man	Respiratory or direct contact	Yes	
Shingles: herpes-zoster (*see* Chickenpox)	During vesicular stage	Endogenous in man—virus latent in nerve cells and may reactivate, causing disease	Lesion exudate and possible respiratory	Yes to protect susceptible patients	Patients appear to be less likely to transmit virus than from chickenpox. Staff hands or equipment may be implicated. *Exclude non-immune staff*

Table 14.4 Continued.

Disease and/or infective agent	Period of infectivity to others	Source	Route of transmission	Isolation required	Comments
Staphylococcal infection: *S. aureus*	While shedding from infected lesions	Infected person or carrier	Direct or indirect contact. (Airborne)	Yes if antibiotic-resistant or virulent strain	Isolate if MRSA (see Care Plan 1) or other multiresistant strain. Staff hands or equipment may be implicated. Isolate heavy shedders (e.g. patients with burns, eczema, boils)
Streptococcus pyogenes: Group A β-haemolytic streptococcus	While shedding	Infected person or carrier. Neonatal infection from mother's vaginal carriage	Respiratory. Direct contact	At least for first 24 h. antibiotic therapy	Can cause serious infection on burns, plastic and surgical units

472

Disease		Reservoir/source	Transmission	Person-to-person	Comments
Syphilis: *Treponema pallidum*	Primary chancre (1°). Secondary stage (2°).	Infected person	Direct sexual transmission; transplacentally. Chancre exudate (1°), blood and other secretions (2°)	No	Infectivity rapidly reduced by treatment. Wear gloves when dealing with (1°) or (2°) lesions
Tetanus: (*C. tetani*)	NA	Contaminated soil; harmless inhabitant of intestines of many animals (e.g. horses)	Direct inoculation from contaminated source	No	Booster immunization required every 5–10 years
Toxoplasmosis: *T. gondii*	NA	Undercooked food containing cysts, or soil contaminated with cat faeces	Ingestion; transplacental or intrapartum	No	No person-to-person spread (except by transfusion—unusual)

473

Table 14.4 Continued.

Disease and/or infective agent	Period of infectivity to others	Source	Route of transmission	Isolation required	Comments
Tuberculosis: *M. tuberculosis*, etc.	While excreting bacilli	Primarily man; cattle in some areas	Respiratory tract. Ingestion of contaminated milk. Rarely, direct or indirect contact	Yes	Pulmonary TB usually for first 14 days of treatment (aerosol spread)
Urinary tract infections: especially in catheterised patients e.g. (*E. coli*, *Klebsiella* spp.)	While excreting bacilli	Patients' faecal flora or environment	Direct contact (usually hands)	If multiply antibiotic resistant	Cross-infection with coliforms in urological and other wards is not uncommon. Hand hygiene essential
Viral haemorrhagic fevers: Lassa, Ebola, Marburg, Congo–Crimean viruses (see Chapter 9)	Variable	Rats, monkeys, others (depending on particular virus)	Blood and secretions, inoculation. *Needlestick injury* greatest hazard in hospitalised patients	Yes— transfer to High Security Unit, IDU	Only one documented case of transmission of a VHF in the UK (in a laboratory worker)

474

Whooping cough: *Bordetella pertussis*	Before and during catarrhal phase	Infected person	Respiratory spread. Direct contact	Yes	Infectivity reduced by antibiotic treatment, e.g. 3 days erythromycin. Staff hands/equipment may be implicated
Wounds (infected)	While shedding organisms	May be patient's own flora, or staff or other patient origin	Direct or indirect contact	Not usually	If organism multiresistant (e.g. MRSA), or group A streptococcus or gentamicin-resistant coliform, isolate patient. *Hand hygiene* of great importance in wound management

IDU, infectious diseases unit. RSV, respiratory syncytial virus. NA, not applicable. TB, tuberculosis. VHF, viral haemorrhagic fever.

Glossary

Abscess: a localised collection of pus.

Acid-fast stain: a differential stain used to detect and identify some types of bacteria, especially mycobacteria.

Acquired immunity: immunity which develops in response to a stimulus, e.g. an infection.

Active immunity: immunity depending on the production of antibodies or sensitised cells by the host animal; contrasted with passive immunity.

Acute infection: an infection which runs its course in a relatively short period.

Adherence (adhesion): the 'sticking' of a microbe to a body surface or other surface; this is an important phase in the initiation of infection.

Aerobe: a microbe that grows in the presence of oxygen. A *strict aerobe* requires oxygen. *See* anaerobe.

Agar: a polysaccharide made from seaweed and used in solidifying bacteriological media.

Agglutinate: to stick to one another, clump (of particles, red cells, etc.); the result is agglutination.

Algae: photosynthetic microbes; the blue–green algae are procaryotes and the others eucaryotes.

Allergy: an undesirable immune response due to hypersensitivity. (*See* hypersensitivity.)

Aminoglycoside: a type of antibiotic; examples are gentamicin, amikacin and streptomycin. The aminoglycosides are active against Gram-negative organisms, including *Pseudomonas* species, and some Gram-positive species.

Amoeba: a eukaryotic organism that lacks a rigid cell wall and moves by pseudopods.

Anaerobe: a microbe that grows in the absence of oxygen. A *strict anaerobe* will not grow in the presence of oxygen, a *facultative anaerobe* grows in the presence or absence of oxygen.

Anaphylaxis: one of the forms of hypersensitivity.

Antagonism: one antimicrobial interfering with another so that the sum of the effect is *less* than if either were given alone, e.g. penicillin and tetracycline.

Antibiotic: a substance which is toxic for certain microbes; the first antibiotics to be used were produced by microbes, but many are now partly or wholly synthesised by the pharmaceutical chemists. = antimicrobial agent.

Antibody: a protein which appears in the body fluids of an animal after contact with a foreign molecule, 'antigen', and which combines specifically with that antigen.

Antimicrobial agent: *see* antibiotic.

Antiseptic: a chemical used to reduce the numbers of microbes on body surfaces.

Antiserum: a serum that contains antibodies to a particular antigen.

Antitoxin: a serum containing antibodies to a toxin, either as a result of natural infection or, more often, in response to injection of toxoid.

Arthropod: an animal which has a hard outer 'skeleton' and jointed legs; examples are insects, ticks and lice.

Aseptic: free of contaminating microbes.

Attenuated: a microbe that is *attenuated* has lost its virulence and may be suitable for use as a vaccine.

Autoclave: a machine in which materials can be exposed to steam under pressure and therefore at a temperature higher than that of boiling water.

Autogenous: arising within the individual.

Bacillus: any rod-shaped bacterium; also the name of a genus of bacteria, Gram-positive rods which are often found in soil and dust.

Bacteraemia: the presence of bacteria in the blood *without* clinical signs or symptoms of infection.

Bactericidal: capable of killing bacteria, e.g. penicillins.

Bacteriophage: an 'eater of bacteria', a bacterial virus which enters a bacterial cell and multiplies within it by directing the bacterial metabolic machinery to manufacture bacteriophage components.

Bacteriostatic: prevents bacteria from replicating; if the drug is withdrawn, bacteria can multiply again, e.g. tetracycline. (A drug that is bacteriostatic may in high concentration or in certain circumstances become bactericidal, e.g. chloramphenicol in typhoid.)

Bacterium: a prokaryotic microbe.

Basophil: a white cell of the blood, so called because it takes up basic dyes; in the usual stains for blood films, basophils have large black granules.

B-cell: one of the two main cell types of the immune system, chiefly involved in the production of antibodies.

BCG strain of tubercle bacilli: an attenuated strain that is used as a vaccine against tuberculosis.

Binary fission: division of one cell into two daughter cells, the usual method of reproduction in bacteria.

Broad-spectrum: agents which work against many bacteria and often used initially while the cause of an infection is unknown.

Carrier: an individual who persistently excretes a microbe or who has a body surface colonised by a microbe, but who is not obviously ill of this infection.

Cell-mediated immunity: a form of immune response carried out by cells.

Cell wall: the rigid outer layer of most prokaryotic cells and of some eukaryotic cells.

Centrifuge: an instrument which can spin liquids in containers at high speed, thus depositing particles on the bottom of the tube. It is often used to concentrate bacteria from body fluids for examination.

Cephalosporin: an antibiotic containing a β-lactam ring; many different types are now available, (see Chapter 5).

Cercaria: the final larval stage of a fluke (trematode).

Chemotaxis: movement of a cell in response to the presence of a chemical.

Chemotherapy: treatment of disease with chemicals; with reference to infection, this means antibiotics.

Clone: a group of organisms descended from a single parent by asexual reproduction and therefore exact copies of it. The term is now extended to the production of copies of DNA molecules.

Coccobacillus: a short oval rod, i.e. between a coccus and a bacillus in shape.

Coccus: a bacterium that is a sphere or almost so.

Colonisation: a microbe that establishes itself in a particular environment such as a body surface without producing disease is said to 'colonise' the site. Capable of causing invasion and disease if virulent or if the host is immunocompromised.

Colony: when a bacterial cell (or a few cells) multiplies on a solid medium until the group is visible to the naked eye, the group is called a *colony*. A typical colony contains 10–100 million cells.

Commensal: a commensal organism lives in association with another, without benefiting or harming it. Many members of the gut flora appear to be commensals. Commensals may be pathogenic if the host is immunocompromised.

Communicable: a disease that can be transmitted from one person to another is communicable (= contagious, = infectious).

Complement: a complex of proteins in the blood; sequential reactions between the component proteins (often after reacting with an antigen–antibody complex) promote the movement of phagocytes and the phagocytosis and killing of bacteria.

Compromised person (host, patient): a person whose normal defences against infection are impaired.

Conjugation: the transfer of genetic material from one bacterial cell to another by cell-to-cell contact; a form of sexual reproduction.

Conjugative plasmid: a plasmid which bears the genes needed to bring about the conjugation of its host bacterium with another bacterium.

Contagious: *see* communicable.

Counterstain: a stain used to enhance contrast in a differential stain.

Culture: a culture of microbes is the result of inoculating a medium with them and incubating it until large numbers are present.

Cutaneous: relating to the skin.

Cyst: (a) a sac or closed cavity in the (human or animal) body, filled with fluid or other material; (b) a stage in the lifecycle of some protozoan parasites, in which the organism is encased in a tough outer wall.

Cysticercus: a larval stage of some tapeworms, in which a fluid-filled cyst is formed.

Cystitis: a urinary infection confined to the bladder.

Cytoplasm: in a prokaryote, everything inside the cytoplasmic membrane; in a eukaryote, everything inside the cytoplasmic membrane, except the nucleus.

Cytoplasmic membrane: the membrane which constitutes the outer boundary of the cell except for the cell wall (when one is present) and which prevents the escape of the large and small molecules making up the cytoplasm of the cell.

Cytotoxic: toxic to cells. Some T-cells are cytotoxic.

Dane particle: a complete and infectious hepatitis B virion; it consists of DNA enclosed in a protein capsid.

Definitive host: the host organism in which the adult form of a parasite lives.

Delayed(-type) hypersensitivity: a hypersensitivity reaction carried out by cells and requiring 24 or more hours to be manifest.

Denaturation: (a) of proteins, the loss of folding brought about by heat or chemicals; denatured proteins have lost their normal biological activity. (b) of DNA, breaking the hydrogen bonds that hold two DNA strands together, resulting in their separation.

Deoxyribonucleic acid (DNA): the large molecule in which genetic information is encoded, the genetic material. The component nucleotides contain the sugar deoxyribose.

Dermatophyte: a fungus that attacks the skin, hair and nails without invading the deeper tissues.

Differential stain: a staining procedure that can dye some objects in the preparation but not others.

Diffusion: the process whereby the random movement of molecules tends to equalize their concentration in regions initially of higher and lower concentration.

Diploid: a diploid cell contains two copies of each chromosome. The body cells of most eukaryotic organisms are diploid.

Disc diffusion: a method of testing bacteria for susceptibility to antibiotics.

DNA: *see* deoxyribonucleic acid.

Dysentery: a severe form of infectious diarrhoea, characterised by blood and mucus in the stools.

DNA probe: *see* probe.

Ectoparasite: a parasite that lives on the outer surface of the host, e.g. a tick or louse.

Electron: a negatively charged particle in orbit round the nucleus of an atom.

Electron microscope: a microscope in which a beam of

electrons is used instead of light rays to produce an image.

Electrophoresis: the separation of molecules by subjecting them to an electric field in which they move at different rates.

ELISA (enzyme-linked immunosorbent assay): a technique for detecting and estimating antigens and antibodies, in which a coloured compound is formed by the enzyme linked to the detector antibody.

Embolus: material, especially a blood clot, which is carried by the circulation and blocks a blood vessel at a distance from the site where it originally formed.

Encephalitis: inflammation of the brain.

Endemic: if a disease is endemic, cases regularly appear in the population with little variation in incidence. *See* epidemic.

Endocarditis: an inflammation, especially one due to infection, of the lining of the heart, including its valves.

Endogenous: arising within the body; an *endogenous* infection is caused by the normal flora.

Endoplasmic reticulum: a complicated membrane system extending throughout the cytoplasm of the eukaryotic cell. During protein synthesis, ribosomes are often attached to it.

Endotoxin: part of the outer membrane of Gram-negative cells; it consists of various sugars and a lipid and possesses toxic properties, causing activation of complement, inflammation, blood clotting and fever. = lipopolysaccharide.

Envelope: in some viruses, an outer coat that surrounds the capsid and may be derived partly or wholly from the host cell.

Enzyme: a protein which catalyses a biochemical reaction.

Eosinophil: a white cell of the blood, so called because it takes up the dye eosin; in the usual stains for blood films, eosinophils have large orange-red granules.

Epidemic: when an unusually high incidence of an endemic infection occurs, or occurrence of an infection not usually seen in that population.

Epidemiology: the study of the occurrence of diseases, how and when they occur, how they are transmitted, etc.

Eukaryotic cell: one of two chief types of living cells, in which the nucleus is delimited from the cytoplasm by a membrane.

Exogenous: derived from outside the body; compare '*endogenous*'.

Extracellular: outside the cell.

Facultative: an organism which is not restricted to a particular way of life; thus a facultative anaerobe can live in the absence or presence of oxygen.

Facultative anaerobe: *see* anaerobe.

Fermentation: production of energy from carbohydrates in the absence of oxygen. The electrons generated are passed to organic molecules.

Fibrin: When blood clots, a meshwork of fibrin is formed from the fibrinogen in the plasma.

Fix: to prepare a specimen for staining; heating causes most bacterial specimens to adhere to the glass slide and is an adequate preparation for staining, other specimens need to be soaked in liquids such as formalin.

Flagellum: an organ attached to the surface of the cell and used for locomotion.

Flatworm: any of the flat-bodied worms, especially the flukes and tapeworms, which are important parasites.

Flora: originally the plant life of an area or period (*Flora* was the Roman goddess of flowers); bacteria were originally considered to be plants, hence the term is still applied in microbiology to the community of microbes colonising a body region.

Fluke: a parasitic flatworm (= trematode). Adult flukes are important parasites of man—*Fasciola*, the liver fluke, or *Schistosoma*.

Fluorescent antibody technique: a technique for detecting microbes in which the antibody is tagged with fluorescent dyes and thus rendered visible when viewed with a special microscope (*fluorescence microscope*) in which ultraviolet light is used.

Fomites: inanimate objects or material on which disease-producing agents may be conveyed, e.g. patients' personal possessions such as bedding, clothes.

Gamete: a male or female sex cell; it is haploid.

Gangrene: Death of body tissue such as a limb, because of interference with the blood supply.

Gas gangrene: Death of body tissue such as a limb, because of infection with *Clostridium perfringens*.

Gene: a 'unit of heredity', a segment of DNA that encodes the structure of a protein.

Generation time: the time required for a microbe to undergo division, producing two individuals.

Genetics: the science of heredity.

Genome: the complete set of hereditary factors contained in the haploid set of chromosomes.

Genus: in biological nomenclature the *genus* is the larger grouping and is written with a capital; the *species* is the smaller grouping. Both words are modern Latin and are printed in italics.

Glycocalyx: a more or less diffuse layer outside the cell wall of prokaryotes; it consists of polysaccharide, polypeptide or both.

Glycogen: a polysaccharide stored by animals and some bacteria.

Golgi complex: an organelle present in the cytoplasm of eucaryotic cells; it is involved in the secretion of proteins from the cell.

Gram stain: a staining procedure that distinguishes two types of prokaryotes: Gram-positive and Gram-negative.

Habitat: the part of an ecosystem (environment) in which a creature lives.

Haemolysin: a molecule that lyses red cells. Many bacteria produce haemolysins.

Haploid: a haploid cell contains only one copy of each chromosome. The cells of prokaryotic organisms are haploid. Compare '*diploid*'.

Heat-labile: easily destroyed by heat.

Helix, helical: spiral.

Hermaphrodite: possessing both male and female sex organs.

Histamine: a molecule released by mast cells; it causes increased permeability of blood vessels, and is responsible for the signs of inflammation; excess is associated with hay fever, asthma, etc.

Histocompatibility antigens: cell-surface antigens involved in many aspects of immunological recognition; they are the main antigens recognised in the rejection of grafts. In humans the chief group of such antigens is called the *HLA antigens*.

HLA antigens: *See* histocompatibility antigens.

Hypersensitivity: an exaggerated or inappropriate immune response, leading to inflammation or tissue damage.

Icosahedron: a solid figure with 12 (vertices) corners and 20 triangular faces.

Immunity: the result of infection by a particular microbe or of immunisation against that microbe.

Immunisation: the process of artificially inducing immunity to infection by a microbe.

Immunoglobulin: an antibody.

Incubation period: the interval between contact with the microbe and the development of the symptoms and signs of infection.

Infection: entry of a harmful microbe into the body and its multiplication in the tissues.

Inflammation: a response to infection or other injury characterised by swelling, heat, redness and pain.

Innate resistance: resistance which does not depend on previous exposure to microbes.

Inoculum: material (containing bacteria) added to a growth medium to initiate a culture; hence '*inoculate*'.

Interleukins: immunological proteins, messenger molecules released during immunological reactions.

Intermediate host: a host organism in which the larval form of a parasite lives; there may be more than one intermediate host.

In vitro: 'in glass', i.e. carried out in the test-tube, in the laboratory.

In vivo: 'in the living', i.e. in the animal (or patient).

Intracellular: inside cells.

Latent infection: a condition in which the clinical signs of infection are absent and the causative organism may be temporarily undetectable; under certain conditions the infection may again become obvious.

Leucocyte: white blood cell.

Lipid: a fat, a molecule made up of glycerol and fatty acids.

Lipopolysaccharide: a constituent of the Gram-negative bacterial cell wall, in which chains of various sugars are linked to lipid A. = endotoxin.

Lymphocyte: any one of several different types of cells involved in the immune response. They have a round or oval nucleus and the cytoplasm is usually free of granules.

Lymphokines: polypeptides released chiefly by T-cells and activating macrophages.

Lyse: to cause or produce disintegration of a compound, susbtance or cell, to undergo *lysis*.

Lysis: destruction or decomposition of a cell under the influence of a specific agent.

Lysosome: an intracellular organelle, a bag of enzymes.

Lysozyme: an enzyme that can dissolve the cell walls of certain bacteria.

Malaise: a general feeling of being unwell.

Macrophage: a type of phagocyte.

Mantoux test: a tuberculin skin test.

Mast cell: a cell involved in the type I hypersensitivity response. In appearance it closely resembles the basophil. It contains histamine and other substances the release of which causes inflammation.

Meiosis: a form of cell division, characteristic of eukaryotic cells; it results in haploid progeny cells (male and female gametes).

Membrane filter: a filter, usually made from a cellulose derivative, which contains large numbers of pores of a specified size.

Messenger RNA: the transcript of the DNA from which a polypeptide is synthesised by the ribosome.

Metabolism: a general term for all the biochemical processes that occur in a living cell.

Metabolite: break-down products of the process of metabolism. This may pertain to bacterial or human cell metabolism. It may also refer to parts of a drug excreted.

Microbe: a creature too small to be seen with the naked eye (or only just visible); the term includes bacteria, fungi, protozoa, some of the algae and the viruses. = microorganism.

Micrometre (μm): a unit of length, $= 10^{-6}$ metres. Formerly called *micron*.

Microorganism: *see* microbe.

Minimal inhibitory concentration (MIC): the lowest concentration of an antibiotic or other agent that will inhibit the growth of a microbe.

Miracidium: the first-stage larva of a parasitic fluke; it emerges from the egg in water.

Mitochondrion: an intracellular organelle that contains the energy-generating systems of eukaryotic cells.

Mitosis: division of a eukaryotic cell into two diploid daughter cells.

Monocyte: a white cell of the blood, which develops into the tissue macrophage of the mononuclear phagocytic system.

Mononuclear phagocytic system: a system of phagocytic cells consisting of the blood monocytes, the wandering monocytes and macrophages of the lung and other tissues, and the fixed phagocytes in the liver and spleen.

Motility: the ability to move.

Mould: a fungus that forms a mycelium which may be seen as a 'furry' growth on the surface of e.g. bread or a fruit.

Mutation: a change in the sequence of the bases in the DNA strand.

Myalgia: pain in the muscles, a feature of many viral infections.

Mycelium: an intertwined mass of filaments (*hyphae*), typical of the growth of moulds.

Nanometer: a unit of length, $= 10^{-9}$ m (10^{-3} micrometer).

Narrow-spectrum: an antibiotic having activity against only one or a limited range of bacteria.

Natural killer cells: large lymphoid cells capable of killing cells with the appropriate receptors on the surface.

Nematode: one of the large group of worms which have an unsegmented, cylindrical body tapering at each end (= roundworm). Some are free-living, in soil and water, others are parasites of plants and animals.

Neutrophil: a white cell of the blood, actively phagocytic.

Nitrogen cycle: the series of reactions whereby nitrogen is converted from atmospheric nitrogen gas to organic compounds and back to gas again.

Normal flora: the community of microbes that colonises a body surface.

Nosocomial: acquired or occurring in a hospital; e.g. a nosocomial infection. = a hospital-acquired infection.

Nucleolus: an area in the nucleus of a eukaryotic cell where RNA is synthesised.

Nucleotide: a constituent of DNA or RNA, made up of a sugar, an organic base and a phosphate group.

Nucleus: (a) the central part of an atom, made up of protons and neutrons. *Or* (b) the part of the eukaryotic cell that contains the genetic material.

Objective lens: the lens of a microscope which forms the primary image of the specimen.

Obligate: an obligate organism is restricted to a particular way of life; e.g. an obligate parasite cannot live free without a host.

Obligate aerobe/anaerobe: *see* aerobe, anaerobe.

Ocular lens: the lens of a microscope which further magnifies the primary image formed by the objective lens.

Opportunistic organism: one capable of causing infection when the immune system of the host is impaired.

Organelle: a distinct structure within the cytoplasm of a eukaryotic cell that possesses a separate function; e.g. the mitochondria, Golgi complex.

Organic: an organic compound is one that contains carbon.

Oxidation: the addition of oxygen to, or the removal of electrons from, a substance.

Pandemic: a worldwide outbreak of an infectious disease.

Parasite: an organism that lives in or on another creature and obtains food and shelter without benefitting the host. Hence '*parasitism*'. *See* commensal, symbiosis.

Parenteral: administered by injection directly into the tissues, e.g. subcutaneously, intramuscularly, intravenously.

Passive immunity: immunity conferred on the host animal by antibodies made in another host.

Pathogen: a microbe capable of causing disease.

Pathogenicity: the ability of a microbe to invade and cause disease. (See Chapter 3.)

Penicillins: a group of antibiotics containing a β-lactam ring; some are natural products, but most are at least partially synthesised.

Peptide: a chain of amino acids.

Peptidoglycan: a major structural component of bacterial cell walls, consisting of chains of sugars cross-linked by peptides.

Peptones: short chains of amino acids derived from the breakdown of proteins.

pH: the symbol denoting hydrogen ion concentration; the pH ranges between 0 and 14 and its value indicates the relative acidity or alkalinity of a solution.

Phagocyte: a cell capable of phagocytosis.

Phagocytosis: the ingestion of material by a cell either in order to destroy foreign matter or for its own nutrition.

Phase-contrast microscope: a microscope which is fitted with a special illumination system that reveals the structure of living cells without the need for staining.

Photosynthesis: the use of solar energy by green plants and some bacteria to synthesise carbon compounds from CO_2 and water.

Plasma: the liquid portion of blood.

Plasma cell: a cell that develops from a B-cell and that manufactures a specific antibody.

Plasmid: a double-stranded circle of DNA which may be present in the cytoplasm of a microbial cell; it may be able to bring about conjugation between bacterial cells and it may carry genes for antibiotic resistance, for virulence and for various biochemical pathways.

Pleomorphic: varied in shape.

Polymer: a molecule made up of similar subunits.

Polymorphonuclear leucocyte: the blood contains three polymorphonuclear leucocytes, the neutrophil, the eosinophil and the basophil.

Polypeptide: a chain of amino acids, containing at least four and usually more.

Precipitate: the result of a reaction between two soluble substances to form an insoluble material that 'falls' out of solution.

Precipitin reaction: a reaction between antigen and antibody which results in a visible precipitate.

Primary response: the production of antibody in response to the first contact with the antigen.

Probe: a short single-stranded segment of DNA or RNA which is identical in base sequence to a part of a gene, plasmid, ribosome, etc., and which can be used to detect the presence of the gene or plasmid, and hence to identify the microbe of which it is a part, or to detect a hereditary defect.

Prokaryotic cell: one of two chief types of living cells, in which the nucleus is not delimited from the cytoplasm by a membrane. In general prokaryotic cells are smaller and of less complex structure than eukaroyotic cells.

Proglottid: a segment of a tapeworm; it contains male and female reproductive organs and eggs.

Prophylaxis: treatment which is intended to prevent disease rather than cure it after it has developed; e.g. prophylactic antibiotic therapy.

Protein: a large molecule, one of the main constituents of living matter; it consists of one or more polypeptide chains.

Protozoa: microscopic single-celled eukaryotic microbes; some are free-living, others are important parasites.

Pseudopod: an extension of the cytoplasm of a cell; pseudopods are formed for the purposes of feeding and locomotion.

Pus: an accumulation of fluid due to infection; it consists of living and dead microbes, phagocytes and tissue cells, together with the fluid that has accumulated in the tissue because of inflammation.

Pyelonephritis: an infection of the kidney.

Replication: the synthesis of copies of a DNA molecule or a virus.

Reservoir (of infection): the permanent source of infection; e.g. foxes are a reservoir of rabies in Western Europe.

Respiration: the generation of energy by the conversion of organic compounds to carbon dioxide and water.

Reverse transcriptase: an enzyme that works 'in reverse', synthesising DNA from an RNA template. The human immunodeficiency virus contains a reverse transcriptase.

Ribonucleic acid (RNA): a nucleic acid in which the component nucleotides contain the sugar ribose. The ribonucleic acids of cells are messenger RNA, transfer RNA and ribosomal RNA; in addition the genome of some viruses consists of RNA.

Ribosomal RNA: RNA which forms part of the ribosome.

Ribosome: the protein-synthesising 'factory' of the cytoplasm.

Roundworm: *see* nematode.

Saprophyte: an organism that lives on dead organic matter.

Scolex: the head of a tapeworm, armed with suckers and often with hooks.

Sensitivity: the susceptibility of certain organisms to specific agents.

Septicaemia: bacteraemia accompanied by symptoms and signs of infection and illness with no other recognised cause.

Serotype: a strain of a bacterial species which can be differentiated by the antigens present on its surface; these are detected by antibodies (*serological* methods).

Serum: the liquid which remains when plasma clots.

Sign: *see* symptoms and signs.

Species: *see* genus.

Subclinical infection: an infection which produces no symptoms or signs of disease; said of the early stages or a very mild form of the disease.

Subcutaneous: beneath the skin.

Subphrenic abscess: a collection of pus below the diaphragm and usually between it and the liver.

Substrate: the substance(s) with which an enzyme reacts.

Superinfection: acquisition of a more resistant strain of the organism already causing infection, or replacement of normal flora by antibiotic-resistant organisms because of antibiotic use.

Symbiosis: an association between two species in which there is mutual benefit.

Symptoms and signs: symptoms are the patient's complaints; signs are the physical evidence of disease.

Syndrome: a set of symptoms and signs that forms a distinctive clinical picture suggesting a particular disease.

Synergy: when the effect of two antibiotics (or other drugs) given together is greater than can be accounted for by the effect of each acting alone, this is said to be due to synergy.

Systemic: involving the whole body.

Tapeworm: a long segmented flatworm parasitic in the intestine.

Teichoic acid: a polymer of an alcohol, phosphate and other molecules found in Gram-positive cell walls.

Tetracyclines: a group of broad-spectrum antibiotics which interfere with protein synthesis.

Titre (titer): a means of expressing the concentration of an antibody.

Topical: a drug that is applied directly to the affected part (e.g. skin or eye) is applied *topically*.

Toxin: any poisonous susbtance produced by a living organism, especially a microbe.

Toxoid: a microbial toxin treated (usually with dilute formaldehyde) so that its toxic activity is destroyed, but it is still capable of stimulating the production of antibodies which react with and inactivate the parent toxin.

Trace element: a chemical element required for growth, but only needed in very small amounts.

Transcription: copying the sense strand of the DNA into messenger RNA.

Transduction: the introduction into a bacterial cell, by a bacteriophage, of new genes which are not bacteriophage genes and which are derived from the bacterium in which the phage previously replicated.

Transfer RNA: RNA molecules which carry individual amino acids to the ribosome.

Transformation: the introduction of new genes into a cell by the uptake of 'naked' DNA from solution.

Translation: synthesising a polypeptide chain from the messenger RNA template.

Transposon: a 'jumping gene', a segment of DNA which can move from one DNA molecule to another, or from one site to another in the same DNA molecule.

Trematode: *see* fluke.

Trophozoite: the normal actively feeding form of a parasite, which is often too frail to survive the conditions involved in transfer to a new host.

Tuberculin test: a skin test used to detect infection by mycobacteria.

Ubiquitous: present everywhere.

Ultraviolet light: invisible light of wavelength shorter than the light at the violet end of the visible spectrum.

Uracil: an organic base found in RNA.

Vaccination: the process of inducing immunity by administering a vaccine.

Vaccine: a preparation of killed microbes, inactivated

microbial toxins or microbial antigens used to induce immunity.

Vector: an animal, usually an arthropod (insect or tick) that transfers an infectious microbe from one host to another.

Virulence: the ability of an organism to cause disease. (See Chapter 3.)

Zoonosis: an infectious disease of animals that may be transmitted to man. Brucellosis, rabies and toxoplasmosis are examples. (See Table 3.2.)

Index

acid-fast bacilli, 25, 225–9
Acinetobacter, 216–17
Acne, 205
Acquired immunity
  defined, 476
  mechanisms, 81
Actinomyces israeli, presence,
    pathogenicity and
    treatment, 205
Activities of daily living, nursing
    model, 429
Acyclovir, indications and side-
    effects, 107
Adenoviruses, 243
Aerobe, defined, 22
Agar, defined, 476
Agglutination, 73
  agglutination tests, 174
AIDS and AIDS-related
    complex, 261–2
  patient care plan, 437–46
Alcohols, cleaning use, 133, 382,
    396–402
Alcoholic handrub, 372, 396
Aldehydes, cleaning use, 131,
    133
Amantadine, indications and
    side-effects, 108
Amikacin, indications and side-
    effects, 101
P-aminobenzoic acid, 93
Aminoglycosides
  defined, 476
  indications and side-effects,
    101–2, 111
  summary, 109–11
Amoebae

amoebic dysentery, 291
  faecal specimens, 161–2
Amoxycillin
  amoxycillin + clavulanic acid,
    99
  indications and side-effects, 98
Amphotericin B, indications and
    side-effects, 106
Ampicillin, indications and side-
    effects, 98
Anaerobe, defined, 24, 477
Anaesthetic machines, care, 389
Ancylostoma duodenale, 297
Animals, transmitted infections
    see Zoonoses
Anthrax, 197
  historical notes, 6
Antibiotics *see* Antimicrobials
Antibodies
  antibody-producing cells, 70
  classes, 71–4
  monoclonal antibodies, 83–5
  serum for, 158–9
  structure and function, 71
Anti-fungal agents, 106, 113
Antigen-antibody reactions, 174
  complement fixation test, 176
  cytopathic effect (CPE), 175
  skin tests, 78–80
  specific immune response,
    68–78
Antigenic drift, 245
Antigenic shift, 244
Antigens
  defined, 69
  see also Immunity
Antimicrobials

broad-spectrum, 112
disc diffusion, 173–4, 184
historical notes, 93–4
indications, 98–108
main groups, 96–113
mechanisms of action, 94–6
resistance, 114–17
sensitivity to, 173–4, 184
side-effects, 98–113
sites of action, 95
summary and list, 98–113
Antisepsis, historical notes, 7,
    130–1, *see also* Glossary
    and skin cleaning
Antitoxins
defined, 477
historical notes, 8
production, 87
Antituberculous drugs,
    indications and side-
    effects, 105
Antiviral agents, 107–8, 113–14
Aprons, 421–2
Architectural design and
    function, 338–42
Arenaviruses, 272
Argentinian haemorrhagic fever,
    273
Arthropod-borne viruses, 269–70
Ascaris lumbricoides, 295, 296
Aseptic techniques, 366–7
Aspergillus flavus, 285–6
Aspergillus fumigatus, 285–6
Aspergillus niger, 285–6
Athlete's foot, 285
Augmentin, 99
Autoclave, 136–8, 139–40
definition, 477
Azlocillin, 99
Aztreonam, 100

B-cells *see* Lymphocytes
Babesia, 293
Bacillus anthracis, 195, 197
Bacillus cereus, presence, and
    pathogenicity, 195, 197

Bacillus subtilis, presence, and
    pathogenicity, 195, 198
Bacillus(i) defined, 22, 478
Bacteria
AAFB (acid/alcohol fast), 25,
    225–9
bacteriocine typing, 179
biochemical tests,
    identification, 172
capsule, 19, 25
cell division, -18, 17, 26
classification, 21, 186
conjugation, 27
death *see* Sterilization
genetics, 26–7
    conjugation, 27
    plasmids, 26, 27
    transformation, 26
Gram-staining, 24–5, 40
    Gram-negative division,
        205–25
    Gram-positive division,
        187–205
identification
    biochemical tests, 172
    serological tests, 174–7
    see also Diagnosis
infections
    *guide to transmission and
        management*, 451–75
    see also Infection process;
        *specific organisms and
        conditions*
macroscopy, 171–2
morphology, 22
natural history, 20–1
normal body flora, 41–5,
    369
normal carriage, 369
nutrition, 22–4
resistance and sensitivity,
    173–4
size, 19–20
spores, 23, 24
structure, 14–37
typing, 178–9

Bacteriophage, 178, 478
  defined, 478
Bacteroides, 209, 219, 225
Barrier nursing *see* Isolation
  nursing
Bathing
  postoperative, 384
  preoperative, 380
BCG test, immunisation, 80
Bed-pan, disposal of excreta,
  360–1
Bedbugs, 310
Beds and bedding
  cleaning and maintenance,
    343–4
  duvets, 344
  mattresses, 343–4
  see also Linen
von Behring, 8
Benzylpenicillin, indications and
  side-effects, 98
Bilharzia, 299, 304–5
Binary fission, 17, 18
Biochemical tests, identification
  of bacteria, 172
Biotyping, 179
BK virus, 276
Blastomyces dermatitidis, 287
Blastomycosis, 287
Blood, culture, 158–9
Blood agar, 167
Blood-borne viruses, 256–62
Body louse, 307–8
Body substance isolation, 414–5
Bolivian haemorrhagic fever, 273
Bordetella pertussis,
  pathogenicity and
    treatment, 221–2
Bornholm disease, 251
Borrelia borgderferi, 231–2
Borrelia duttoni, 231
Borrelia recurrentis, 231
Borrelia vincentii, Vincent's
  angina, 231
Botulism, 204

Bovine spongiform
  encephalopathy, 278
Branhamella see Moraxella
Bronchial tree, mucous surfaces,
  62–3
Brucella abortus, 222
Brucella melitensis, 222
Brucella suis, 222
Burkitt lymphoma, 268

Campylobacter, 211
Campylobacter jejuni,
  pathogenicity, 218
Candida albicans, presence and
  pathogenicity, 284–5
Capreomycin, indications and
  side-effects, 105
Capsule, structure/function, 19,
  25
Care planning
  for infected patient (Roper's),
    429–34
  Orem's self-care nursing
    model, 435–6
  partial care plans, 429–34,
    435–46
Carriage of infections
  defined, 478
  infection process, 47
    asymptomatic, 47
    convalescent, 47
  normal body flora, 41–5, 369
Catering services, maintenance
  of hygiene, 345–9
Catheters
  administration sets, 394, 397–8
  catheterized patient, 372–9
  filters, 395
  infection process, 44, 47
  infections, organisms, 392
  material and type, 394
  preparation of the site, 396–7
  site, 394
  see also Intravenous
    catheterization
CD4, CD8 cell surface antigens,
  77, 78

Cell division
  eukaryotes, 19, 20
  prokaryotes (including
    bacteria), 17, 26
Cell-mediated immunity, 75–8
Centers for Disease Control, 332
  postoperative pneumonia
    prevention, 389
Cephalosporins
  indications and side-effects,
    99–100, 109–11
  summary, 109–11
Cerebrospinal fluid (CSF),
    collection, 159
Cestodes, 298–9, 301–4
Chaga's disease, 294
Chain, E, 94
Chemotaxins, 68
Chemotherapy
  historical notes, 92–4
  mechanisms of action, 94
Chickenpox, 265–7
  infection process, 49, 56
Chlamydia pneumoniae, 236
Chlamydia psittaci, 235
Chlamydia trachomatis
  serogroups, 234–5
  treatment, 235
Chlamydiae, occurrence, 33
Chloramphenicol
  indications and side-effects,
    111
  summary, 109–11
Chlorhexidine, cleaning use, 130,
    133, 371
Chlorine-releasing agents,
    128–32, 426
Chocolate agar, 167
Cholera, 217
  historical notes, 6
Chromosomes, number, 19
Cimex lectularius, 310
Ciprofloxacin, indications and
    side-effects, 104
Clavulanic acid, indications and
    side-effects, 99

Cleaning, 112–24
  definition, 119
  domestic, 426–7
  floors and walls, 341–2
  spillages, chlorine-releasing
    granules, 426
  surface maintenance, 336–7
  terminal, 342, 427
  see also Beds and bedding;
    Hospital environment;
    Laundry; Waste disposal
Clindamycin, indications and
    side-effects, 111
Clonorchiasis, 300
Clostridium, presence,
    pathogenicity and
    treatment, 201–4
Clostridium botulinum, 204
Clostridium difficile, 204
Clostridium perfringens (welchii),
    201–3
Clostridium tetani, 203–4
Clothing, isolation nursing,
    420–1
Clotrimazole, indications and
    side-effects, 107
Cloxacillin, indications and side-
    effects, 98
CMV (cytomegalovirus), 267–8
Cocci, 22
Coccidioides immitis, 287
Coccidioidomycosis, 287
Cold sores, 263–4
Colitis, pseudomembranous
    colitis, 204
Collection of specimens,
    diagnostic microbiology,
    148–9, 153–64
Communicable Disease
    Surveillance Centre, 332
Communication problems,
    laboratory reports, 181–2
Community infections, 53,
    317–18
  see also Infection control
Complement fixation test,

antigen-antibody
reactions, 176
Complement system, 65–8
complement-binding site, 127
defined, 480
receptors, 74
Conjugation, 27, 480
Conjunctivitis, haemorrhagic,
251
Contact–direct and indirect, 55
see also Appendix to Chapter
14
Coronaviruses, 249
Corynebacterium diphtheriae
presence, pathogenicity and
treatment, 198–9
Schick test, 80
Corynebacterium hofmannii, 199
Corynebacterium ulcerans, 199
Corynebacterium xerosis, 199
Co-trimoxazole, indications and
side-effects, 93, 102
Coxiella burnetii, 233–4
Coxsackie viruses, 251
Crab lice, 308
Creutzfeld-Jakob disease, 278
Crockery and cutlery, in
isolation nursing, 425
Cross-infection, 44–5
Cross-infection carousel, 319
Crown immunity, National
Health Services, 345, 358
Cryptococcus neoformans, 283–5
Cryptosporidiosis, 292
Ctenocephalodes felis (or canis),
309–10
Culture media, 167–8
chocolate agar, 167
viral transport media (VTM),
163
Cycloserine, 105
Cysticercosis, 298, 303
Cytomegalovirus, 267–8
Cytotoxic T-cells, 77

Dane particle, 259

Davaine, 6
Definitions, glossary, 476–95
Delayed hypersensitivity, 79
Delhi boil, 293
Dengue fever, 270
Dermatophytes, 285–6
Diagnostic microbiology, 147–84
collection of specimens,
148–9, 153–64
fungal investigations, 162–3
viral investigations, 163–4
laboratory isolation of
microorganisms, 164–72
culture, 167–72
microscopy, 165–7
laboratory report, 180–4
laboratory request forms,
151–3
transport of specimens, 149–51
Dichloroisocyanurates, 128,
128–32, 132
Diguanides, cleaning use, 130,
133
Diphtheria, historical notes, 8
Diphyllobothrium latum, 299,
302, 303
Disc diffusion, antimicrobials,
173–4, 184
Disinfection
community practice, 144
defined, 119
methods
chemical agents, 126–34
heat, 124–6, 135–9
risk categories, 121
see also Sterilisation
Disposable equipment
re-use, 143
see also Sharps; Waste
disposal
DNA
DNA typing, 179
in prokaryotes, 15, 26–7
viral, 30
Domagk, 8, 92
Domestic cleaning, 426–7

Domestic services, 361
Doxycycline, indications and side-effects, 101
Drainage of surgical wounds, 382–3
Dressings
  ‡ideal', 385
  intravenous catheterization, 398
  surgical wounds, 383–6
Dysentery
  amoebic, 291
  faecal specimens, 161–2

Ear swabs, 156
Ebola virus, 273
EBV (Epstein-Barr virus), 268–9
Echinococcus granulosus, 298, 304
Echoviruses, 251–2
Econazole, indications and side-effects, 107
Ectoparasites, 306–10
Education of nurses, 332–4, 360
Electron microscopy, 166
Elek test, 198
Elephantiasis, 297
ELISA technique, 176
Encephalitis, arthropod-borne disease, 270
Endoparasites
  helminths, 294–306
  see also Protozoa
Endotracheal suction techniques, 390
Entamoeba histolytica, 291
Enteral feeding, food hygiene, 349
Enteric fever, *Salmonella*, 213–14
Enterobacter, presence and pathogenicity, 210
Enterobius vermicularis, 295, 296–7, 301
Enterococcus faecalis, 195
Enteroviruses, 250–2

Environment *see* Hospital environment
Enzyme cascade, complement system, 65–8
Epidemic myalgia, 251
Epidemiology of disease, 330–2
  organizations, 330–2
Epidermophyton cruris, 285
Epstein-Barr virus, 268–9
Equipment, cleaning
  clinical, 342–3
  disposable, re-use, 143–4
  isolation, 426
  patient equipment, 343–4
Erlich, 8–9
Erysipelas, 194
Erythema infectiosum, 277
Erythromycin, indications and side-effects, 101
Escherichia coli, presence and pathogenicity, 210
Ethambutol, indications and side-effects, 105
Ethanol, cleaning use, 130, 133
Ethylene oxide, 140
Eukaryotes
  defined, 14, 483
  structure, 17–19
Excreta, disposal, 360–1
Exotoxins, 87

Fab and Fc fragments, 70
Faeces, specimens, 161–2
Fascioliasis, 300
Fasciolopsiasis, 300
Fifth disease, 277
Filariasis, 297
Filoviruses, 273–4
Filters, care, 395
Filtration, for sterilisation, 141
Fimbriae, structure, 17
Fixtures, fittings and furnishings, 341–2
Flagella, structure, 16
Fleas, 309–10
Fleming, Alexander, 9–10, 93

Floors and walls, cleaning, 341–2
Flora, normal carriage, 41–5, 369
Florey, Howard, 94
Flucloxacillin, 98
Fluconazole, 107
Flucytosine, 106
Folic acid, 93
Food
  catering services, 345–9
  preserving, 141–2
Food hygiene, 345–9
  common abuses, 347–8
  enteral feeding, 349
  legislation, 346
  ten-point catering code, 347
Food poisoning
  common causes (summary), 348
  gastroenteritis *Salmonella* group, 214
  organisms involved, 345
  staphylococcal, 189
Formaldehyde, cleaning, 134, 139–40
Fracostoro, 4
Francisella tularensis, 220
Freezing, 141
Fungal infections
  dimorphic fungi, 286–8
  filamentous fungi, 285–6
  host, effects on, 34–7
  investigations, collection of specimens, diagnostic microbiology, 162–3
  species, 282–3
  superficial/deep, 283
  yeasts and yeast-like fungi, 283–5
Fungi
  classification, 34
  forms, 36
Fusidic acid, indications and side-effects, 111
Fusobacterium

presence and pathogenicity, 225
in Vincent's angina, 231

Ganciclovir, indications and side-effects, 107
Gangrene, 203
Gastritis, *Helicobacter pylori*, 218
Gastroenteritis food poisoning, *Salmonella* group, 214
Gastrointestinal viruses, 250–5
Genital tract, swab-taking, 157
Gentamicin, indications and side-effects, 101
German measles, 249–50
Giardia intestinalis (lamblia), 290
Giardiasis, 290
Glossary, 476–95
Gloves, materials and care, 422–3
Glutaraldehydes
  cleaning use, 133–4
  sterilisation, 140
Glycopeptides, lymphocytes, 82, 83
Goggles, 423
Gonococcus *see Neisseria gonorrhoeae*
Gowns, 421–2
Gram-negative division of bacteria, 205–25
  aerobic bacilli, 215–24
  aerobic cocci, 205–9
  anaerobic bacilli, 225
  anaerobic cocci, 209–15
  summary, 190–1
Gram-positive division of bacteria, 187–205
  aerobic bacilli, 195–201
  aerobic cocci, 187–95
  anaerobic bacilli, 201–5
  anaerobic cocci, 195
  summary, 188
Gram-staining, 24–5, 40

Griseofulvin, indications and
side-effects, 106

Haemadsorption, 171
Haemolysis, beta-haemolysis,
171
Haemophilus ducreyi,
pathogenicity and
treatment, 220–1
Haemophilus influenzae
infection process, 40, 41
presence, pathogenicity and
treatment, 220–1
Haemorrhagic fevers,
Argentinian, 273
Hair
collection of specimens, 162
removal, for surgery, 382
Halogens, 128–32
Hand washing, 367–72
missed areas, 371
problems, 372
residual/transient organisms
remaining, 367–9
soaps and disinfectants, 371–2
techniques, 370
why and when, 369–70
Head louse, 306–7
Heaf test, 79
Heat *see* Disinfection;
Sterilization
Helicobacter pylori, 218
Helminth infections, 294–306
Helper T-cells, 77
Hepatitis (viral infections)
A, 253–4, 255
B, 45, 256–9
C, 260
D, 259–60
E, 254, 255
summary, 255
Herpangina, 251
Herpesviruses, 262–9
herpes simplex, 262–5
human herpes virus 6, 268–9
Hexachlorophane, cleaning use,
131, 132

Histoplasma capsulatum, 286–7
History of microbiology, 3–31
HIV *see* Human
immunodeficiency virus
HLA system *see* Major
histocompatibility complex
HNIG *see* Immunoglobulins,
human normal
Holmes, Oliver Wendell, 5
Hookworms, 297
Hospital environment, 336–61
architectural design and
function, 338–42
equipment, 342–5
microbes present, 336–8
sampling, 338
services, 345–61
Hospital Infection Working
Group, 323
Hospital-acquired infections, 53,
313–27
UTI prevention, catheterized
patient, 372–9
see also Infection control
HTLV-1, tropical spinal
paralysis, 261
Human herpes virus 6, 268–9
Human immunodeficiency virus
(HIV), 261–2
CD4, CD8 cell surface
antigens, 77, 78
HIV-positive patient, care
plan, 437–46
Human leucocyte antigen system
see Major
histocompatibility complex
Humidifiers, care, 390
Humoral immunity, 70, 70–1
Hybridoma, Mabs, 84–5
Hydatid disease, 298, 304
Hymenolepis nana, 299, 302
Hypersensitivity, delayed, 79
Hypochlorites, 128, 128–32

Idoxuridine
indications and side-effects, 107

uses, 113
Ig *see* Immunoglobulins
Imidazoles, 107
Imipenem, 100
Immune response, specific,
    68–78
  antibody classes, 71–4
  cell-mediated immunity, 75–8
  humoral immunity, 70–1
  imbalance in immune system, 78
  induction, 69–70
Immunisation
  BCG test, 80
  defined, 84–5
  schedules, 88–90
  status, checklist, 330
  vaccines, 84–90
Immunity, 58–91
  acquired, 81
    mechanisms, 81
  active immunity, 87–8
  artificial acquired, 85
  humoral, 70
  length of protection, 88
  new developments, 82–4
  non-specific defence
    mechanisms, 59, 60–8
  passive immunity, 86–7
  skin tests, 78–80
  specific immune responses,
    68–78
  summary, 80–2
Immunofluorescence assay, 176
Immunogenetics, 83
Immunoglobulins
  classes, 71–4
  defined, 70
  human normal (HNIG), 86
  specific, 86
  structure/function, 71–4
Immunosuppressive therapy, risk
    of VZV infection, 267
Impetigo, 194
Incineration of waste, 139
  legislation, 357–8
Infection control

aseptic techniques, 366–7
catheterized patient, 372–9
community-acquired
    infections, 317–18
education, 332–4
epidemiology, 330–2
hand washing, 367–72
hospital-acquired infections,
    313–17
  associated factors, 318–21
  costs, 316–17
  National Survey of
    Infection in Hospitals,
    314–15
  prevention of transmission,
    322–7
  reasons for increase, 312–13
intravenous catheterization,
    391–400
  central venous catheters,
    400–2
and occupational health,
    327–30
respiratory tract infections,
    386–90
Study on Efficacy of
    Nosocomial Infection
    Control, 314–16
surgical wounds, 379–86
urinary tract infections,
    catheterized patient, 372–9
Infection Control Committee,
    323–4, 333
Infection Control Nurse, 326–8
Infection Control Nursing,
    Certificate in, 334
Infection Control Officer, 324–5
Infection process, 38–57
  barriers to infection, 60–3
  carriage of infections, 47
  chain of infection, 39
  control *see* Infection control
  cross-infection, 44–6
  opportunistic infections, 209
  pathogenicity, 39–40
  prodromal phase, 45

sources of infection, 41–8
  animals, 48, 50–2
  humans, 41–7
  inanimate sources, 47–8
  susceptible host, 49, 53–4,
    320–1
  three elements, 321
  transmission routes, 55–6
  prevention, 322–7
  viral infections, 239–81
Infectious diseases, *guide to
  transmission and
  management*, 451–75
Infectious patients *see* Isolation
  nursing
Inflammation process, 63–4
Influenza
  viral, 244–6
  vaccines, 246
Inosine pranobex, 108
Insect-borne viruses, 269–70
Instruments
  cleaning, 133–4
  sterilisation, 136–8, 139–40
    community problems, 144
  see also Equipment
Interferons, 239
  indications and side-effects,
    108
  non-specific defence, 64
  types, 64
  see also Lymphokines
Interleukins, T-cells, 83
Intravenous catheterization
  administration sets, 397–8
  central venous catheters,
    400–2
    infection hazards, 400–2
  dressings, 398
  fluids, 397
  infection control, 391–400
  site care, 399
  summary, 399–400
  see also Catheters
Iodines and iodophors, 128, 132
Irradiation, for sterilisation, 141

Isolation nursing
  decontamination of rooms,
    342, 427
  disposal of excreta, 360–1
  historical notes, 409–10
  measures for care of patients,
    418–20
  methods of isolation, 410–15
  protective clothing, 420–4
  rationale for precautions,
    416–18
  staff responsibility, 419–20
  terminal cleaning, 342, 427
Izoniazid, indications and side-
  effects, 105

JC virus, 276, 278
Jenner, Edward, 5

Kala-azar, 293
Ketoconazole, indications and
  side-effects, 107
Klebs, 8
Klebsiella, 210, 212
Klebsiella pneumoniae, 212
Koch, E., 7–8
Kuru, 278

Laboratory reports, 180–4
  communication problems,
    181–2
  request forms, 151–3
Laboratory Services, Public
  Health Laboratory
  Service, 331
Lancefield groups, *Streptococcus*,
  194
Lassa fever, 272
Laundry, 349–54
  categories of linen, 350
  colour coding, 352
  dangerous objects, 350
  infected linen, 352
  isolation nursing, 424

nursing guidelines, 354
problem areas, 353–4
risks to handlers, 352
temperature control, 351
Legionella, infection process, 48
Legionella pneumophila,
        presence, pathogenicity
        and treatment, 223–4
Leishmania braziliensis, 293
Leishmania donovani, 293–4
Leishmania tropica, 293
Leishmaniasis, 293–4
Leprosy, 228
Leptospira biflexa, 230
Leptospira interrogans,
        serogroups, 230–1
Lice, 306–8
Light microscopy, 165–6
Lincomycin, indications and
        side-effects, 111
Linen *see* Laundry
Lister, Lord, 7
Listeria monocytogenes,
        presence, pathogenicity
        and treatment, 199–201
Listeriosis, 199–201
Liver fluke, 300
Lockjaw, 203–4
Loeffler, 8, 10
Louping-ill, 269
Lyme disease, 231–2
Lymphatic system, 68–71
Lymphocytes
  B-cells, 70–1, 73, 78
  immunogenetics, 83
  interleukins, 83
  memory B-cells, 71
  memory T-cells, 78
  receptors, 69
  specific immune response,
        68–78
  T-cells, 70, 75–8
Lymphocytic choriomeningitis,
        272–3
Lymphokines
  defined, 75

see also Interferons
Lysosomes, defined, 68
Lytic pathway, 67, 68, 74

Mabs *see* Monocloncal
        antibodies
MacConkey agar, 167
Madura foot, 201
Major histocompatibility
        complex, 82
Malaria, 288–90
Mantoux test, 79
Marburg virus, 273
Masks, materials and care, 423
Measles, 247–9
  immunisation, 87
Media *see* Culture media
Meiosis *see* Cell division
Memory B-cells, 71
Memory T-cells, 77, 78
Meningitis
  aseptic, HSV, 262–5
  lymphocytic choriomeningitis,
        272–3
  neonatal, 194, 200
Meningococcus *see* Neisseria
        meningitidis
Methicillin
  indications and side-effects, 98
  MRSA, 116
  methicillin-resistant
        Staphylococcus aureus
        (MRSA), 116, 132, 189
  care plan for infected patient,
        429
Metronidazole
  indications and side-effects,
        104
  summary, 112
  uses, 111
Mezlocillin, 99
MHC *see* Major
        histocompatibility complex
Miconazole, 107
Microscopy
  electron, 166

fluorescence, 166
light, 165–6
Microsporum capitis, ringworm, 285
Minocycline, indications and side-effects, 101
Mitochondria, structure/function, 17
Mitosis *see* Cell division
Molluscum contagiosum, 275
Monkeypox, 274
Monobactams, indications and side-effects, 100
Monoclonal antibodies, 83–4, 83–5
Mononucleosis, infectious, 268
Moraxella (Branhamella) catarrhalis, pathogenicity and treatment, 209
MRSA *see* Methicillin-resistant *Staphylococcus aureus*
Mucor, presence and pathogenicity, 286
Mucous surfaces, skin, 61
Mumps, 247
Mycobacterium, atypical species, 228–9
Mycobacterium bovis, treatment, 227
Mycobacterium leprae, pathogenicity and treatment, 228
Mycobacterium tuberculosis, presence, pathogenicity and treatment, 225–7
Mycoplasma hominis, 232
Mycoplasma pneumoniae, 232
Mycoplasmas, occurrence, 33
Mycoses, 34–7

Nails, collection of specimens, 162
Nalidixic acid, indications and side-effects, 104
Nasal swabs, 153–4
National Health Services, Crown immunity, 345, 358

Nebulisers, care, 390
Necator americanus, 297
Needlestick injuries, 258
disposal of sharps, 358–60
Neisseria gonorrhoeae, 207, 208
Neisseria meningitidis, 205–7
Nematodes (roundworms), 295–301
Neomycin, indications and side-effects, 102
Neonatal meningitis, 194, 200
Neonatal septicaemia, 194
Netilmicin, 101
Nitrofurantoin, 104
Nits, 307
Nocardia asteroides, pathogenicity, 201
Nocardia madurae, pathogenicity, 201
Normal body flora, humans, 41–5, 369
Nosocomial infections *see* Hospital-acquired infections
Notifiable diseases, 324
Nucleic acids *see* DNA; RNA
Nursing model
activities of daily living (Roper's), 429
Orem's self-care, 435–6
Nursing process
four stages, 428
for infected patient, 429–34
see also Care planning
Nystatin, indications and side-effects, 106

Occupational health, 327–30
OH nurse, 329–30
Onchocerca volvulus, 297
Operating theatre, ventilation systems, 340–1
Operative care *see* Surgical wounds
Ophthalmia neonatorum, 208
Opsonization, 73

Orem's self-care nursing model, 435–6
Orf, 275
Organizations for study of epidemiology, 330–2
Orthomyxoviruses, 244–6
Oven, hot-air, 139
Oxytetracycline, indications and side-effects, 101

Papillomavirus, 275
Paracoccidioides brasiliensis, 287
Paracoccidioidomycosis, 287
Paragonimiasis, 300
Parainfluenza viruses, 247
Paramyxoviruses, 246–9
Parasites
  faecal specimens, 161
  see also Ecto-; Endo-
Parenteral nutrition, and central venous catheters, infection control, 400–2
Parvobacteria, 220–4
Pasteur, Louis, 7
Pasteurella multocida, presence, pathogenicity and treatment, 218–19
Pasteurization, 126
Pathogens
  classification, 186
  failure to identify, 182
  handling, 150
  infection process, 39–40
  pathogenicity tests, experimental animals, 179–80
  sensitivity, 184
  see also Diagnostic microbiology; Infection control; Infection process
Patient's environment *see* Hospital environment
Paul Bunnell test, 268
Pediculus humanus capitis, 306–7
Pediculus humanus corporis, 307–8

Penicillins, 98
  antipseudomonal, 99
Penicillium notatum, historical notes, 93–4
Peptidoglycans, 25
Peptostreptococcus, 195
Phage typing, 178
Phagocytosis, leucocytes, 65–8, 73
  mononuclear phagocytes, 65
  polymorphonuclear leucocytes, 65
Phagosomes, defined, 68
Phenolics, 129, 131, 132
Phenoxymethylpen, 98
Phthiris pubis, 308
Picornaviruses, 250–2
Pili, structure, 17
Pinta, 230
Pinworms, 295, 296
Piperacillin, 99
Plague, bubonic, pneumonic, 219
Planning of care *see* Care planning
Plasmids, 26, 27, 29
Plasmodium falciparum, 288–90
Plasmodium malariae, 288–90
Plasmodium ovale, 288–90
Plasmodium vivax, 288–90
Pleurodynia, 251
Pneumocystis carinii pneumonia, 293
Pneumonia, postoperative, 388–9
Poliomyelitis, 251
  historical notes, 10
Poliovirus, 251
Polymorphonuclear leucocytes, 65
Pontiac fever, 224
Precipitation tests, 174
Prodromal phase, infection process, 45
Progressive multifocal leucoencephalopathy, 278
Prokaryotes
  defined, 14
  structure, 14–17

Propionibacterium acnes, 205
Protective clothing, isolation nursing, 420–4
Protein typing, 179
Proteus mirabilis, 212
Protozoa
    forms, 35
    occurrence, 33–4
Protozoal infections, 288–94
Pseudomembranous colitis, 204
Pseudomonas, antipseudomonal penicillins, 99
Pseudomonas aeruginosa, 215–16
Psittacosis, 235
Pubic lice, 308
Public Health Laboratory Service, 331
Puerperal sepsis, 194
    historical notes, 5
Pyocyanea, 216
Pyrazinamide, indications and side-effects, 105
Pyrexia of unknown origin (PUO), *Brucella*, 222

Quarantine, historical notes, 4
Quinolones
    indications and side-effects, 104
    uses, 111–12

Rabies virus, 271–2
Radioimmunoassay, 176
Rat-borne disease, 231
Receptors, lymphocytes, 69
Refrigeration, 142
Reoviruses, 252
Resistance and sensitivity, microorganisms, 173–4
Respiratory equipment, care, 389–90
Respiratory tract infections
    infection control, 386–90
    postoperative pneumonia, 388–9
    prevention measures, 387–8
    risk factors, 387
Respiratory viruses, 243–50
    respiratory syncytial virus, 247
Retroviruses, 261–2
Reye's syndrome, 246
Rhabdoviruses, 270–2
Rhinoviruses, 249
Rhizopus, presence and pathogenicity, 286
Ribavirin, indications and side-effects, 108
Rickettsiae
    infections, 232–4
    occurrence, 33
Rifampicin, 105
Ringworm, 285–6
River blindness, 297
RNA, in prokaryotes, 16, 17
Rocky Mountain spotted fever, 233
Roseola infantum, 269
Rotavirus, 252–3
Roundworms, 295–301
Rubella virus, 249–50
Rubeola, 247–9

Salmonella
    carriage, 209, 210
    enteric fever group, 213–14
    presence and pathogenicity, 212–13
Salvarsan, historical notes, 9, 92
Sampling
    hospital environment, 338
    ventilation systems, 339–40
Saprophytes, 195
Sarcoptes scabei, 308–9
Savlon, cleaning use, 133
Scabies, 308–9
Scalded skin syndrome, 189
Schick test, *Corynebacterium diphtheria*, 80
Schistosoma haematobium, 299, 304–5
Schistosoma japonicum, 299, 304–5

Schistosoma mansoni, 299, 304–5
Scrapie, 278
Semmelweiss, 5
SENIC *see* Study on Efficacy of
    Nosocomial Infection
    Control
Serotyping, 178
Serratia, 209
Serum assay, 184
Sharps
    disposal, 358–9, 425
    needlestick injuries, 53
Shaving, preoperative, 382
Sheep liver fluke, 300
Shigella boydii, 215
Shigella dysenteriae, 215
    carriage, 209, 210
    resistance to antimicrobials, 116
Shigella flexneri, 215
Shigella sonnei, 215
Shingles, 266–7
Skin
    cleaning
        preoperative, 382
        preparation for intravenous
            catheterization, 396–7
        for surgery, 380
    collection of specimens, 163
    defence mechanisms, 60
    mucous surfaces, 61
    secretions, 62
Skin disinfectants, hand washing,
    371–2
Skin tests, immunity, 78–80
Slapped cheek syndrome, 277
Sleeping sickness, 294
Smallpox, historical notes, 5, 9,
    274
Snow, J., 6
Sodium dichloroisocyanurates,
    128–32
Sodium fusidate *see* Fusidic acid
Source isolation, 410
Spallanzani, 5
Specimens
    collection of swabs, 153–7

faeces, 161–2
information to be provided,
    151–3
urine
    catheter specimen, 160
    MSU, 159–60
Spectinomycin, indications and
    side-effects, 102
Spillages, 128, 426
Spirilla, 22
Spirochaetes, 22, 229–32
Sporothrix schenki, 287–8
Sporotrichosis, 287–8
Sputum, collection, 157–8
Staining techniques, 166
Stanley Royd Report 1986,
    gastroenteritis food
    poisoning, 214
Staphylococcal food poisoning,
    189
Staphylococcus aureus
    clumping', 192
    presence, pathogenicity and
        treatment, 187–9
    resistance to antimicrobials
        (MRSA), 116, 429, 435
Staphylococcus epidermidis,
    presence, pathogenicity
    and treatment, 189
Staphylococcus saprophyticus,
    192
Statutory notifiable diseases, 324
Steam *see* Disinfection;
    Sterilization
Sterilization
    community practices, 144
    defined, 119
    methods
        chemical agents, 139–40
        cold, 141–2
        drying, 142
        filtration, 141
        heat (inc. steam), 135–9
        irradiation, 141
        UV light, 142
    risk categories, 121

see also Disinfection
Streptococcus
  alpha and beta-haemolysis, 194
  illnesses caused, 196
  Lancefield groups, 194
Streptococcus agalactiae, 194
Streptococcus pneumoniae, 192–5
Streptococcus pyogenes, 192–4
Streptomyces, 94
Streptomycin, indications and side-effects, 102
Strongyloides stercoralis, 297
Structure of microorganisms, 14–37
Study on Efficacy of Nosocomial Infection Control, 314–16
Subacute sclerosing panencephalitis, 248, 278
Suction techniques, 390
Sulphonamides
  historical notes, 9–10, 93
  indications and side-effects, 102
Superinfection, 109
Suppressor T-cells, 77
Surgical wounds, 379–86
  drainage, 382–3
  dressings, 383–6
  incidence, factors influencing, 380–1
  nursing process, 386
  risk of infection, 379–80
  routine cleaning, contraindications, 385
Swabs, collection, 153–7
Syphilis
  historical notes, 8
  see also Treponema pallidum

T-cells *see* Lymphocytes
Taenia saginata, 298, 303
Taenia soleum, 298, 303
Taiwanese adult respiratory agent (TWAR), 236
Tapeworms, 298–9, 301–4

Teichoic acid, 25
Teicoplanin, 111
Tetanus (lockjaw), 203–4
Tetracycline, 101
Threadworms, 295, 296–7
Throat swabs, 156
Thrush, 284–5
Thymus gland, 75
Ticarcillin, 99
Tick-borne disease, 231–2, 233, 269–70
Timentin, 99
Tinea fungi, 285–6
Tobramycin, 101
Toxic epidermal necrolysis, 189
Toxic shock syndrome, 187–8
Toxins
  endotoxins, 40
  exotoxins, 40
Toxocara canis, 296, 301
Toxocara cati, 296, 301
Toxoid, defined, 88
Toxoplasma gondii, 292
Transformation, 26
Transmission routes
  guide and summary, 451–75
  infection process, 55–6
Transport of specimens, diagnostic microbiology, 149–51
Trematodes, 299–300, 304–6
Treponema carateum, 230
Treponema pallidum, 229
Treponema pertenue, 230
Trichinella spiralis, 295, 297
Trichomonas vaginalis, 291
Trichomoniasis, 291
Trichophyton pedis, athlete's foot, 285
Trimethoprim, indications and side-effects, 93, 102
Tropical spastic paralysis, HTLV-1, 261
Trosch, 10
Trypanosoma cruzi, 294
Trypanosoma gambiense, 294

Trypanosoma rhodesiense, 294
Tuberculosis *see Mycobacterium*
          tuberculosis
Tuberculosis, drugs, 105
Typhus fever, 233
Typing of bacteria, 178–9

Ultraviolet light, anti-infection,
          142
Universal precautions, 415
Ureoplasma urealyticum, 232
Urethral care, 377
Urinary tract infections
    common pathogens, 374
    prevention, catheterized
          patient, 372–9
    risk factors, 375
Urine
    catheter specimen, 160
    MSU, 159–60

Vaccines, 84–90
    historical notes, 5, 10–11
    production, 87
    vaccination, 84–90
    see also Immunisation
Vaccinia virus, 274
Vancomycin, 111
Varicella-zoster virus, 265–7
Variola, 274
Veillonella, 209
Vein, catheterization *see*
          Intravenous
          catheterization
Ventilation systems, 339–41
Ventilators, care, 389–90
Vibrio cholerae, pathogenicity
          and treatment, 217
Vibrio parahaemolyticus,
          pathogenicity, 217
Vidarabine, indications and side-
          effects, 107
Vincent's angina, 225, 231
Viral infections
    *guide to transmission and
          management*, 451–75

mode of infection, 239
Virulence, defined, 40
Viruses, 239–81
    antibody reporting, 177
    characteristics, 29–30
    culture, 170–80
    destruction, 240
    diagnosis, DEAFF, 267
    groups, 241, 242
        arthropod-borne, 269–70
        blood-borne viruses, 256–62
        gastrointestinal group,
              250–5
        herpesviruses, 262–9
        papovaviruses, 275–6
        parvoviruses, 277
        poxviruses, 274–5
        respiratory group, 243–50
        unconventional virus-like
              agents, 277–9
        zoonoses, 270–4
        summary, 242
    historical notes, 10
    host, effects on, 32–3
    infectivity, sources,
          transmission routes and
          care, 241
        see also Appendix
          (451–475)
    investigations, collection of
          specimens, diagnostic
          microbiology, 163–4
    plasmid transfer, 29
    replication, 30–3
    serology, 175–7
    structure/function, 30–3
    transduction, 28
    transport medium (VTM),
          163, 171
Visors, 423

Warts, plantar/genital, 275
Waste disposal, 355–61
    categories of waste, 355–6
    clinical waste
        isolation nursing, 425

LWRA definition, 356
legislation, 358
problem areas, 357–8
waste collection management, 356–7
see also Disposable equipment
Water therapy, checks necessary, 344–5
Weil's disease, 231
Western blot assay, 176
Whooping cough, 221–2
Woolsorter's disease, 197
World Health Organization, functions, 331
Wound swabs, 157
Wounds *see* Surgical wounds
Wucheraria bancrofti, 295, 297

Yaws, 230

Yeasts and yeast-like fungi
occurrence, 34
presence, pathogenicity and treatment, 283–5
Yellow fever, 270
Yersinia enterocolitica, 219
Yersinia pestis, 219
Yersinia pseudotuberculosis, 219

Zidovudine (AZT), indications and side-effects, 108
Ziehl-Neelsen staining, *Mycobacterium tuberculosis*, 25
Zoonoses, 48, 50–2
Pasteurella multocida, 218–19
viruses, 270–1
Zoster, 266–7
Zygomyctes, infections, 286